INSTRUCTOR'S SOLUTIONS MANUAL

HOSSEIN HAMEDANI
Marquette University

CALCULUS
FOR BUSINESS, ECONOMICS, LIFE SCIENCES, AND SOCIAL SCIENCES

TENTH EDITION

RAYMOND A. BARNETT
MICHAEL R. ZIEGLER
KARL E. BYLEEN

PEARSON

Prentice
Hall

Upper Saddle River, NJ 07458

Editor-in-Chief: Sally Yagan
Acquisitions Editor: Petra Recter
name_9 Supplement Editor: Joanne Wendelken
Executive Managing Editor: Vince O'Brien
Production Editor: Allyson Kloss
Supplement Cover Manager: Paul Gourhan
Supplement Cover Designer: Joanne Alexandris
Manufacturing Buyer: Ilene Kahn

© 2005 Pearson Education, Inc.
Pearson Prentice Hall
Pearson Education, Inc.
Upper Saddle River, NJ 07458

Printed in the United States of America

10 9 8 7 6 5 4 3 2 1

ISBN 0-13-143654-6

Pearson Education Ltd., *London*
Pearson Education Australia Pty. Ltd., *Sydney*
Pearson Education Singapore, Pte. Ltd.
Pearson Education North Asia Ltd., *Hong Kong*
Pearson Education Canada, Inc., *Toronto*
Pearson Educación de Mexico, S.A. de C.V.
Pearson Education—Japan, *Tokyo*
Pearson Education Malaysia, Pte. Ltd.

CONTENTS

1 A BEGINNING LIBRARY OF ELEMENTARY FUNCTIONS

2. The table specifies a function, since for each domain value there corresponds one and only one range value.

4. The table does not specify a function, since more than one range value corresponds to a given domain value.
   (Range values 1, 2 correspond to domain value 9.)

6. This is a function.

8. The graph specifies a function; each vertical line in the plane intersects the graph in at most one point.

10. The graph does not specify a function. There are vertical lines which intersect the graph in more than one point. For example, the y-axis intersects the graph in two points.

12. The graph does not specify a function.

16. $f(x) = \dfrac{3x^2}{x^2 + 2}$. Since the denominator is bigger than 1, we note that the values of f are between 0 and 3. Furthermore, the function f has the property that $f(-x) = f(x)$. So, adding points $x = 3$, $x = 4$, $x = 5$, we have:

x	-5	-4	-3	-2	-1	0	1	2	3	4	5
$f(x)$	2.78	2.67	2.45	2	1	0	1	2	2.45	2.67	2.78

The sketch is:

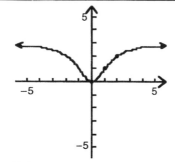

18. (A)

x	0	5	10	15	20
$f(x)$	0	750	1,000	750	0
$g(x)$	200	450	700	950	1,200
$f(x) - g(x)$	-200	300	300	-200	-1,200

(B)

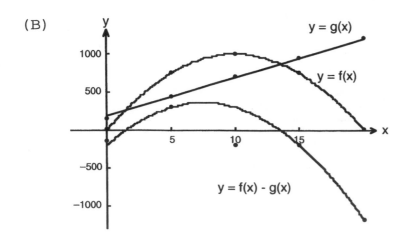

20. $y = f(4) = 0$

22. $y = f(-2) = 3$

24. $f(x) = 3$, $x < 0$ at $x = -4, -2$

26. $f(x) = 4$ at $x = 5$

28. $f(x) = 2x - 3$
$f(1) = 2(1) - 3 = -1$

30. $g(x) = x^2 + 2x$
$g(1) = (1)^2 + 2(1) = 3$

32. $g(-2) = (-2)^2 + 2(-2) = 0$

34. $f(3) - g(3) = [2(3) - 3] - [(3)^2 + 2(3)] = -12$

36. $g(0) \cdot f(-2) = [(0)^2 - 2(0)] \cdot [2(-2) - 3] = 0$

38. $\dfrac{g(-3)}{f(2)} = \dfrac{(-3)^2 + 2(-3)}{2(2) - 3} = \dfrac{3}{1} = 3$

40. domain: all real numbers or $(-\infty, \infty)$

42. domain: all real numbers except 2

46. f is not defined at the values of x where $x^2 - 9 = 0$, that is, at 3 and -3; f is defined at $x = -2$, $f(-2) = \dfrac{0}{-5} = 0$.

48. $f(x) = -3x + 4$

50. $F(x) = -8x^3 + 3\sqrt{3}$

52. Function g multiplies the domain element by -2 and adds 7 to the result.

54. Function G multiplies the square root of the domain element by 4 and subtracts the square of the domain element from the result.

56. Given $3y - 7x = 15$. Solving for y, we have:
$3y = 7x + 15$
$y = \dfrac{7}{3}x + 5$

Since each input value x determines a unique output value y, the equation specifies a function. The domain is R, the set of real numbers.

58. Given $x - y^2 = 1$. Solving for y, we have:

$$y^2 = x - 1$$
$$y = \pm\sqrt{x - 1}$$

This equation does not specify a function, since each value of x, $x > 1$, determines two values of y. For example, corresponding to $x = 5$, we have $y = 2$ and $y = -2$; corresponding to $x = 10$, we have $y = 3$ and $y = -3$.

60. Given $x^2 + y = 10$. Solving for y, we have:

$$y = 10 - x^2$$

This equation specifies a function. The domain is R.

62. Given $xy + y - x = 5$. Solving for y, we have:

$$(x + 1)y = x + 5 \quad \text{or} \quad y = \frac{x + 5}{x + 1}$$

This equation specifies a function. The domain is all real numbers except $x = -1$.

64. Given $x^2 - y^2 = 16$. Solving for y, we have:

$$y^2 = x^2 - 16 \quad \text{or} \quad y = \pm\sqrt{x^2 - 16}$$

Thus, the equation does not specify a function since, for $x = 5$, we have $y = \pm 3$, when $x = 6$, $y = \pm 2\sqrt{5}$, and so on.

66. Given $G(r) = 3 - 5r$. Then:

$$\frac{G(2 + h) - G(2)}{h} = \frac{3 - 5(2 + h) - (3 - 5 \cdot 2)}{h}$$

$$= \frac{-7 - 5h + 7}{h} = \frac{-5h}{h} = -5$$

68. Given $P(x) = 2x^2 - 3x - 7$. Then:

$$\frac{P(3 + h) - P(3)}{h} = \frac{2(3 + h)^2 - 3(3 + h) - 7 - (2 \cdot 3^2 - 3 \cdot 3 - 7)}{h}$$

$$= \frac{2(9 + 6h + h^2) - 9 - 3h - 7 - (2)}{h}$$

$$= \frac{2h^2 + 9h}{h} = 2h + 9$$

70. (A) $f(x) = -3x + 9$ (B) $f(x + h) = -3x - 3h + 9$

(C) $f(x + h) - f(x) = -3h$ (D) $\dfrac{f(x + h) - f(x)}{h} = -3$

72. (A) $f(x) = 3x^2 + 5x - 8$ (B) $f(x + h) = 3x^2 + 6xh + 3h^2 + 5x + 5h - 8$

(C) $f(x + h) - f(x) = 6xh + 3h^2 + 5h$

(D) $\dfrac{f(x + h) - f(x)}{h} = 6x + 3h + 5$

74. (A) $f(x) = x(x + 40) = x^2 + 40x$

(B) $f(x + h) = x^2 + 2xh + h^2 + 40x + 40h$

(C) $f(x + h) - f(x) = 2xh + h^2 + 40h$ (D) $\dfrac{f(x + h) - f(x)}{h} = 2x + h + 40$

76. Given $A = \ell w = 81$.

Thus, $w = \dfrac{81}{\ell}$. Now $P = 2\ell + 2w = 2\ell + 2\left(\dfrac{81}{\ell}\right) = 2\ell + \dfrac{162}{\ell}$.

The domain is $\ell > 0$.

78. Given $P = 2\ell + 2w = 160$ or $\ell + w = 80$ and $\ell = 80 - w$.

Now $A = \ell w = (80 - w)w$ and $A = 80w - w^2$.

The domain is $0 \le w \le 80$. [Note: $w \le 80$ since $w > 80$ implies $\ell < 0$.]

80.

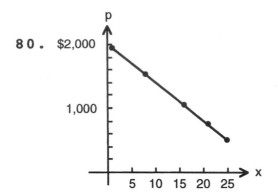

$p(11) = 1,340$ dollars per computer
$p(18) = 920$ dollars per computer

82. (A) $R(x) = xp(x)$
$= x(2,000 - 60x)$ thousands of dollars

Domain: $1 \le x \le 25$

(B) Table 11 Revenue

x(thousands)	$R(x)$ (thousands)
1	$1,940
5	8,500
10	14,000
15	16,500
20	16,000
25	12,500

(C)

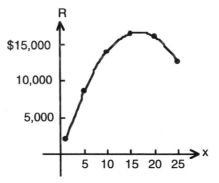

84. (A) $P(x) = R(x) - C(x)$
$= x(2,000 - 60x) - (4,000 + 500x)$ thousand dollars
$= 1,500x - 60x^2 - 4,000$

Domain: $1 \le x \le 25$

(B) Table 13 Profit

x(thousands)	$P(x)$ (thousands)
1	-$2,560
5	2,000
10	5,000
15	5,000
20	2,000
25	-4,000

(C)

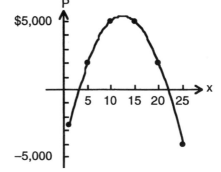

86. (A) 1.2 inches

(B) Evaluate the volume function for $x = 1.21$, 1.22, ..., and choose the value of x whose volume is closest to 65.

(C) $x = 1.23$ to two decimal places

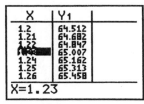

(D)

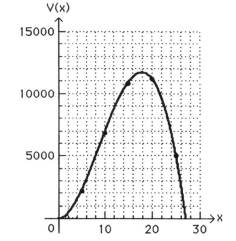

88. (A) $V(x) = x^2(108 - 4x)$

(B) $0 \leq x \leq 27$

(C) Table 15 Volume

x	$V(x)$
5	2,200
10	6,800
15	10,800
20	11,200
25	5,000

90. (A) Given $5v - 2s = 1.4$. Solving for v, we have:
$v = 0.4s + 0.28$.
If $s = 0.51$, then $v = 0.4(0.51) + 0.28 = 0.484$ or 48.4%.

(B) Solving the equation for s, we have:
$s = 2.5v - 0.7$.
If $v = 0.51$, then $s = 2.5(0.51) - 0.7 = 0.575$ or 57.5%.

EXERCISE 1-2
_____

2. $g(x) = -0.3x$
Domain: all real numbers; range: all real numbers

4. $k(x) = 4\sqrt{x}$
Domain: $[0, \infty)$; range: $[0, \infty)$

6. $n(x) = -0.1x^2$
Domain: all real numbers; range: $(-\infty, 0]$

8. $S(x) = 5\sqrt[3]{x}$
Domain: all real numbers; range: all real numbers

10.

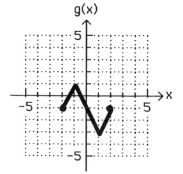

12.

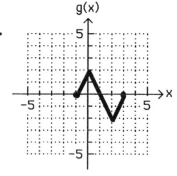

14.

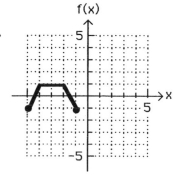

16.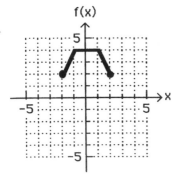

18.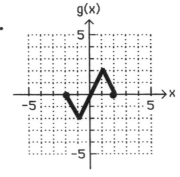

20.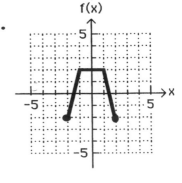

22. The graph of $h(x) = -|x - 5|$ is the graph of $y = |x|$ reflected in the x axis and shifted 5 units to the right.

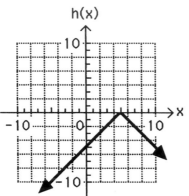

24. The graph of $m(x) = (x + 3)^2 + 4$ is the graph of $y = x^2$ shifted 3 units to the left and 4 units up.

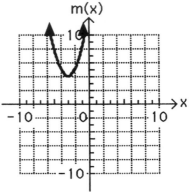

26. The graph of $g(x) = -6 + \sqrt[3]{x}$ is the graph of $y = \sqrt[3]{x}$ shifted 6 units down.

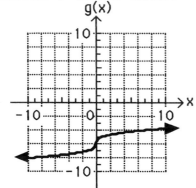

28. The graph of $m(x) = -0.4x^2$ is the same as the graph of $y = x^2$ reflected in the x axis and vertically contracted by a factor of 0.4.

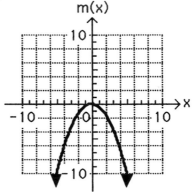

30. The graph of the basic function $y = |x|$ is shifted 3 units to the right and 2 units up. $y = |x - 3| + 2$

32. The graph of the basic function $y = |x|$ is reflected in the x axis, shifted 2 units to the left and 3 units up. Equation: $y = 3 - |x + 2|$

34. The graph of the basic function $\sqrt[3]{x}$ is reflected in the x axis and shifted up 2 units. Equation: $y = 2 - \sqrt[3]{x}$

36. The graph of the basic function $y = x^3$ is reflected in the x axis, shifted to the right 3 units and up 1 unit. Equation: $y = 1 - (x - 3)^3$

38. $g(x) = \sqrt[3]{x + 3} + 2$ **40.** $g(x) = -|x - 1|$ **42.** $g(x) = 4 - (x + 2)^2$

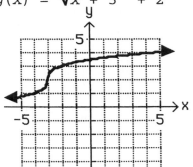 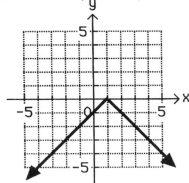 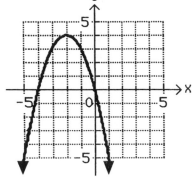

44. $g(x) = \begin{cases} x + 1 & \text{if} \quad x < -1 \\ 2 + 2x & \text{if} \quad x \geq -1 \end{cases}$ **46.** $h(x) = \begin{cases} 10 + 2x & \text{if} \quad 0 \leq x \leq 20 \\ 40 + 0.5x & \text{if} \quad x > 20 \end{cases}$

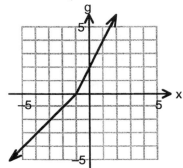 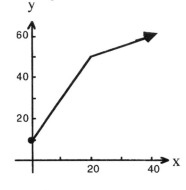

48. $h(x) = \begin{cases} 4x + 20 & \text{if} \quad 0 \leq x \leq 20 \\ 2x + 60 & \text{if} \quad 20 < x \leq 100 \\ -x + 360 & \text{if} \quad x > 100 \end{cases}$

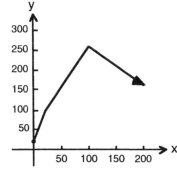

50. The graph of the basic function $y = x$ is reflected in the x axis and vertically expanded by a factor of 2. Equation: $y = -2x$

52. The graph of the basic function $y = |x|$ is vertically expanded by a factor of 4. Equation: $y = 4|x|$

54. The graph of the basic function $y = x^3$ is vertically contracted by a factor of 0.25. Equation: $y = 0.25x^3$.

56. Vertical shift, reflection in y axis.
Reversing the order does not change the result. Consider a point (a, b) in the plane. A vertical shift of k units followed by a reflection in y axis moves (a, b) to $(a, b + k)$ and then to $(-a, b + k)$. In the reverse order, a reflection in y axis followed by a vertical shift of k units moves (a, b) to $(-a, b)$ and then to $(-a, b + k)$. The results are the same.

58. Vertical shift, vertical expansion.
Reversing the order can change the result. For example, let (a, b) be a point in the plane. A vertical shift of k units followed by a vertical expansion of h ($h > 1$) moves (a, b) to $(a, b + k)$ and then to $(a, bh + kh)$. In the reverse order, a vertical expansion of h followed by a vertical shift of k units moves (a, b) to (a, bh) and then to $(a, bh + k)$; $(a, bh + kh) \neq (a, bh + k)$.

60. Horizontal shift, vertical contraction.
Reversing the order does not change the result. Consider a point (a, b) in the plane. A horizontal shift of k units followed by a vertical contraction of h ($0 < h < 1$) moves (a, b) to $(a + k, b)$ and then to $(a + k, bh)$. In the reverse order, a vertical contraction of h followed by a horizontal shift of k units moves (a, b) to (a, bh) and then to $(a + k, bh)$. The results are the same.

62. (A) The graph of the basic function $y = \sqrt{x}$ is vertically expanded by a factor of 4.

64. (A) The graph of the basic function $y = x^2$ is reflected in the x axis, vertically contracted by a factor of 0.013, and shifted 10 units to the right and 190 units up.

(B)

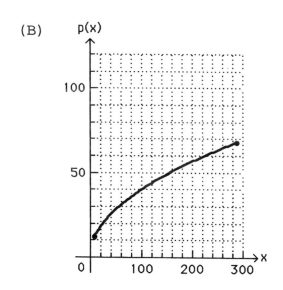

(B)

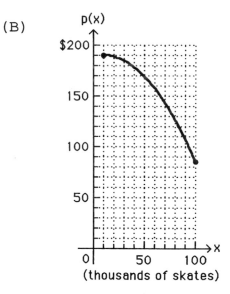

(thousands of skates)

66. (A) Let x = number of kwh used in a winter month. For $0 \leq x \leq 700$, the charge is $8.5 + .065x$. At $x = 700$, the charge is $54. For $x > 700$, the charge is $54 + .053(x - 700) = 16.9 + 0.053x$. Thus,

$$W(x) = \begin{cases} 8.5 + .065x & \text{if} \quad 0 \leq x \leq 700 \\ 16.9 + 0.053x & \text{if} \quad x > 700 \end{cases}$$

(B)

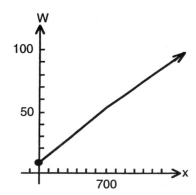

68. (A)   Let x = taxable income.
          If $0 \le x \le 15,000$, the tax due is
          $\$.035x$. At $x = 15,000$, the tax due is
          $\$525$. For $15,000 < x \le 30,00$, the tax
          due is $525 + .0625(x - 15,000) =$
          $.0625x - 412.5$. For $x > 30,000$,
          the tax due is
          $1,462.5 + .0645(x - 30,000)$
          $= .0645x - 472.5$.

          Thus,

$$T(x) = \begin{cases} 0.035x & \text{if} \quad 0 \le x \le 15,000 \\ 0.0625x - 412.5 & \text{if} \quad 15,000 < x \le 30,000 \\ 0.0645x - 472.5 & \text{if} \quad x > 30,000 \end{cases}$$

(B)
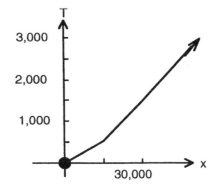

(C) $T(20,000) = \$837.50$
    $T(35,000) = \$1,785$

70. (A) The graph of the basic
       function $y = x^3$ is vertically
       expanded by a factor of 463.

(B) w(x)
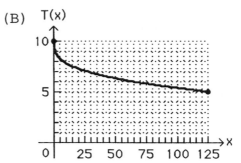

72. (A) The graph of the basic
       function $y = \sqrt[3]{x}$ is reflected in
       the x axis and shifted up 10
       units.

(B) T(x)
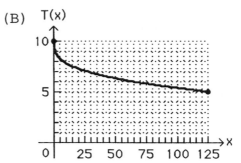

EXERCISE 1-3
_____

2. (a)

4. (b); slope is not defined for a vertical line

6. $y = \dfrac{x}{2} + 1$

x	y
0	1
2	2
4	3

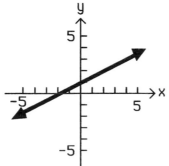

8. $8x - 3y = 24$

x	y
0	-8
3	0
6	8

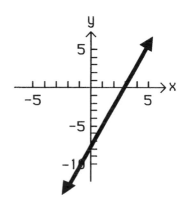

10. Slope $m = \dfrac{1}{5}$

y intercept $b = -2$

12. Slope $m = 0.7$

y intercept $b = 5$

14. $m = \dfrac{3}{4}$

$b = -5$

Using <u>6</u>, $y = \dfrac{3}{4}x - 5$.

16. $m = -5$

$b = 9$

Using <u>6</u>, $y = -5x + 9$.

18. $y = -\dfrac{3}{2}x + 1$

$m = -\dfrac{3}{2}$, $b = 1$

x	y
0	1
2	-1
-2	4

20. $5x - 6y = 15$

x	y
0	-2.5
3	0
-3	-5

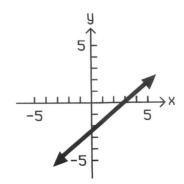

22.

$x = -3$ $y = 2$

24. $5x - y = -2$

$\quad -y = -5x - 2$

Multiply both sides by (-1);

$y = 5x + 2$

$m = 5$ (using <u>6</u>)

26. $2x - 3y = 18$

$\quad -3y = -2x + 18$

Divide both sides by (-3);

$y = \dfrac{2}{3}x - 6$

$m = \dfrac{2}{3}$ (using <u>6</u>)

28.

(A) $x = 4$

(B) $y = 3$

(C) $y = -\dfrac{2}{3}x + 8$

30. $g(x) = 40x + 160$, $x \geq 0$

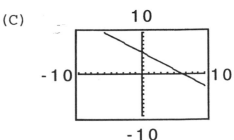

(B) x intercept: 6.5;
y intercept: 5.2

32. (A) Set $f(x) = 0$, $-0.8x + 5.2 = 0$, $x = 6.5$.
Set $x = 0$, $y = 5.2$.

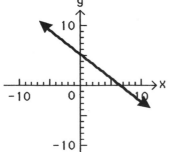

(C)

10

-10 | | 10

-10

(D) x intercept: 6.5;
y intercept: 5.2

34. Using $\underline{3}$ with $a = -5$ for the vertical line and $b = 6$ for the horizontal line, we find that the equation of the vertical line is $x = -5$ and the equation of the horizontal line is $y = 6$.

36. Using $\underline{3}$ with $a = 2.6$ for the vertical line and $b = 3.8$ for the horizontal line, we find that the equation of the vertical line is $x = 2.6$ and the equation of the horizontal line is $y = 3.8$.

38. $m = -6$
For the point $(-4, 1)$, $x_1 = -4$ and $y_1 = 1$. Using $\underline{7}$, we get:
$$y - 1 = -6[x - (-4)]$$
$$y - 1 = -6x - 24$$
$$y = -6x - 23$$

40. $m = \dfrac{4}{3}$
For the point $(-6, 2)$, $x_1 = -6$ and $y_1 = 2$. Using $\underline{7}$, we get:
$$y - 2 = \frac{4}{3}[x - (-6)]$$
$$y - 2 = \frac{4}{3}x + 8$$
$$y = \frac{4}{3}x + 10$$

42. $y - (-2.7) = 0[x - 3.1]$
$y + 2.7 = 0$ or $y = -2.7$

44. (A) $m = \dfrac{5 - 2}{3 - 1} = \dfrac{3}{2}$

(B) Using $y - y_1 = m(x - x_1)$, where $m = \dfrac{3}{2}$ and $(x_1, y_1) = (1, 2)$ or $(3, 5)$, we get:
$$y - 2 = \frac{3}{2}(x - 1) \quad \text{or} \quad y - 5 = \frac{3}{2}(x - 3)$$
Those two equations are equivalent. After simplifying either one of these, we obtain:
$$y - 2 = \frac{3}{2}(x - 1) \quad \text{or} \quad 3x - 2y = -1.$$

(C) Linear function

46. (A) $m = \dfrac{7 - 3}{-3 - 2} = -\dfrac{4}{5}$

(B) Using $y - y_1 = m(x - x_1)$, where $m = -\dfrac{4}{5}$ and (x_1, y_1) is either of these points, we obtain:
$$y - 7 = -\frac{4}{5}(x + 3) \quad \text{or} \quad 4x + 5y = 23.$$

(C) Linear function

48. (A) $m = \dfrac{4 - 4}{0 - 1} = \dfrac{0}{-1} = 0$

(B) The line through $(1, 4)$ and $(0, 4)$ is horizontal; $y = 4$.

(C) Constant function

50. (A) $m = \dfrac{-3 - 0}{2 - 2} = \dfrac{-3}{0}$ which is not defined.

   (B) The line through (2, 0) and (2, -3) is vertical; $x = 2$.

   (C) Neither

52. The graphs are parallel lines with slope -0.5

54. (A) 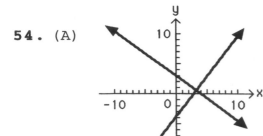   (B)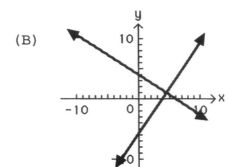

56. The graph of $g(x) = m|x| + b$ coincides with the graph of $f(x) = mx + b$ for all $x \geq 0$. For $x < 0$, the graph of g is the reflection of the graph of f for $x > 0$ in the y axis.

58. We are given $A = 75t + 1,000 = t \geq 0$

   (A) At $t = 5$,
   we have $A = 75(5) + 1,000 = \$1,375$

   At $t = 20$,
   we have $A = 75(20) + 1,000 = \$2,500$

   (B)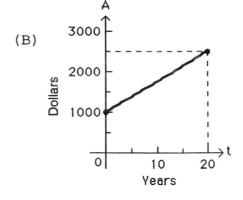

   (C) The equation $A = 75t + 1,000$ is in slope-intercept form. Thus, the slope is 75. The amount in the account is growing at the rate of \$75 per year.

60. (A) We find an equation $C(x) = mx + b$ for the line passing through (0, 300) and (20, 5100).
   $$m = \dfrac{5100 - 300}{20 - 0} = \dfrac{4800}{20} = 240$$
   Also, since $C(x) = 300$ when $x = 0$, it follows that $b = 300$. Thus, $C(x) = 240x + 300$.

   (B) The total costs at 12 boards per day are:
   $$C(12) = 240(12) + 300 = \$3,180$$

   (C)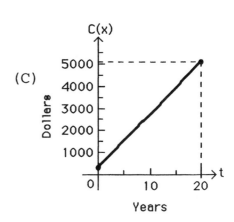

62. (A) Slope: $m = \dfrac{20{,}000 - 2{,}000}{0 - 10}$

$= -1{,}800$

y intercept: 20,000

equation:

$V(t) = -1{,}800t + 20{,}000$

(B) $V(6) = -1{,}800(6) + 20{,}000 = \$9{,}200$

(C)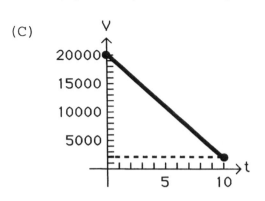

(D) The equation $V(t) = -1{,}800t + 20{,}000$ is in slope-intercept form. Thus the slope is $-1{,}800$. The value decreases \$1,800 per year.

64. (A) Supply: $p(5.50) = 2.4$ and $p(7.30) = 2.8$. Thus, the slope of the price-supply line is $m = \dfrac{2.8 - 2.4}{7.30 - 5.50} = \dfrac{2}{9}$, and hence

$p - 2.4 = \dfrac{2}{9}(x - 5.5)$ or $p = \dfrac{2}{9}x + \dfrac{53}{45}$.

Demand: $p(5.50) = 2.9$ and $p(7.30) = 2.4$. Thus the slope of the price-demand line is $m = \dfrac{2.9 - 2.4}{5.5 - 7.3} = -\dfrac{5}{18}$, and hence

$p - 2.4 = -\dfrac{5}{18}(x - 7.3)$ or $p = -\dfrac{5}{18}x + \dfrac{79.7}{18}$.

(B) Equilibrium point: $\dfrac{2}{9}x + \dfrac{53}{45} = -\dfrac{5}{18}x + \dfrac{79.7}{18}$ which implies $x = 6.5$

and $p(6.5) = \dfrac{118}{45} \approx 2.62$ million bushels.

66. (A)

x	0	1	2	3	4
Net Income	3.3	3.8	4.6	5.2	5.9
$f(x)$	3.2	3.9	4.6	5.2	5.9

(B)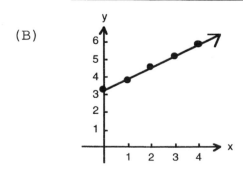

(C) $f(10) = \$9.84$ billion;
$f(15) = \$13.14$ billion

68. (A) The slope of the line is
$$m = \frac{44 - 11}{60 - 20} = \frac{33}{40} = .825.$$
Thus the equation of the linear function is
$f(x) - 11 = .825(x - 20)$ or
$f(x) = 0.825x - 5.5.$

(B) $f(32) = 20.9\%,$ $f(56) = 40.7\%$

(C) Near the end of 2027.

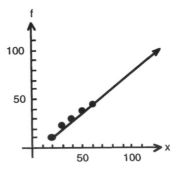

70. (A) The slope is: $m = \frac{30 - 15}{33 - 0} = \frac{15}{33} = \frac{5}{11}.$

Thus, the equation is $p - 15 = \frac{5}{11}(x - 0)$ or $p = \frac{5}{11}d + 15.$

(B) $p(12,540) = \frac{5}{11}(12,540) + 15 = 5,715$ pounds per square inch.

(C)

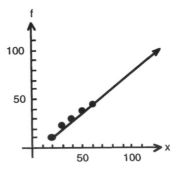

(D) The slope is $\frac{5}{11} \approx 0.45.$ The pressure increases approximately 0.45 pounds per square inch for each one foot increase in depth.

EXERCISE 1-4

---

2. $x^2 - 2x - 5 = x^2 - 2x + 1 - 6$
$ = (x - 1)^2 - 6$

4. $-x^2 + 8x - 9 = -(x^2 - 8x + 9)$
$ = -(x^2 - 8x + 16 - 7)$
$ = -(x - 4)^2 + 7$

6. The graph of $g(x)$ is the graph of $y = x^2$ shifted right 1 unit and down 6 units.

8. The graph of $n(x)$ is the graph of $y = x^2$ reflected in the x axis, then shifted right 4 units and up 7 units.

10. (A) g (B) m (C) n (D) f

12. (A) x intercepts: -5, -1; y intercept: -5   (B) Vertex: (-3, 4)
(C) Maximum: 4   (D) Range: $y \leq 4$ or $(-\infty, 4]$
(E) Increasing interval: $x \leq -3$ or $(-\infty, -3]$
(F) Decreasing interval: $x \geq -3$ or $[-3, \infty)$

14. (A) x intercepts: 1, 5; y intercept: 5   (B) Vertex: (3, -4)
(C) Minimum: -4   (D) Range: $y \geq 4$ or $[-4, \infty)$
(E) Increasing interval: $x \geq 3$ or $[3, \infty)$
(F) Decreasing interval: $x \leq 3$ or $(-\infty, 3]$

16. $g(x) = -(x + 2)^2 + 3$

    (A) x intercepts: $-(x + 2)^2 + 3 = 0$

$$(x + 2)^2 = 3$$
$$x + 2 = \pm\sqrt{3}$$
$$x = -2 - \sqrt{3}, \; -2 + \sqrt{3}$$

       y intercept: -1

    (B) Vertex: $(-2, 3)$ (C) Maximum: 3   (D) Range: $y \leq 3$ or $(-\infty, 3]$

18. $n(x) = (x - 4)^2 - 3$

    (A) x intercepts: $(x - 4)^2 - 3 = 0$

$$(x - 4)^2 = 3$$
$$x - 4 = \pm\sqrt{3}$$
$$x = 4 - \sqrt{3}, \; 4 + \sqrt{3}$$

       y intercept: 13

    (B) Vertex: $(4, -3)$ (C) Minimum: -3 (D) Range: $y \geq -3$ or $[-3, \infty)$

20. $y = -(x - 4)^2 + 2$

22. $y = [x - (-3)]^2 + 1$ or $y = (x + 3)^2 + 1$

24. $g(x) = x^2 - 6x + 5 = x^2 - 6x + 9 - 4 = (x - 3)^2 - 4$

    (A) x intercepts: $(x - 3)^2 - 4 = 0$

$$(x - 3)^2 = 4$$
$$x - 3 = \pm 2$$
$$x = 1, \; 5$$

       y intercept: 5

    (B) Vertex: $(3, -4)$ (C) Minimum: -4 (D) Range: $y \geq -4$ or $[-4, \infty)$

26. $S(x) = -4x^2 - 8x - 3 = -4\left[x^2 + 2x + \dfrac{3}{4}\right] = -4\left[x^2 + 2x + 1 - \dfrac{1}{4}\right]$

$$= -4\left[(x + 1)^2 - \dfrac{1}{4}\right] = -4(x + 1)^2 + 1$$

    (A) x intercepts: $-4(x + 1)^2 + 1 = 0$

$$4(x + 1)^2 = 1$$
$$(x + 1)^2 = \dfrac{1}{4}$$
$$x + 1 = \pm\dfrac{1}{2}$$
$$x = -\dfrac{3}{2}, \; -\dfrac{1}{2}$$

       y intercept: -3

    (B) Vertex: $(-1, 1)$ (C) Maximum: 1   (D) Range: $y \leq 1$ or $(-\infty, 1]$

28. $V(x) = .5x^2 + 4x + 10 = .5[x^2 + 8x + 20] = .5[x^2 + 8x + 16 + 4]$
$$= .5[(x + 4)^2 + 4]$$
$$= .5(x + 4)^2 + 2$$

(A) x intercepts: none
y intercept: 10

(B) Vertex: $(-4, 2)$ (C) Minimum: 2   (D) Range: $y \geq 2$ or $[2, \infty)$

30. $g(x) = -0.6x^2 + 3x + 4$

(A) $g(x) = -2$: $-0.6x^2 + 3x + 4 = -2$
$$0.6x^2 - 3x - 6 = 0$$

(B) $g(x) = 5$: $-0.6x^2 + 3x + 4 = 5$
$$-0.6x^2 + 3x - 1 = 0$$
$$0.6x^2 - 3x + 1 = 0$$

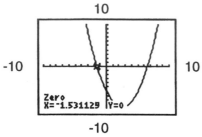

$x = -1.53, 6.53$

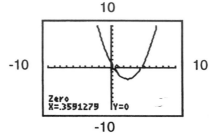

$x = 0.36, 4.64$

(C) $g(x) = 8$: $-0.6x^2 + 3x + 4 = 8$
$$-0.6x^2 + 3x - 4 = 0$$
$$0.6x^2 - 3x + 4 = 0$$

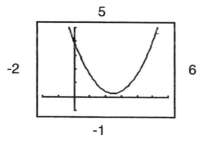

No solution

32. Using a graphing utility with $y = 100x - 7x^2 - 10$ and the calculus option with maximum command, we obtain 347.1429 as the maximum value.

34. The graph is entirely above or below the x axis.

36. $m(x) = 0.20x^2 - 1.6x - 1 = 0.20(x^2 - 8x - 5)$
$$= 0.20[(x - 4)^2 - 21]$$
$$= 0.20(x - 4)^2 - 4.2$$

(A) x intercepts: $0.20(x - 4)^2 - 4.2 = 0$
$$(x - 4)^2 = 21$$
$$x - 4 = \pm\sqrt{21}$$
$$x = 4 - \sqrt{21} = -0.6, \quad 4 + \sqrt{21} = 8.6;$$

y intercept: -1

(B) Vertex: $(4, -4.2)$ (C) Minimum: -4.2
(D) Range: $y \geq -4.2$ or $[-4.2, \infty)$

38. $n(x) = -0.15x^2 - 0.90x + 3.3$
$\qquad = -0.15(x^2 + 6x - 22)$
$\qquad = -0.15[(x + 3)^2 - 31]$
$\qquad = -0.15(x + 3)^2 + 4.65$

(A) x intercepts: $-0.15(x + 3)^2 + 4.65 = 0$
$$(x + 3)^2 = 31$$
$$x + 3 = \pm\sqrt{31}$$
$$x = -3 - \sqrt{31} = -8.6, \quad -3 + \sqrt{31} = 2.6;$$

y intercept: 3.30

(B) Vertex: $(-3, 4.65)$ (C) Maximum: 3.30

(D) Range: $x \leq 4.65$ or $(-\infty, 4.65]$

40.

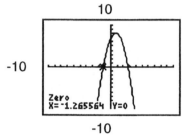

$x = -1.27, \ 2.77$

42.

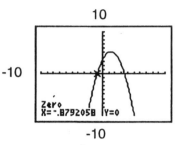

$-0.88 \leq x \leq 3.52$

44.

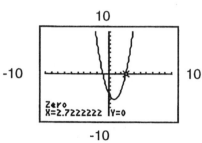

$x < -1$ or $x > 2.72$

46. f is a quadratic function and max $f(x) = f(-3) = -5$
Axis: $x = -3$
Vertex: $(-3, -5)$
Range: $y \leq -5$ or $(-\infty, -5]$
x intercepts: None

48. (A)

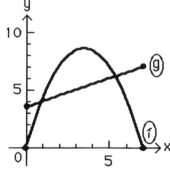

(B) $f(x) = g(x)$: $-0.7x(x - 7) = 0.5x + 3.5$
$$-0.7x^2 + 4.4x - 3.5 = 0$$
$$x = \frac{-4.4 \pm \sqrt{(4.4)^2 - (0.7)(3.5)}}{-1.4} = 0.93, \ 5.35$$

(C) $f(x) > g(x)$ for $0.93 < x < 5.35$

(D) $f(x) < g(x)$ for $0 \leq x < 0.93$ or $5.35 < x \leq 7$

50. (A)

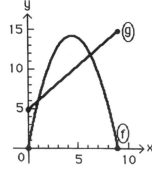

(B) $f(x) = g(x)$: $-0.7x^2 + 6.3x = 1.1x + 4.8$

$$-0.7x^2 - 5.2x - 4.8 = 0$$
$$0.7x^2 + 5.2x + 4.8 = 0$$
$$x = \frac{-5.2 \pm \sqrt{(5.2)^2 - (0.7)(4.8)}}{1.4} = 1.08, \; 6.35$$

(C) $f(x) > g(x)$ for $1.08 < x < 6.35$

(D) $f(x) < g(x)$ for $0 \le x < 1.08$ or $6.35 < x \le 9$

52. $f(x) = x^2$ and $g(x) = -(x - 4)^2$ are two examples. The vertex of the graph is on the x axis.

54. (A) $f(x) = .04x^2 - 0.8x + 22$

x	0	5	10	15	20
Market share	23.6	17.2	18.8	20	20.7
$f(x)$	22	19	18	19	22

(B)

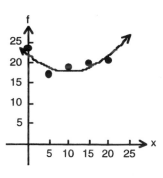

(C) $f(25) = 27\%$, $f(30) = 34\%$

56. (A)

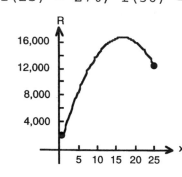

(B) $R(x) = 2,000x - 60x^2$

$$= -60\left(x^2 - \frac{100}{3}x\right)$$
$$= -60\left[x^2 - \frac{100}{3}x + \frac{2500}{9} - \frac{2500}{9}\right]$$
$$= -60\left[\left(x - \frac{50}{3}\right)^2 - \frac{2500}{9}\right]$$
$$= -60\left(x - \frac{50}{3}\right) + \frac{50,000}{3}$$

16.667 thousand computers (16,667 computers);
16,666.667 thousand dollars ($16,666,667)

(C) $p\left(\dfrac{50}{3}\right) = 2,000 - 60\left(\dfrac{50}{3}\right) = \$1,000$

58. (A)

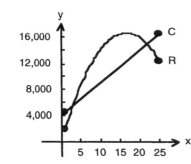

(B) $R(x) = C(x)$

$$x(2,000 - 60x) = 4,000 + 500x$$
$$2,000x - 60x^2 = 4,000 + 500x$$
$$60x^2 - 1,500x + 4,000 = 0$$
$$6x^2 - 150x + 400 = 0$$
$$x = 3.035, 21.965$$

Break-even at 3.035 thousands (3,035) and 21.965 thousand (21,965)

(C) Loss: $1 \leq x < 3.035$ or $21.965 < x \leq 25$;
Profit: $3.035 < x < 21.965$

60. (A) $P(x) = R(x) - C(x)$
$$= 1,500x - 60x^2 - 4,000$$

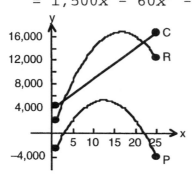

(C) Intercepts and break-even points: 3,035 computers and 21,965 computers

(E) Maximum profit is $5,375,000 when 12,500 computers are produced. This is much smaller than the maximum revenue of $16,666,667.

62. (A) Solve: $f(x) = 1,000(0.04 - x^2) = 30$
$$40 - 1000x^2 = 30$$
$$1000x^2 = 10$$
$$x^2 = 0.01$$
$$x = 0.10 \text{ cm}$$

(B)

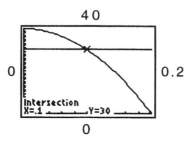

2 ADDITIONAL ELEMENTARY FUNCTIONS

2. (A) 1 (B) $\dfrac{4}{3}$ (C) 4   **4.** (A) 2 (B) 2, 3 (C) –6

6. (A) 2 (B) –7, 4 (C) –28   **8.** (A) 3 (B) –1, $\dfrac{2}{5}$, 6 (C) –12

10. (A) 20 (B) None (C) 35   **12.** (A) 1 (B) 2 (C) negative

14. (A) 2 (B) 3 (C) negative   **16.** (A) 3 (B) 4 (C) positive

18. (A) 4 (B) 5 (C) positive

20. It is one less than the degree of the polynomial. In this case it is 11 – 1 = 10.

22. It is equal to the degree of the polynomial. In this case it is 7.

24. Since the degree is an even number as x approaches $-\infty$ or $+\infty$, the graph of the polynomial approaches ∞. So, its graph may have no intersection with x axis. The minimum number of x intercepts, therefore, is 0.

26. $f(x) = \dfrac{x - 3}{x + 3}$

(A) *Intercepts:*

x intercepts: $f(x) = 0$ only if $x - 3 = 0$ or $x = 3$.
The x intercept is 3.

y intercept: $f(0) = \dfrac{0 - 3}{0 + 3} = -1$
The y intercept is –1.

(B) *Domain:* The denominator is 0 at $x = -3$. Thus, the domain is the set of all real numbers except –3.

(C) *Asymptotes:*

Vertical asymptotes: $f(x) = \dfrac{x - 3}{x + 3}$

The denominator is 0 at $x = -3$. Therefore, the line $x = -3$ is a vertical asymptote.

Horizontal asymptotes: $f(x) = \dfrac{x - 3}{x + 3} = \dfrac{1 - \dfrac{3}{x}}{1 + \dfrac{3}{x}}$

As x increases or decreases without bound, the numerator tends to 1 and the denominator tends to 1. Therefore, the line $y = 1$ is a horizontal asymptote.

(D)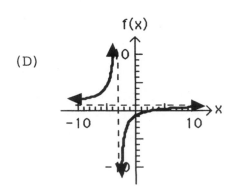

(E)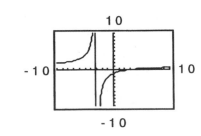

28. $f(x) = \dfrac{2x}{x - 3}$

(A) *Intercepts*:

x intercepts: $f(x) = 0$ only if $2x = 0$ or $x = 0$.
The x intercept is 0.

y intercept: $f(0) = \dfrac{2(0)}{0 - 3} = 0$
The y intercept is 0.

(B) *Domain*: The denominator is 0 at $x = 3$. Thus, the domain is the set of all real numbers except 3.

(C) *Asymptotes*:

Vertical asymptotes: $f(x) = \dfrac{2x}{x - 3}$

The denominator is 0 at $x = 3$. Therefore, the line $x = 3$ is a vertical asymptote.

Horizontal asymptotes: $f(x) = \dfrac{2x}{x - 3} = \dfrac{2}{1 - \dfrac{3}{x}}$

As x increases or decreases without bound, the numerator is 2 and the denominator tends to 1. Therefore, the line $y = 2$ is a horizontal asymptote.

(D)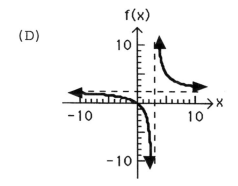

(E)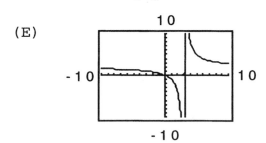

30. $f(x) = \dfrac{3 - 3x}{x - 2}$

(A) *Intercepts:*

x intercepts: $f(x) = 0$ only if $3 - 3x = 0$ or $x = 1$.
The x intercept is 1.

y intercept: $f(0) = \dfrac{3 - 3(0)}{0 - 2} = \dfrac{3}{-2} = -\dfrac{3}{2}$.

The y intercept is $-\dfrac{3}{2}$.

(B) *Domain:* The denominator is 0 at $x = 2$. Thus, the domain is the set of all real numbers except 2.

(C) *Asymptotes:*

Vertical asymptotes: $f(x) = \dfrac{3 - 3x}{x - 2}$

The denominator is 0 at $x = 2$. Therefore, the line $x = 2$ is a vertical asymptote.

Horizontal asymptotes: $f(x) = \dfrac{3 - 3x}{x - 2} = \dfrac{\dfrac{3}{x} - 3}{1 - \dfrac{2}{x}}$

As x increases or decreases without bound, the numerator tends to -3 and the denominator tends to 1. Therefore, the line $y = -3$ is a horizontal asymptote.

(D)

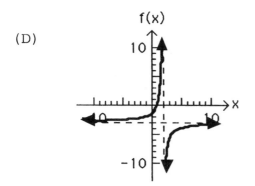

(E)

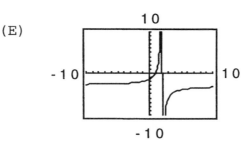

32. The graph of $f(x) = x^3 - 2x + 2 = x^3\left(1 - \dfrac{2}{x^2} + \dfrac{2}{x^3}\right)$ will "look like" the graph of $y = x^3$. For large x, $f(x) \approx x^3$.

34. The graph of $f(x) = -x^5 + 5x^3 + 4x - 1 = -x^5\left(1 - \dfrac{5}{x^2} - \dfrac{4}{x^4} + \dfrac{1}{x^5}\right)$ will "look like" the graph of $y = -x^5$. For large x, $f(x) \approx -x^5$.

36. (A)

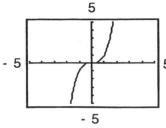

$$y = x^3 \qquad\qquad y = x^3 - 2x + 2$$

(B)

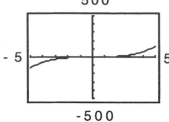

$$y = x^3 \qquad\qquad y = x^3 - 2x + 2$$

38. (A)

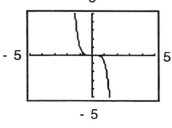

$$y = -x^5 \qquad\qquad y = -x^5 + 5x^3 - 5x + 2$$

(B)

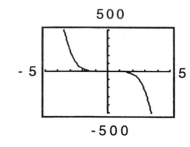

$$y = -x^5 \qquad\qquad y = -x^5 + 5x^3 - 5x + 2$$

40. $P(x) = 3x^3 + 10x^2 + 6x - 2$

Let $Q(x) = \dfrac{1}{3}P(x) = x^3 + \dfrac{10}{3}x^2 + 2x - \dfrac{2}{3}$; $P(x)$ and $Q(x)$ have the same zeros. If x is a zero of $Q(x)$, then, by Theorem 1,

$$|x| < 1 + \max\left\{ \left|\frac{10}{3}\right|, |2|, \left|\frac{-2}{3}\right| \right\} = 1 + \frac{10}{3} = \frac{13}{3}.$$

Thus an interval containing all zeros of

$P(x)$ is $\left[-\dfrac{13}{3}, \dfrac{13}{3} \right]$.

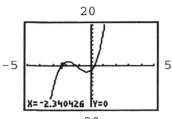

Graph $P(x)$ on $[-5, 5]$

$P(x) = 0$ at $x = -2.37, -1.20, 0.23$.

42. $P(x) = x^4 - 3x^3 - 4x^2 + 3x + 1$
By Theorem 1, if x is a zero of $P(x)$, then

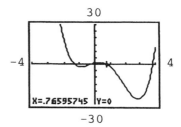

$|x| < 1 + \max\{|-3|, |-4|, |3|, |1|\} = 1 + 4 = 5$
An interval containing all zeros of
$P(x)$ is $[-5, 5]$.

Graph $P(x)$ on $[-5, 5]$

$P(x) = 0$ at $x = -1.32, -0.26, 0.76, 3.82$.

44. $P(x) = x^5 + 14x^4 - 10x^2 - 15$
By Theorem 1, if x is a zero of $P(x)$, then

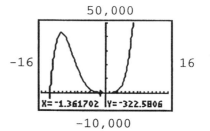

$|x| < 1 + \max\{|14|, |-10|, |-15|\} = 1 + 15 = 16$

An interval containing all zeros of
$P(x)$ is $[-16, 16]$.
Graph $P(x)$ on $[-16, 16]$

$P(x) = 0$ at $x = -13.95, -1.24, 1.17$.

46. The quadratic regression model for the data set consisting of three
points on the graph of the parabola $y = x^2 - 5x$ is simply the parabola
$y = x^2 - 5x$.

48. $f(x) = \dfrac{3x^2}{x^2 + x - 6}$

(A) *Intercepts:*

　　x intercepts: $f(x) = 0$ only if $3x^2 = 0$ or $x = 0$.
　　　　　　　　The x intercept is 0.

　　y intercept: $f(0) = \dfrac{3(0^2)}{0^2 + 0 - 6} = 0$
　　　　　　　　The y intercept is 0.

(B) *Asymptotes:*

　　Vertical asymptotes: $f(x) = \dfrac{3x^2}{x^2 + x - 6} = \dfrac{3x^2}{(x + 3)(x - 2)}$
　　　　　　　　The denominator is 0 at $x = -3$ and $x = 2$.
　　　　　　　　Thus, the lines $x = -3$ and $x = 2$ are vertical
　　　　　　　　asymptotes.

　　Horizontal asymptotes: $f(x) = \dfrac{3x^2}{x^2 + x - 6} = \dfrac{3}{1 + \dfrac{1}{x} - \dfrac{6}{x}}$

　　　　　　　　As x increases or decreases without bound,
　　　　　　　　the numerator is 3 and the denominator
　　　　　　　　tends to 1. Therefore, the line $y = 3$ is a
　　　　　　　　horizontal asymptote.

(C)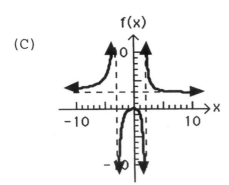

(D)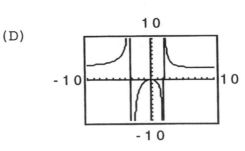

50. $f(x) = \dfrac{3 - 3x^2}{x^2 - 4}$

(A) *Intercepts:*

x intercepts: $f(x) = 0$ only if $3 - 3x^2 = 0$

$$3x^2 = 3$$
$$x^2 = 1$$
$$x = \pm 1$$

The x intercepts are ± 1.

y intercept: $f(0) = \dfrac{3 - 3(0^2)}{0^2 - 4} = \dfrac{3}{-4} = -\dfrac{3}{4}$

The y intercept is $-\dfrac{3}{4}$.

(B) *Asymptotes:*

Vertical asymptotes: $f(x) = \dfrac{3 - 3x^2}{x^2 - 4} = \dfrac{3 - 3x^2}{(x - 2)(x + 2)}$

The denominator is 0 at $x = -2$ and $x = 2$. Thus, the lines $x = -2$ and $x = 2$ are vertical asymptotes.

Horizontal asymptotes: $f(x) = \dfrac{3 - 3x^2}{x^2 - 4} = \dfrac{\dfrac{3}{x^2} - 3}{1 - \dfrac{4}{x^2}}$

As x increases or decreases without bound, the numerator tends to -3 and the denominator tends to 1. Therefore, the line $y = -3$ is a horizontal asymptote.

(C)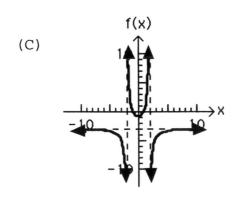

(D)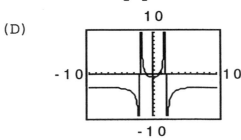

52. $f(x) = \dfrac{5x}{x^2 + x - 12}$

   (A) *Intercepts:*

      x intercepts: $f(x) = 0$ only if $5x = 0$ or $x = 0$.
                  The x intercept is 0.

      y intercept: $f(0) = \dfrac{5(0)}{0^2 + 0 - 12} = 0$
                  The y intercept is 0.

   (B) *Asymptotes:*

      Vertical asymptotes: $f(x) = \dfrac{5x}{x^2 + x - 12} = \dfrac{5x}{(x + 4)(x - 3)}$

                        The denominator is 0 at $x = -4$ and $x = 3$. Thus, the lines $x = -4$ and $x = 3$ are vertical asymptotes.

      Horizontal asymptotes: $f(x) = \dfrac{5x}{x^2 + x - 12} = \dfrac{\dfrac{5}{x}}{1 + \dfrac{1}{x} - \dfrac{12}{x}}$

                        As x increases or decreases without bound, the numerator tends to 0 and the denominator tends to 1. Therefore, the line $y = 0$ (the x axis) is a horizontal asymptote.

(C)

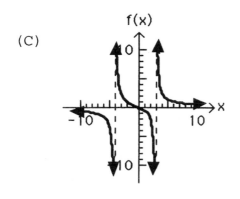

(D)

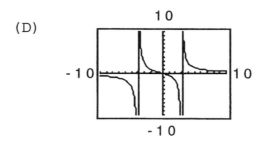

54. The graph has 1 turning point which implies $n = 2$. The x intercepts are $x = -2$ and $x = 1$. The direction of the graph indicates that leading coefficient is negative.
Thus, $f(x) = -(x + 2)(x - 1) = 2 - x - x^2$.

56. The graph has 2 turning points which implies degree $n = 3$. The x intercepts are $x = -1$, $x = 0$, and $x = 1$.
Thus, $f(x) = (x + 1)(x)(x - 1) = x^3 - x$.

58. (A) Since $C(x)$ is a linear function of x, it can be written in the form
        $C(x) = mx + b$
Since the fixed costs are \$300, $b = 300$.
Also, $C(20) = 5100$, so
      $5100 = m(20) + 300$
       $20m = 4800$
         $m = 240$
Therefore, $C(x) = 240x + 300$

   (B) $\overline{C}(x) = \dfrac{C(x)}{x} = \dfrac{240x + 300}{x}$

(C)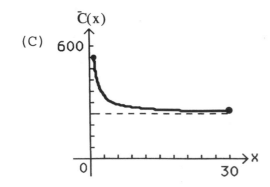

(D) $\overline{C}(x) = \dfrac{240x + 300}{x}$

$\qquad = \dfrac{240 + \dfrac{300}{x}}{1}$

As x increases, the numerator tends to 240 and the denominator is 1. Therefore, $\overline{C}(x)$ tends to 240 or $240 per board.

60. (A) $\overline{C}(x) = \dfrac{x^2 + 2x + 2000}{x}$

(B)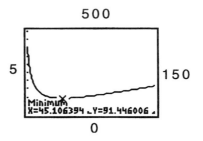

(C) Using the graph, we calculate
$\overline{C}(40) = 92$
$\overline{C}(45) = 91.44$
$\overline{C}(50) = 92$
Thus, it appears that the average cost per unit is a minimum at $x = 45$ units; at 45 units, the minimum average cost per player is $91.44.

(D) 45 units; $91.44 per player

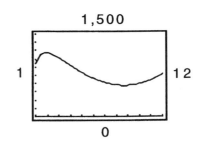

62. (A) $\overline{C}(x) = \dfrac{20x^3 - 360x^2 + 2300x - 1000}{x}$

(B)

(C) The caseload which yields the minimum average cost per case is 8.667 thousand cases per month. At 8.667 thousand cases per month, the average cost per case is $567.

64. (A) Quadratic regression model for Table 5.

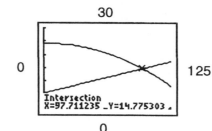

Linear regression model for Table 6.

```
LinReg
y=ax+b
a=.0942446043
b=5.566546763
```

(B) Graphing the two models, we have

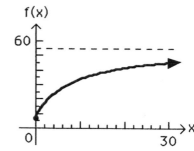

The equilibrium price is $\bar{p}$ = \$14.78 and the equilibrium quantity is $\bar{x}$ = 98.

66. (A)

```
CubicReg
y=ax³+bx²+cx+d
a=.0166666667
b=-.2514285714
c=-2.688095238
d=271.3285714
■
```

(B) $y(30) = 414$

68. (A) $f(x) = \dfrac{55(x + 1)}{(x + 8)} = \dfrac{55\left(1 + \dfrac{1}{x}\right)}{1 + \dfrac{8}{x}}$

(B)

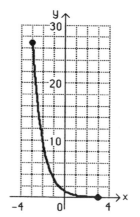

As x increases, the numerator tends to 55 and the denominator tends to 1. Therefore, $f(x)$ approaches 55 words per minute as x increases.

70. (A)

```
CubicReg
y=ax³+bx²+cx+d
a=-2.760943ε-5
b=-.0023419913
c=.2762097162
d=-.5841269841
■
```

(B) $y(50) = 1.7$ divorces per 1,000 population.

EXERCISE 2-2

2. (A) g (B) f (C) h (D) k

4. $y = 3^x$, $-3 \le x \le 3$

x	y
-3	$\frac{1}{27}$
-1	$\frac{1}{3}$
0	1
1	3
3	27

6. $y = \left(\dfrac{1}{3}\right)^x = 3^{-x}$, $-3 \le x \le 3$

x	y
-3	27
-1	3
0	1
1	$\frac{1}{3}$
3	$\frac{1}{9}$

8. $g(x) = -3^{-x}$, $-3 \le x \le 3$

x	$f(x)$
-3	-27
-1	-3
0	-1
1	$-\frac{1}{3}$
3	$-\frac{1}{27}$

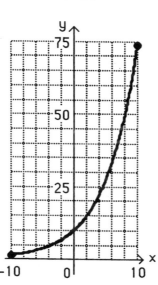

10. $y = -e^x$, $-3 \le x \le 3$

x	y
-3	≈ -0.05
-1	≈ -0.4
0	-1
1	≈ -2.7
3	≈ -20

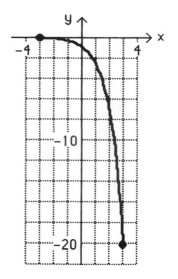

12. $y = 10e^{0.2x}$, $-10 \le x \le 10$

x	y
-10	≈ 1.4
-8	≈ 2.0
-6	≈ 3.0
0	10.0
6	≈ 33.2
8	≈ 49.5
10	≈ 73.9

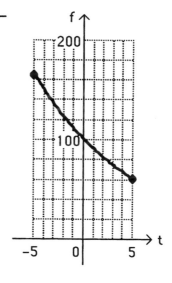

14. $f(t) = 100e^{-0.1t}$, $-5 \le t \le 5$

t	$f(t)$
-5	≈ 165
-3	≈ 135
-1	≈ 111
0	100
1	≈ 90
3	≈ 74
5	≈ 60

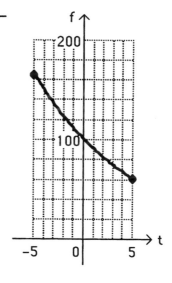

16. $10^{2x + 3}$ **18.** $\dfrac{e^x}{e^{1-x}} = e^{x-(1-x)} = e^{2x - 1}$ **20.** $(3e^{-1.4x})^2 = 9e^{-2.8x}$

22. $g(x) = f(x - 2)$; the graph of g is the graph of f shifted 2 units to the right.

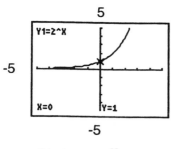

$f(x) = 2^x$

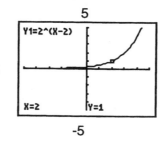

$g(x) = 2^{x-2}$

24. $g(x) = -f(x)$; the graph of g is the graph of f reflected in the x axis.

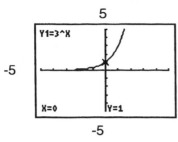

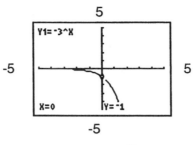

$$f(x) = 3^x$$

$$g(x) = -3^x$$

26. $g(x) = f(x) - 2$; the graph of g is the graph of f shifted two units down.

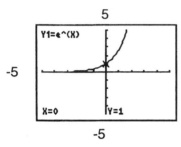

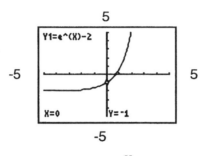

$$f(x) = e^x$$

$$g(x) = e^x - 2$$

28. $g(x) = 0.5f(x - 1)$; the graph of g is the graph of f vertically contracted by a factor of 0.5 and shifted to the right 1 unit.

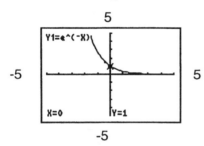

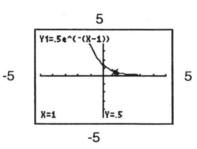

$$f(x) = e^{-x}$$

$$g(x) = 0.5e^{-(x-1)}$$

30. (A)   (B)   (C)   (D)

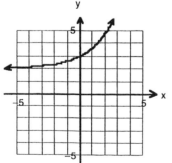
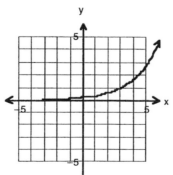
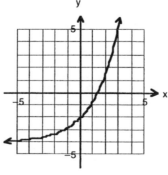
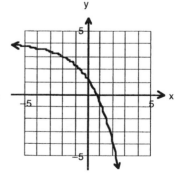

32. $G(t) = 3^{t/100}$, $-200 \le t \le 200$

t	$G(t)$
-200	$\frac{1}{9}$
-100	$\frac{1}{3}$
0	1
100	3
200	9

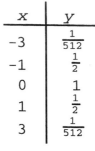

34. $y = 2 + e^{x-2}$, $-1 \le x \le 5$

x	y
-1	$\approx\ 2.0$
0	$\approx\ 2.1$
1	$\approx\ 2.4$
3	$\approx\ 4.7$
5	$\approx\ 22.0$

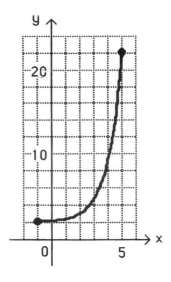

36. $y = e^{-|x|}$, $-3 \le x \le 3$

x	y
-3	$\approx\ 0$
-1	$\approx\ 0.4$
0	1
1	$\approx\ 0.4$
3	$\approx\ 0$

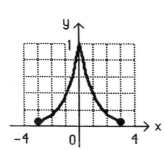

38. $M(x) = e^{x/2} + e^{-x/2}$, $-5 \le x \le 5$

x	y
-5	$\approx\ 12.2$
-3	$\approx\ 4.7$
-1	$\approx\ 2.3$
0	2
1	$\approx\ 2.3$
3	$\approx\ 4.7$
5	$\approx\ 12.2$

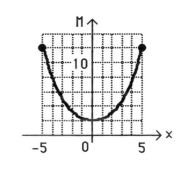

40. $y = 2^{-x^2}$, $-3 \le x \le 3$

x	y
-3	$\frac{1}{512}$
-1	$\frac{1}{2}$
0	1
1	$\frac{1}{2}$
3	$\frac{1}{512}$

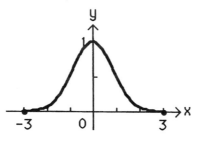

42. $a = 2$, $b = -2$ for example. The exponential function property: For $x \ne 0$, $a^x = b^x$ if and only if $a = b$ assumes $a > 0$, $b > 0$.

44. $5^{3x} = 5^{4x-2}$ implies $3x = 4x - 2$ or $x = 2$

46. $7^{x^2} = 7^{2x + 3}$ implies $x^2 = 2x + 3$
$$x^2 - 2x - 3 = 0$$
$$(x - 3)(x + 1) = 0 \text{ or } x = -1, 3$$

48. $(1 - x)^5 = (2x - 1)^5$ implies $1 - x = 2x - 1$ if $x < 1$ and $x > \frac{1}{2}$.

So $3x = 2$ or $x = \frac{2}{3}$ is a solution since $\frac{1}{2} < x - \frac{2}{3} < 1$.

50. $2xe^{-x} = 0$

$\quad\quad 2x = 0 \quad$ (since $e^{-x} \neq 0$)

$\quad\quad\quad x = 0$

52. $x^2 e^x - 5xe^x = 0$

$\quad\quad x(x - 5)e^x = 0$

$\quad\quad\quad x(x - 5) = 0 \quad$ (since $e^x \neq 0$)

$\quad\quad\quad\quad\quad x = 0, 5$

54. $m(x) = x(3^{-x}), \ 0 \leq x \leq 3$

x	$m(x)$
0	0
1	$\frac{1}{3}$
2	$\frac{2}{9}$
3	$\frac{1}{9}$

56. $N(t) = \dfrac{200}{1 + 3e^{-t}}, \ 0 \leq t \leq 5$

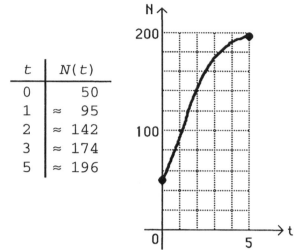

t	$N(t)$
0	50
1	$\approx$ 95
2	$\approx$ 142
3	$\approx$ 174
5	$\approx$ 196

58. $f(x) = 5 - 3^{-x}$

Solve $5 - 3^{-x} = 0$

$\quad\quad\quad x = -1.46$

60. $f(x) = 7 - 2x^2 + 2^{-x}$

Solve $7 - 2x^2 + 2^{-x} = 0$

$\quad\quad\quad x = -6.05, \ -2.53, \ 1.91$

62. $A = P\left(1 + \dfrac{r}{m}\right)^{mt}$, we have:

(A) $P = 4,000, \ r = 0.07, \ m = 52, \ t = \dfrac{1}{2}$

$\quad A = 4,000\left(1 + \dfrac{0.07}{52}\right)^{(52)(1/2)} = 4,142.38$

Thus, $A = \$4,142.38$.

(B) $A = 4,000\left(1 + \dfrac{0.07}{52}\right)^{(52)(10)} = 8,051.22$

Thus, $A = \$8,051.22$.

64. $A = Pe^{rt}$ with $P = 5,250, \ r = 0.0745$, we have:

(A) $A = 5,250e^{(0.0745)(6.25)} = 8,363.30$.

Thus, there will be \$8,363.30 in the account after 6.25 years.

(B) $A = 5,250e^{(0.0745)(17)} = 18,629.16$

Thus, there will be \$18,629.16 in the account after 17 years.

66. Using $A = P\left(1 + \dfrac{r}{m}\right)^{mt}$, we have:

$A = 40,000, \ r = 0.055, \ m = 365, \ t = 17$

Thus, $40,000 = P\left(1 + \dfrac{0.055}{365}\right)^{(365)(17)} = 15,704.54$. Therefore, $P \approx \$15,705$.

68. (A) Oriental Bank of Trust:

$$A = P\left(1 + \frac{r}{m}\right)^{mt} = 10,000\left(1 + \frac{0.0325}{4}\right)^{(4)(5)} = \$11,756.76$$

(B) BMW Bank of North America:

$$A = P\left(1 + \frac{r}{m}\right)^{mt} = 10,000\left(1 + \frac{0.0316}{12}\right)^{(12)(5)} = \$11,709.23$$

(C) Bank First Corporation:

$$A = P\left(1 + \frac{r}{m}\right)^{mt} = 10,000\left(1 + \frac{0.0297}{365}\right)^{(365)(5)} = \$11,600.86$$

70. In $A = Pe^{rt}$, we are given $A = 30,000$, $r = 0.07$, and $t = 10$. Thus:
$30,000 = Pe^{(0.07)(10)}$ or $P = \dfrac{30,000}{e^{0.7}} = 14,897.56$

You should be willing to pay \$14,897.56 for the note.

72. Given $N = 40(1 - e^{-0.12t})$, $0 \le t \le 30$

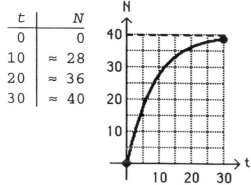

t	N
0	0
10	≈ 28
20	≈ 36
30	≈ 40

Maximum number of boards an average employee can be expected to produce in 1 day is 40.

74. (A)

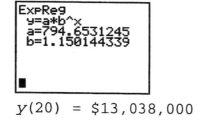

$y(20) = \$13,038,000$

(B) The model gives an average of \$2,116,000 in 1997. Inclusion of the data for 1997 gives

ExpReg
y=a*b^x
a = 798.0806951
b = 1.150556933

and $y(20) = \$13,189,000$.

76. Given $I = I_0 e^{-0.00942d}$

(A) $I = I_0 e^{-0.00942(50)} = I_0 e^{-0.471} \approx I_0(0.62)$

Thus, about 62% of the surface light will reach a depth of 50 feet.

(B) $I = I_0 e^{-0.00942(100)} = I_0 e^{-0.942} \approx I_0(0.39)$

Thus, about 39% of the surface light will reach a depth of 100 feet.

78. (A) The model is $N = N_0 e^{rt} = 24.8 e^{0.19t}$

(B) The number of people (to the nearest million) who had died from AIDS prior to 1999 can be obtained from the equation $24.8 = Pe^{0.19(3)}$ or $P = 24.8 e^{-0.19(3)} \approx 14,000,000$. The number of deaths prior to 2010 is $N(8) = 24.8 e^{0.19(8)} \approx 113,000,000$.

(C)

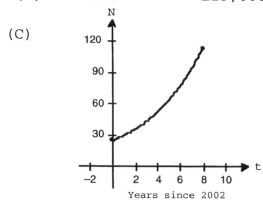

80. (A) With $P_0 = 68$ and $r = 0.026$,

we have $P = 68 e^{0.026t}$

(B) In the year 2010, $t = 8$ and
$$P = 68 e^{0.026(8)} = 68 e^{0.208}$$
$$\approx 84 \text{ million}$$

In the year 2030, $t = 28$ and
$$P = 68 e^{0.026(28)} = 68 e^{0.728}$$
$$\approx 141 \text{ million}$$

(C)

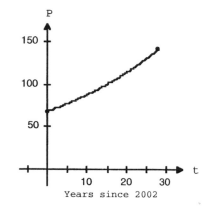

82.

```
ExpReg
 y=a*b^x
 a=71.45321377
 b=1.002572221

■
```

2010: $y(40) \approx 79.2$ years

EXERCISE 2-3

2. $32 = 2^5$　　　　　　**4.** $e^0 = 1$　　　　　　**6.** $27 = 9^{3/2}$

8. $\log_6 36 = 2$　　**10.** $\log_{27} 9 = \dfrac{2}{3}$　　**12.** $\log_b M = x$

14. $\log_e 1 = y$ is equivalent to $e^y = 1$; $y = 0$.

16. $\log_{10} 10 = y$ is equivalent to $10^y = 10$; $y = 1$.

18. $\log_{13} 13 = y$ is equivalent to $13^y = 13$; $y = 1$.

20. $\log_{10} 10^{-5} = -5$　　**22.** $\log_3 3^5 = 5$　　　　**24.** $\log_6 36 = \log_6 6^2 = 2$

26. $\log_b FG = \log_b F + \log_b G$　　**28.** $\log_b w^{15} = 15 \log_b w$

30. $\text{Log}_3 P = (\text{Log}_R P)(\text{Log}_3 R)$ (change of base formula)

or $\text{Log}_R P = \dfrac{\text{Log}_3 P}{\text{Log}_3 R}$

32. $\log_2 x = 2$

$\qquad x = 2^2$

$\qquad x = 4$

34. $\log_3 27 = y$

$\qquad \log_3 27 = \log_3 3^3 = 3 \log_3 3 = 3$

$\qquad$ Thus, $y = 3$

36. $\log_b e^{-2} = -2$

$\qquad -2 \log_b e = -2$ or $\log_b e = 1$

$\qquad$ Thus, $b = e$

38. $\log_{25} x = \dfrac{1}{2}$

$\qquad x = 25^{1/2}$

$\qquad x = 5$

40. $\log_{49}\left(\dfrac{1}{7}\right) = y$

$\qquad \dfrac{1}{7} = 49^y$

$\qquad y = -\dfrac{1}{2}$

42. $\log_b 4 = \dfrac{2}{3}$

$\qquad\quad 4 = b^{2/3}$ Taking square root from both sides, we have

$\qquad b^{1/3} = 2$ Cubing both sides yields

$\qquad\quad b = 8$

44. False. Take $f(x) = x^3 - x$, then $f(-1) = f(0) = f(1) = 0$.

46. True. Indeed the graph of every function (not necessarily one-to-one) intersects each vertical line exactly once.

48. False. $x = -1$ is in the domain of f, but cannot be in the range of g.

50. True. $y = \log_b x$ implies that $x = b^y$. If $b > 1$, then as y increases so does b^y. Therefore, the inverse of $x = b^y$ which is $y = \log_b x$ must be increasing as well.

52. True. Since g is the inverse of f, then (a, b) is on the graph of f if and only if (b, a) is on the graph of g. Therefore, f is also the inverse of g.

54. $\log_b x = \dfrac{2}{3}\log_b 27 + 2 \log_b 2 - \log_b 3$

$\qquad\quad = \dfrac{2}{3}\log_b 3^3 + 2 \log_b 2 - \log_b 3$

$\qquad\quad = 2 \log_b 3 + 2 \log_b 2 - \log_b 3 = \log_b 3 + 2 \log_b 2$

$\qquad\qquad\qquad\qquad\qquad\qquad\qquad\qquad = \log_b 12$

$\qquad$ Thus, $x = 12$.

56. $\log_b x = 3 \log_b 2 + \dfrac{1}{2}\log_b 25 - \log_b 20$

$\qquad\quad = \log_b 8 + \log_b 5 - \log_b 20$

$\qquad\quad = \log_b 40 - \log_b 20 = \log_b \dfrac{40}{20} = \log 2$

$\qquad$ Thus, $x = 2$.

58. $\log_b(x + 2) + \log_b x = \log_b 24$

$\quad\quad \log_b x(x + 2) = \log_b 24$

$\quad\quad\quad\quad x(x + 2) = 24 \quad$ or $\quad x^2 + 2x - 24 = 0 \quad$ or $\quad (x - 4)(x + 6) = 4$

Thus, $x = 4$. [Note: $x = -6$ is not a solution since $\log_b(-6)$ is not defined.]

60. $\log_{10}(x + 6) - \log_{10}(x - 3) = 1$

$\log_{10} \dfrac{x + 6}{x - 3} = 1$ implies that $\dfrac{x + 6}{x - 3} = 10$ or

$x + 6 = 10x - 30$ or $9x = 36$ or $x = 4$.

62. $y = \log_3(x + 2)$

$x + 2 = 3^y$

$x = 3^y - 2$

x	y
$-\frac{53}{27}$	-3
$-\frac{17}{9}$	-2
$-\frac{5}{3}$	-1
-1	0
1	1
7	2
25	3

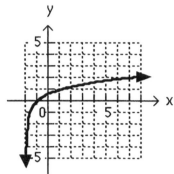

64. The graph of $y = \log_3(x + 2)$ is the graph of $y = \log_3 x$ shifted to the left 2 units.

66. Since logarithmic functions are defined only for positive "inputs", we must have $x - 1 > 0$ or $x > 1$; domain: $(1, \infty)$. The range of $y = \log(x - 1) - 1$ is the set of all real numbers.

68. (A) 1.86096
(B) -1.48095
(C) 10.60304
(D) -5.12836

70. (A) $\log x = 2.0832$
$\quad\quad\quad\quad x = 121.1156$
(B) $\log x = -1.1577$
$\quad\quad\quad\quad x = 0.0696$
(C) $\ln x = 3.1336$
$\quad\quad\quad\; x = 22.9565$
(D) $\ln x = -4.3281$
$\quad\quad\quad\; x = 0.0132$

72. $10^x = 153$ (Take common logarithms of both sides)
$\log 10^x = \log 153 = 2.1847$
$\quad\quad x = 2.1847 \; (\log 10^x = x \log 10 = x; \; \log 10 = 1)$

74. $e^x = 0.3059$ (Take natural logarithms of both sides)
$\ln e^x = \ln \; 0.3059 = -1.1845$
$\quad\; x = -1.1845 \; (\ln e^x = x \ln e = x; \; \ln e = 1)$

76. $1.075^x = 1.837$ (Take either common or natural logarithms of both sides.)
$\quad\quad\quad\quad$ We use natural logarithms.
$\ln 1.075^x = \ln 1.837$
$\quad\quad\quad x = \dfrac{\ln 1.837}{\ln 1.075} = 8.4089$

78. $1.02^{4t} = 2$ (Take either common or natural logarithms of both sides.)
Here we'll use common logarithms.

$$\log 1.02^{4t} = \log 2$$
$$t = \frac{\log 2}{4 \log 1.02} = 8.7507$$

80. $y = -\ln x, \ x > 0$

x	y
0.5	≈ 0.69
1	0
2	≈ -0.69
4	≈ -1.39
5	≈ -1.61

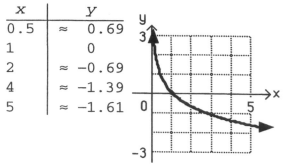

decreasing $(0, \infty)$

82. $y = \ln|x|$

x	y
-5	≈ 1.61
-2	0.69
1	0
2	≈ 0.69
5	≈ 1.61

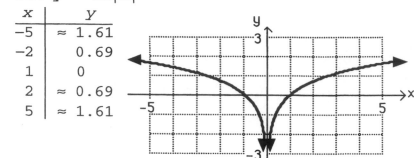

decreasing $(-\infty, 0)$
increasing $(0, \infty)$

84. $y = 2 \ln x + 2$

x	y
0.5	≈ 0.62
1	2
2	≈ 3.38
4	≈ 4.78
5	≈ 5.52

increasing $(0, \infty)$

86. $y = 4 \ln(x - 3)$

x	y
4	0
6	≈ 2.77
8	≈ 6.44
10	≈ 7.78
12	≈ 8.79

increasing $(3, \infty)$

88. It is not possible to find a power of 1 that is an arbitrarily selected real number, because 1 raised to any power is 1.

90. $\log_e x - \log_e 25 = 0.2t$

$$\log_e \frac{x}{25} = 0.2t$$

Therefore, $\frac{x}{25} = e^{0.2t}$, and $x = 25e^{0.2t}$

92.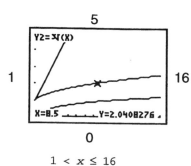

$1 < x \leq 16$

A function f is "larger than" a function g on an interval $[a, b]$ if $f(x) > g(x)$ for $a \leq x \leq b$.
$r(x) > q(x) > p(x)$ for $1 < x \leq 16$, that is $x > \sqrt[3]{x} > \log x$.

94. From the compound interest formula $A = P(1 + r)^t$, we have:

$2P = P(1 + 0.0958)^t$ or $(1.0958)^t = 2$

Take the natural log of both sides of this equation:

$\ln(1.0958)^t = \ln 2$ [Note: The common log could have been used instead of the natural log.]

$t \ln(1.0958) = \ln 2$

$$t = \frac{\ln 2}{\ln(1.0958)} \approx \frac{0.69315}{0.09148} \approx 8 \text{ years}$$

96. $A = P\left(1 + \dfrac{r}{m}\right)^{mt}$, $r = 0.08$, $m = 2$, $P = 5,000$, $A = 7,500$.

$$7,500 = 5,000\left(1 + \frac{0.08}{2}\right)^{2t}$$

$$(1.04)^{2t} = \frac{7500}{5000} = \frac{3}{2} = 1.5$$

$2t \ln(1.04) = \ln(1.5)$

$$t = \frac{\ln 1.5}{2 \ln 1.04} \approx 5.17 \text{ years}$$

$A = Pe^{rt}$, $r = 0.08$, $P = 5,000$, $A = 7,500$

$7,500 = 5,000e^{0.08t}$

$e^{0.08t} = 1.5$

$0.08t = \ln 1.5$ or $t = \dfrac{\ln 1.5}{0.08} \approx 5.07$ years.

98. $A = Pe^{rt}$, $P = 20,000$, $A = 60,000$, $t = 17$

$60,000 = 20,000e^{17r}$

$$e^{17r} = \frac{60,000}{20,000} = 3$$

$17r = \ln 3$ or $r = \dfrac{\ln 3}{17} \approx 6.462\%$

100. 6,145 screwdrivers at $46.77 each.

102. (A) $N = 10 \log \dfrac{I}{I_0} = 10 \log \dfrac{10^{-13}}{10^{-16}} = 10 \log 10^3 = 30$

(B) $N = 10 \log \dfrac{3.16 \times 10^{-10}}{10^{-16}} = 10 \log 3.16 \times 10^6 \approx 65$

(C) $N = 10 \log \dfrac{10^{-8}}{10^{-16}} = 10 \log 10^8 = 80$

(D) $N = 10 \log \dfrac{10^{-1}}{10^{-16}} = 10 \log 10^{15} = 150$

104. (A) Logarithmic regression
model, Table 3:

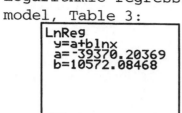

2010: $y(110) = 10,324$ million bushels

(B) The actual yield is 243 million bushels less than the estimated yield. If a new model is calculated using the 1996 value, then the estimate for 2010 will decrease.

106. $A = A_0 e^{-0.000124t}$, $A = 0.1A_0$ yields

$$0.1A_0 = A_0 e^{-0.000124t} \quad \text{or}$$

$$0.1 = e^{-0.000124t} \quad \text{or}$$

$$-0.000124t = \ln 0.1,$$

so $\quad t = \dfrac{\ln 0.1}{-0.000124} \approx 18,600$ years.

3 THE DERIVATIVE

2. (A) $\lim_{x \to 1^-} f(x) = 2$ (B) $\lim_{x \to 1^+} f(x) = 2$ (C) $\lim_{x \to 1} f(x) = 2$ (D) $f(1) = 2$

4. (A) $\lim_{x \to 4^-} f(x) = 4$ (B) $\lim_{x \to 4^+} f(x) = 4$ (C) $\lim_{x \to 4} f(x) = 4$

    (D) $f(4)$ does not exist   (E) Yes, define $f(4) = 4$

6. (A) $\lim_{x \to 2^-} g(x) = 2$ (B) $\lim_{x \to 2^+} g(x) = 2$ (C) $\lim_{x \to 2} g(x) = 2$ (D) $g(2) = 2$

8. (A) $\lim_{x \to 4^-} g(x) = 0$ (B) $\lim_{x \to 4^+} g(x) = 0$ (C) $\lim_{x \to 4} g(x) = 0$ (D) $g(4) = 0$

10. (A) $\lim_{x \to -2^+} f(x) = 3$ (B) $\lim_{x \to -2^-} f(x) = -3$

    (C) Since $\lim_{x \to -2^+} f(x) \neq \lim_{x \to -2^-} f(x)$, $\lim_{x \to -2} f(x)$ does not exist.

    (D) $f(-2) = -3$ (E) No, $\lim_{x \to -2} f(x)$ does not exist.

12. (A) $\lim_{x \to 2^+} f(x) = -3$ (B) $\lim_{x \to 2^-} f(x) = 3$

    (C) $\lim_{x \to 2} f(x)$ does not exist since $\lim_{x \to 2^+} f(x) \neq \lim_{x \to 2^-} f(x)$

    (D) $f(2) = 3$ (E) No, $\lim_{x \to 2} f(x)$ does not exist.

14. $4x \to 12$ as $x \to 3$; thus $\lim_{x \to 3} 4x = 12$

16. $x - 3 \to 5 - 3 = 2$ as $x \to 5$; thus $\lim_{x \to 5} (x - 3) = 2$

18. $x(x + 3) \to (-1)(-1 + 3) = -2$ as $x \to -1$; thus $\lim_{x \to -1} x(x + 3) = -2$

20. $x - 2 \to 4 - 2 = 2$ as $x \to 4$; thus $\lim_{x \to 4} \dfrac{x - 2}{x} = \dfrac{2}{4} = \dfrac{1}{2}$

22. $\sqrt{16 - 7x} \to \sqrt{16 - 7(0)} = \sqrt{16} = 4$ as $x \to 0$; thus $\lim_{x \to 0} \sqrt{16 - 7x} = 4$

24. $\lim_{x \to 1} 2g(x) = 2 \lim_{x \to 1} g(x) = 2(4) = 8$

26. $\lim_{x \to 1} [g(x) - 3f(x)] = \lim_{x \to 1} g(x) - 3 \lim_{x \to 1} f(x) = 4 - 3(-5) = 19$

28. $\lim_{x \to 1} \dfrac{3 - f(x)}{1 - 4g(x)} = \dfrac{\lim_{x \to 1}[3 - f(x)]}{\lim_{x \to 1}[1 - 4g(x)]} = \dfrac{3 - \lim_{x \to 1} f(x)}{1 - 4 \lim_{x \to 1} g(x)} = \dfrac{3 - (-5)}{1 - 4(4)} = -\dfrac{8}{15}$

30. $\lim\limits_{x \to 1} [f(x) - 7x]g(x) = \left\{\lim\limits_{x \to 1}[f(x) - 7x]\right\} \cdot \lim\limits_{x \to 1} g(x)$

$$= \left\{\lim\limits_{x \to 1} f(x) - 7 \lim\limits_{x \to 1} x\right\} \cdot (4)$$

$$= \{-5 - 7\} \cdot (4) = -48$$

32. $\lim\limits_{x \to 1} \sqrt[3]{2x + 2f(x)} = \sqrt[3]{\lim\limits_{x \to 1}[2x + 2f(x)]}$

$$= \sqrt[3]{2 \lim\limits_{x \to 1} x + 2 \lim\limits_{x \to 1} f(x)}$$

$$= \sqrt[3]{2 - 10} = -2$$

34. $\lim\limits_{x \to 1} [2 - g(x)]^3 = [2 - \lim\limits_{x \to 1} g(x)]^3 = [2 - 4]^3 = -8$

36.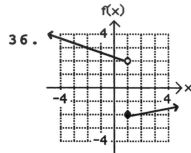

38.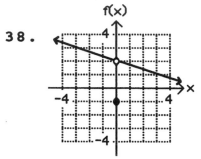

40. $f(x) = \begin{cases} 2 + x & \text{if} \quad x \le 0 \\ 2 - x & \text{if} \quad x > 0 \end{cases}$

(A) $\lim\limits_{x \to 0^+} f(x) = \lim\limits_{x \to 0^+} (2 - x) = 2$

(B) $\lim\limits_{x \to 0^-} f(x) = \lim\limits_{x \to 0^-} (2 + x) = 2$

(C) $\lim\limits_{x \to 0} f(x) = 2$ since $\lim\limits_{x \to 0^+} f(x) = \lim\limits_{x \to 0^-} f(x) = 2$

(D) $f(0) = 2 + 0 = 2$

42. $f(x) = \begin{cases} x + 3 & \text{if} \quad x < -2 \\ \sqrt{x + 2} & \text{if} \quad x > -2 \end{cases}$

(A) $\lim\limits_{x \to -2^+} f(x) = \lim\limits_{x \to -2^+} \sqrt{x + 2} = 0$

(B) $\lim\limits_{x \to -2^-} f(x) = \lim\limits_{x \to -2^-} (x + 3) = 1$

(C) $\lim\limits_{x \to -2} f(x)$ does not exist since $\lim\limits_{x \to -2^+} f(x) \ne \lim\limits_{x \to -2^-} f(x)$

(D) $f(-2)$ does not exist; f is not defined at $x = -2$.

44. $f(x) = \begin{cases} \dfrac{x}{x + 3} & \text{if} \quad x < 0 \\ \dfrac{x}{x - 3} & \text{if} \quad x > 0 \end{cases}$

(A) $\lim\limits_{x \to -3} f(x) = \lim\limits_{x \to -3} \dfrac{x}{x + 3}$ does not exist since $x = -3$ is a non-removable zero of the denominator.

(B) $\displaystyle\lim_{x\to 0} f(x) = \lim_{x\to 0^-} \frac{x}{x+3} = \lim_{x\to 0^+} \frac{x}{x+3} = 0$

(C) $\displaystyle\lim_{x\to 3} f(x)$ does not exist, since $\displaystyle\lim_{x\to 3^+} f(x)$ does not exist.

46. $f(x) = \dfrac{x-3}{|x-3|} = \begin{cases} \dfrac{x-3}{-(x-3)} = -1 & \text{if} \quad x < 3 \\[2mm] \dfrac{x-3}{x-3} = 1 & \text{if} \quad x > 3 \end{cases}$

(<u>Note</u>: Observe that for $x < 3$, $|x-3| = 3 - x = -(x-3)$
and for $x > 3$, $|x-3| = x - 3$)

(A) $\displaystyle\lim_{x\to 3^+} f(x) = \lim_{x\to 3^+} 1 = 1$ (B) $\displaystyle\lim_{x\to 3^-} f(x) = \lim_{x\to 3^-} (-1) = -1$

(C) $\displaystyle\lim_{x\to 3} f(x)$ does not exist, since $\displaystyle\lim_{x\to 3^+} f(x) \neq \lim_{x\to 3^-} f(x)$

(D) $f(3)$ does not exist; f is not defined at $x = 3$.

48. $f(x) = \dfrac{x+3}{x^2+3x} = \dfrac{x+3}{x(x+3)}$

(A) $\displaystyle\lim_{x\to -3} \frac{x+3}{x(x+3)} = \lim_{x\to -3} \frac{1}{x} = -\frac{1}{3}$

(B) $\displaystyle\lim_{x\to 0} f(x) = \lim_{x\to 0} \frac{1}{x}$ does not exist.

50. $f(x) = \dfrac{x^2+x-6}{x+3} = \dfrac{(x+3)(x-2)}{(x+3)}$

(A) $\displaystyle\lim_{x\to -3} f(x) = \lim_{x\to -3} \frac{(x+3)(x-2)}{(x+3)} = \lim_{x\to -3} (x-2) = -5$

(B) $\displaystyle\lim_{x\to 0} f(x) = \lim_{x\to 0} \frac{x^2+x-6}{x+3} = \frac{-6}{3} = -2$

(C) $\displaystyle\lim_{x\to 2} f(x) = \lim_{x\to 2} \frac{x^2+x-6}{x+3} = \frac{0}{5} = 0$

52. $f(x) = \dfrac{x^2-1}{(x+1)^2} = \dfrac{(x-1)(x+1)}{(x+1)^2}$

(A) $\displaystyle\lim_{x\to -1} f(x) = \lim_{x\to -1} \frac{(x-1)(x+1)}{(x+1)^2} = \lim_{x\to -1} \frac{x-1}{x+1}$ does not exist since
$\displaystyle\lim_{x\to -1} (x-1) = -2$ but $\displaystyle\lim_{x\to -1} (x+1) = 0$.

(B) $\displaystyle\lim_{x\to 0} f(x) = \lim_{x\to 0} \frac{x^2-1}{(x+1)^2} = \frac{-1}{1} = -1$ (C) $\displaystyle\lim_{x\to 1} f(x) = \lim_{x\to 1} \frac{x^2-1}{(x+1)^2} = \frac{0}{4} = 0$

54. $f(x) = \dfrac{3x^2 + 2x - 1}{x^2 + 3x + 2} = \dfrac{(3x - 1)(x + 1)}{(x + 2)(x + 1)}$

(A) $\displaystyle\lim_{x \to -3} f(x) = \lim_{x \to -3} \dfrac{3x^2 + 2x - 1}{x^2 + 3x + 2} = \dfrac{20}{2} = 10$

(B) $\displaystyle\lim_{x \to -1} f(x) = \lim_{x \to -1} \dfrac{(3x - 1)(x + 1)}{(x + 2)(x + 1)} = \lim_{x \to -1} \dfrac{3x - 1}{x + 2} = \dfrac{-4}{1} = -4$

(C) $\displaystyle\lim_{x \to 2} f(x) = \lim_{x \to 2} \dfrac{3x^2 + 2x - 1}{x^2 + 3x + 2} = \dfrac{15}{12} = \dfrac{5}{4}$

56. $f(x) = 5x - 1$

$\displaystyle\lim_{h \to 0} \dfrac{f(2 + h) - f(2)}{h} = \lim_{h \to 0} \dfrac{5(2 + h) - 1 - (10 - 1)}{h}$

$\displaystyle\qquad = \lim_{h \to 0} \dfrac{10 + 5h - 1 - 9}{h} = \lim_{h \to 0} \dfrac{5h}{h} = \lim_{h \to 0} 5 = 5$

58. $f(x) = x^2 - 2$

$\displaystyle\lim_{h \to 0} \dfrac{f(2 + h) - f(2)}{h} = \lim_{h \to 0} \dfrac{(2 + h)^2 - 2 - (4 - 2)}{h} = \lim_{h \to 0} \dfrac{4 + 4h + h^2 - 2 - 2}{h}$

$\displaystyle\qquad = \lim_{h \to 0} \dfrac{4h + h^2}{h} = \lim_{h \to 0} (4 + h) = 4$

60. $f(x) = 1 + \sqrt{x}$

$\displaystyle\lim_{h \to 0} \dfrac{f(2 + h) - f(2)}{h} = \lim_{h \to 0} \dfrac{1 + \sqrt{2 + h} - \left(1 + \sqrt{2}\right)}{h} = \lim_{h \to 0} \dfrac{\sqrt{2 + h} - \sqrt{2}}{h}$

$\displaystyle\qquad = \lim_{h \to 0} \dfrac{\sqrt{2 + h} - \sqrt{2}}{h} \cdot \dfrac{\sqrt{2 + h} + \sqrt{2}}{\sqrt{2 + h} + \sqrt{2}}$

$\displaystyle\qquad = \lim_{h \to 0} \dfrac{2 + h - 2}{h\left(\sqrt{2 + h} + \sqrt{2}\right)} = \lim_{h \to 0} \dfrac{h}{h\left(\sqrt{2 + h} + \sqrt{2}\right)}$

$\displaystyle\qquad = \lim_{h \to 0} \dfrac{1}{\sqrt{2 + h} + \sqrt{2}} = \dfrac{1}{2\sqrt{2}}$

62. $f(x) = 2 + |x - 2|$

$\displaystyle\lim_{h \to 0} \dfrac{f(2 + h) - f(2)}{h} = \lim_{h \to 0} \dfrac{2 + |2 + h - 2| - (2 + |2 - 2|)}{h}$

$\displaystyle\qquad = \lim_{h \to 0} \dfrac{2 + |h| - 2}{h} = \lim_{h \to 0} \dfrac{|h|}{h}$ does not exist.

64. $f(x) = \dfrac{1}{x + 2}$

$$\lim_{h \to 0} \frac{f(2 + h) - f(2)}{h} = \lim_{h \to 0} \frac{\dfrac{1}{h + 4} - \dfrac{1}{4}}{h} = \lim_{h \to 0} \frac{\dfrac{4 - h - 4}{4(h + 4)}}{h} = \lim_{h \to 0} \frac{-1}{4(h + 4)} = -\frac{1}{16}$$

66. (A) $\displaystyle\lim_{x \to 2^-} f(x) = \lim_{x \to 2^-} (0.5x) = 1$

$\displaystyle\lim_{x \to 2^+} f(x) = \lim_{x \to 2^+} (-x) = -2$

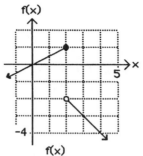

(B) $\displaystyle\lim_{x \to 2^-} f(x) = \lim_{x \to 2^-} (-3 + 0.5x) = -2$

$\displaystyle\lim_{x \to 2^+} f(x) = \lim_{x \to 2^+} (3 - x) = 1$

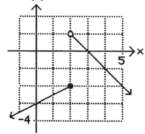

(C) $\displaystyle\lim_{x \to 2^-} f(x) = \lim_{x \to 2^-} (-3m + 0.5x) = -3m + 1$

$\displaystyle\lim_{x \to 2^+} f(x) = \lim_{x \to 2^+} (3m - x) = -3m - 2$

$-3m + 1 = 3m - 2$

$6m = 3$

$m = \dfrac{1}{2} = 0.5$

$\displaystyle\lim_{x \to 2^-} f(x) = \lim_{x \to 2^+} f(x) = -0.5$

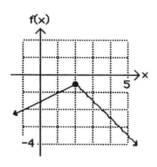

(D) The graph in (A) is broken when it jumps from (2, 1) down to (2, -2), the graph in (B) is also broken when it jumps from (2, -2) up to (2, 1), while the graph in (C) is one continuous piece with no jumps or breaks.

68. $\displaystyle\lim_{h \to 0} \frac{[3(a + h) - 2] - (3a - 2)}{h} = \lim_{h \to 0} \frac{3a + 3h - 2 - 3a + 2}{h}$

$$= \lim_{h \to 0} \frac{3h}{h} = \lim_{h \to 0} 3 = 3$$

70. $\displaystyle\lim_{h \to 0} \frac{\dfrac{1}{a + h} - \dfrac{1}{a}}{h} = \lim_{h \to 0} \frac{\dfrac{a - (a + h)}{a(a + h)}}{h} = \lim_{h \to 0} \frac{-h}{ah(a + h)}$

$$= -\lim_{h \to 0} \frac{1}{a(a + h)} = -\frac{1}{a^2}$$

72. (A) If a state-to-state long   (B)
distance call lasts x minutes,
then for $0 < x < 10$, the charge
will be $0.18x$ and for $x \geq 10$,
the charge will be $0.09x$. Thus,

$$G(x) = \begin{cases} 0.18x\;, & 0 < x < 10 \\ 0.09x\;, & x \geq 10 \end{cases}$$

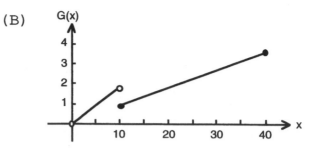

(C) As x approaches 10 from the left, $G(x)$ approaches 1.8, thus,
the left limit of $G(x)$ at $x = 10$ exists, $\lim\limits_{x \to 10^-} G(x) = 1.8$.

Similarly, $\lim\limits_{x \to 10^+} G(x) = 0.09$. However, $\lim\limits_{x \to 10} G(x)$ does not exist,

since $\lim\limits_{x \to 10^-} G(x) \neq \lim\limits_{x \to 10^+} G(x)$.

74. For calls lasting more than 20 minutes, the charge for the service given
in Problem 71 is $0.07x - 0.41$ whereas for that of Problem 72 is $0.09x$.
It is clear that the latter is more expensive than the former.

76. (A) Let x be the volume of a purchase before the discount is applied.
Then $P(x)$ is given by:

$$P(x) = \begin{cases} x & \text{if} & 0 \leq x < 300 \\ 300 + 0.97(x - 300) = 0.97x + 9 & \text{if} & 300 \leq x < 1{,}000 \\ 0.97(1{,}000) + 9 + 0.95(x - 1{,}000) = 0.95x + 29 & \text{if} & 1{,}000 \leq x < 3{,}000 \\ 0.95(3{,}000) + 29 + 0.93(x - 3{,}000) = 0.93x + 89 & \text{if} & 3{,}000 \leq x < 5{,}000 \\ 0.93(5{,}000) + 89 + 0.90(x - 5{,}000) = 0.90x + 239 & \text{if} & x \geq 5{,}000 \end{cases}$$

(B) $\lim\limits_{x \to 1{,}000^-} P(x) = 0.97(1{,}000) + 9 = 979$

$\lim\limits_{x \to 1{,}000^+} P(x) = 0.95(1{,}000) + 29 = 979$

Thus, $\lim\limits_{x \to 1{,}000} P(x) = 979$

$\lim\limits_{x \to 3{,}000^-} P(x) = 0.95(3{,}000) + 29 = 2{,}879$

$\lim\limits_{x \to 3{,}000^+} P(x) = 0.93(3{,}000) + 89 = 2{,}879$

Thus, $\lim\limits_{x \to 3{,}000} P(x) = 2{,}879$

(C) For $0 \leq x < 300$, they produce the same price. For $x \geq 300$, the one
in Problem 75 produces a lower price.

78. From Problem 77, we have:

$$F(x) = \begin{cases} 20x & \text{if } 0 < x \leq 4{,}000 \\ 80{,}000 & \text{if } \quad x \geq 4{,}000 \end{cases}$$

Thus

$$A(x) = \frac{F(x)}{x} = \begin{cases} 20 & \text{if } 0 < x \leq 4{,}000 \\ \dfrac{80{,}000}{x} & \text{if } \quad x \geq 4{,}000 \end{cases}$$

$$\lim_{x \to 4,000^-} A(x) = \lim_{x \to 4,000^+} A(x) = 20 = \lim_{x \to 4,000} A(x)$$

$$\lim_{x \to 8,000^-} A(x) = \lim_{x \to 8,000^+} A(x) = \frac{80,000}{8,000} = 10 = \lim_{x \to 8,000} A(x)$$

EXERCISE 3-2

2. f is discontinuous at $x = 1$, since $\lim_{x \to 1} f(x) \neq f(1)$

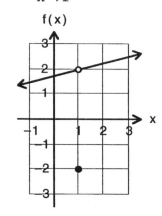

4. f is continuous at $x = 1$, since $\lim_{x \to 1} f(x) = f(1)$

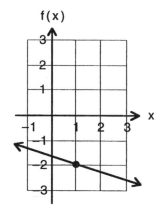

6. f is discontinuous at $x = 1$, since $\lim_{x \to 1} f(x)$ does not exist

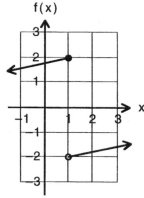

8. (A) $\lim_{x \to 2^-} f(x) = 2$ (B) $\lim_{x \to 2^+} f(x) = 2$ (C) $\lim_{x \to 2} f(x) = 2$

$$\left(\lim_{x \to 2^-} f(x) = \lim_{x \to 2^+} f(x) = 2 \right)$$

(D) $f(2)$ does not exist; f is not defined at $x = 2$.

(E) No, since f is not even defined at $x = 2$.

10. (A) $\lim_{x \to -1^-} f(x) = 0$ (B) $\lim_{x \to -1^+} f(x) = 0$

(C) $\lim_{x \to -1} f(x) = 0$ $\left(\lim_{x \to -1^-} f(x) = \lim_{x \to -1^+} f(x) = 0 \right)$

(D) $f(-1) = 0$ (E) Yes, since $\lim_{x \to -1} f(x) = f(0)$.

12. (A) $\lim\limits_{x \to -2^-} g(x) = 2$ (B) $\lim\limits_{x \to -2^+} g(x) = 4$

(C) $\lim\limits_{x \to -2} g(x)$ does not exist, since $\lim\limits_{x \to -2^-} g(x) \neq \lim\limits_{x \to -2^+} g(x)$

(D) $g(-2)$ does not exist; g is not defined at $x = -2$.

(E) No, since g is not even defined at $x = -2$.

14. (A) $\lim\limits_{x \to 4^-} g(x) = 1$ (B) $\lim\limits_{x \to 4^+} g(x) = 1$ (C) $\lim\limits_{x \to 4} g(x) = 1$

$\left(\lim\limits_{x \to 4^-} g(x) = \lim\limits_{x \to 4^+} g(x) = 1 \right)$

16. $h(x) = 4 - 2x$ is a polynomial function. Therefore, f is continuous for all x [Theorem 1(C)].

18. $k(x) = \dfrac{2x}{x - 4}$ is a rational function and the denominator $x - 4$ is 0 when $x = 4$. Thus, k is continuous for all x except $x = 4$ [Theorem 1(D)].

20. $n(x) = \dfrac{x - 2}{(x - 3)(x + 1)}$ is a rational function and the denominator $(x - 3)(x + 1)$ is 0 when $x = 3$ or $x = -1$. Thus, n is continuous for all x except $x = 3$, $x = -1$ [Theorem 1(D)].

22. $G(x) = \dfrac{1 - x^2}{x^2 + 1}$

$G(x)$ is a rational function and its denominator is never zero, hence by Theorem 1(D), $G(x)$ is continuous for all x.

24. $N(x) = \dfrac{x^2 + 4}{4 - 25x^2}$

$N(x)$ is a rational function and according to Theorem 1(D), $N(x)$ is continuous for all x except $x = \pm\dfrac{2}{5}$ which make a denominator 0.

26. $g(x) = \begin{cases} -1 & \text{if } x \text{ is an even integer} \\ 1 & \text{if } x \text{ is not an even integer} \end{cases}$

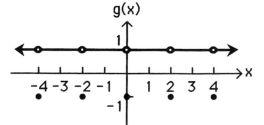

(A) The graph of g is shown at the right.

(B) $\lim\limits_{x \to 1} g(x) = 1$

(C) $g(1) = 1$

(D) g is continuous at $x = 1$ since $\lim\limits_{x \to 1} g(x) = g(1) = 1$.

(E) g is discontinuous at $x = 2n$ for all integers n.

28. $x^2 - 2x - 8 < 0$

Let $f(x) = x^2 - 2x - 8 = (x - 4)(x + 2)$.

Then f is continuous for all x and $f(-2) = f(4) = 0$.

Thus, $x = -2$ and $x = 4$ are partition numbers.

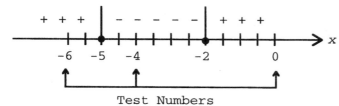

Test Numbers	
x	$f(x)$
-3	7 $(+)$
0	-8 $(-)$
5	7 $(+)$

Thus, $x^2 - 2x - 8 < 0$ for:

$-2 < x < 4 \qquad$ (inequality notation)

$(-2, 4) \qquad\qquad$ (interval notation)

30. $x^2 + 7x > -10$ or $x^2 + 7x + 10 > 0$

Let $f(x) = x^2 + 7x + 10 = (x + 2)(x + 5)$.

Then f is continuous for all x and $f(-5) = f(-2) = 0$.

Thus, $x = -5$ and $x = -2$ are partition numbers.

Test Numbers	
x	$f(x)$
-6	4 $(+)$
-4	-2 $(-)$
0	10 $(+)$

Thus, $x^2 + 7x + 10 > 0$ for:

$x < -5$ or $x > -2 \qquad$ (inequality notation)

$(-\infty, -5) \cup (-2, \infty) \qquad$ (interval notation)

32. $x^4 - 9x^2 > 0$

$x^4 - 9x^2 = x^2(x^2 - 9)$

Since $x^2 > 0$ for $x \neq 0$, then $x^4 - 9x^2 > 0$ if $x^2 - 9 > 0$ or $x^2 > 9$

or "$x < -3$ or $x > 3$"   or $(-\infty, -3) \cup (3, \infty)$.

34. $\dfrac{x - 4}{x^2 + 2x} < 0$

Let $f(x) = \dfrac{x - 4}{x^2 + 2x} = \dfrac{x - 4}{x(x + 2)}$.   Then f is discontinuous at $x = 0$ and

$x = -2$ and $f(4) = 0$.   Thus, $x = -2$, $x = 0$, and $x = 4$ are partition numbers.

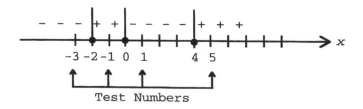

Test Numbers	
x	$f(x)$
-3	$-\frac{7}{3}$ (−)
-1	5 (+)
1	-1 (−)
5	$\frac{1}{35}$ (+)

Thus, $\dfrac{x-4}{x^2+2x} < 0$ for:

$x < -2$ or $0 < x < 4$ (inequality notation)

$(-\infty, -2) \cup (0, 4)$ (interval notation)

36. (A) $g(x) > 0$ for $x < -4$ or $x > 4$; $(-\infty, -4) \cup (4, \infty)$.

     (B) $g(x) < 0$ for $-4 < x < 1$ or $1 < x < 4$; $(-4, 1) \cup (1, 4)$.

38. $f(x) = x^4 - 4x^2 - 2x + 2$
Partition numbers: $x_1 \approx 0.5113$, $x_2 \approx 2.1209$

     (A) $f(x) > 0$ on $(-\infty, 0.5113) \cup (2.1209, \infty)$

     (B) $f(x) < 0$ on $(0.5113, 2.1209)$

40. $f(x) = \dfrac{3 + 6x - x^3}{x^2 - 1}$
Partition numbers: $x_1 \approx -2.3301$, $x_2 \approx -1$, $x_3 \approx 0.2016$, $x_4 = 1$,
$x_5 \approx 2.1284$

     (A) $f(x) > 0$ on $(-2.3301, -1) \cup (0.2016, 1) \cup (2.1284, \infty)$

     (B) $f(x) < 0$ on $(-\infty, -2.3301) \cup (-1, 0.2016) \cup (1, 2.1284)$

42. $\sqrt{7 - x}$
Let $f(x) = 7 - x$. Then $\sqrt{7 - x} = \sqrt[2]{f(x)}$ is continuous whenever $f(x)$ is continuous and nonnegative [Theorem 1(F)]. Since $f(x) = 7 - x$ is continuous for all x [Theorem 1(C)] and $f(x) \geq 0$ for $x \leq 7$, $\sqrt{7 - x}$ is continuous on $(-\infty, 7]$.

44. $\sqrt[3]{x - 8}$
Let $f(x) = x - 8$. Then $\sqrt[3]{x - 8} = \sqrt[3]{f(x)}$ is continuous whenever $f(x)$ is continuous [Theorem 1(E)]. Since $f(x) = x - 8$ is continuous for all x [Theorem 1(C)], $\sqrt[3]{x - 8}$ is continuous on $(-\infty, \infty)$.

46. $\sqrt{4 - x^2}$
Let $f(x) = 4 - x^2$. Then $\sqrt{4 - x^2} = \sqrt[2]{f(x)}$ is continuous whenever $f(x)$ is continuous and nonnegative [Theorem 1(F)]. Since $f(x) = 4 - x^2$ is continuous for all x [Theorem 1(C)] and $f(x)$ is nonnegative on $[-2, 2]$, $\sqrt{4 - x^2}$ is continuous on $[-2, 2]$.

48. $\sqrt[3]{x^2 + 2}$

Let $f(x) = x^2 + 2$. Then $\sqrt[3]{x^2 + 2} = \sqrt[3]{f(x)}$ is continuous whenever $f(x)$ is continuous [Theorem 1(E)]. Since $f(x) = x^2 + 2$ is continuous for all x [Theorem 1(C)], $\sqrt[3]{x^2 + 2}$ is continuous on $(-\infty, \infty)$.

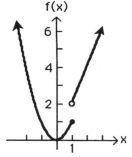

50. The graph of f is shown at the right. This function is discontinuous at $x = 1$.
$[\lim_{x \to 1^-} f(x) = 1$ and $\lim_{x \to 1^+} f(x) = 2$;
Thus, $\lim_{x \to 1} f(x)$ does not exist.]

52. The graph of f is:

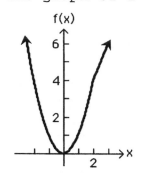

This function is continuous for all x.
$[\lim_{x \to 2} f(x) = f(2) = 4]$

54. The graph of f is:

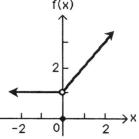

This function is discontinuous at $x = 0$, since $\lim_{x \to 0} f(x) = 1 \neq f(0) = 0$

56. f is discontinuous at $x = -3$:
f is not defined at -3, $\lim_{x \to -3^-} f(x) = -6$ and $\lim_{x \to -3^+} f(x) = 0$.

58. f is discontinuous at $x = -2$: f is not defined at -2, and $\lim_{x \to -2} f(x)$ does not exist. f is discontinuous at $x = 2$: f is not defined at 2, but $\lim_{x \to 2} f(x) = 12$.

60. (A) Yes; f is continuous on $(0, 3)$.

(B) Since $\lim_{x \to 0^+} f(x) = 2 = f(0)$, f is continuous from the right at $x = 0$.

(C) Since $\lim_{x \to 3^-} f(x) = 5 = f(3)$, f is continuous from the left at $x = 3$.

(D) Yes; f is continuous on the closed interval $[0, 3]$.

62. (A) Since $\lim_{x \to 2^+} f(x) = f(2) = 2$, f is continuous from the right at $x = 2$.

(B) Since $\lim_{x \to 2^-} f(x) = 1 \neq f(2) = 2$, f is not continuous from the left at $x = 2$.

(C) f is continuous on the open interval $(1, 2)$.

(D) *f* is *not* continuous on the closed interval [1, 2] since
$\lim\limits_{x\to 2^-} f(x) = 1 \neq f(2) = 2$, i.e., *f* is not continuous from the left at
x = 2.

(E) *f* is continuous on the half-closed interval [1, 2).

64. *x* intercepts: *x* = -4, 3

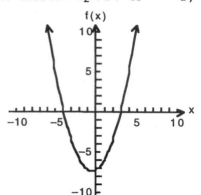

66. *x* intercepts: *x* = -3, 2, 7

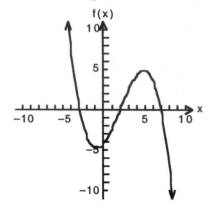

68. $f(x) = \dfrac{6}{x - 4} \neq 0$ for all *x*. This does not contradict Theorem 2 because
f is not continuous on (2, 7); *f* is discontinuous at *x* = 4.

70. The following sketches illustrate that either condition is possible.
Theorem 2 implies that one of these two conditions must occur.

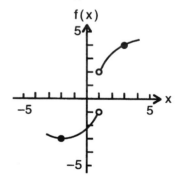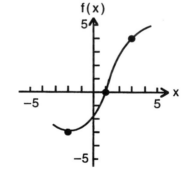

72. (A) $R(x) = \begin{cases} 0.07 & \text{if} & 0 < x \leq 1 \\ 0.12 & \text{if} & 1 < x \leq 2 \\ 0.17 & \text{if} & 2 < x \leq 3 \\ 0.22 & \text{if} & 3 < x \leq 4 \\ 0.27 & \text{if} & 4 < x \leq 5 \\ 0.32 & \text{if} & 5 < x \leq 6 \\ \vdots & & \vdots \end{cases}$ (B)

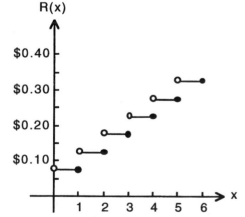

(C) $\lim_{x \to 3.5} R(x) = 0.22 = R(3.5)$; Thus, $R(x)$ is continuous at $x = 3.5$.

$\lim_{x \to 3} R(x)$ does not exist; $R(3) = 0.17$; Thus, $R(x)$ is not continuous at $x = 3$.

74. If x is a positive integer, then $S(x) = R(x) + 0.05$.
$S(x) = R(x)$ for all other values of x in the domain of R.

76. (A) $S(x) = \begin{cases} 5 + 0.69x & \text{if} & 0 \leq x \leq 5 \\ 5.2 + 0.65x & \text{if} & 5 < x \leq 50 \\ 6.2 + 0.63x & \text{if} & 50 < x \end{cases}$

(B) The graph of S is:

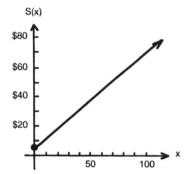

(C) $\lim_{x \to 5} S(x) = 8.45 = S(5)$; thus, $S(x)$ is continuous at $x = 5$.

$\lim_{x \to 50} S(x) = 37.7 = S(50)$; thus, $S(x)$ is continuous at $x = 50$.

78. (A) The graph of $C(x)$ is:

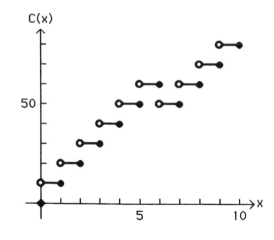

(B) From the graph, $\lim_{x \to 4.5} C(x) = 50$ and $C(4.5) = 50$.

(C) From the graph, $\lim_{x \to 8} C(x)$ does not exist; $C(8) = 60$.

(D) Since $\lim_{x \to 4.5} C(x) = 50 = C(4.5)$, $C(x)$ is continuous at $x = 4.5$. Since $\lim_{x \to 8} C(x)$ does not exist and $C(8) = 60$, $C(x)$ is not continuous at $x = 8$.

80. (A) From the graph, p is discontinuous at $t = t_2$, and $t = t_4$.

(B) $\lim_{t \to t_1} p(t) = 10$; $p(t_1) = 10$.

(C) $\lim_{t \to t_2} p(t) = 30$, $p(t_2) = 10$.

(D) $\lim_{t \to t_4} p(t)$ does not exist; $p(t_4) = 80$.

2. (A) $\dfrac{f(-1) - f(-2)}{-1 - (-2)} = \dfrac{4 - 1}{1} = 3$ is the slope of the secant line through
$(-2,\ f(-2))$ and $(-1,\ f(-1))$.

(B) $\dfrac{f(-2 + h) - f(-2)}{h} = \dfrac{5 - (-2 + h)^2 - 1}{h} = \dfrac{5 - [4 - 4h + h^2] - 1}{h}$

$= \dfrac{5 - 4 + 4h - h^2 - 1}{h} = \dfrac{4h - h^2}{h} = 4 - h;$

slope of the secant line through $(-2,\ f(-2))$ and $(-2 + h,\ f(-2 + h))$

(C) $\lim_{h \to 0} \dfrac{f(-2 + h) - f(-2)}{h} = \lim_{h \to 0} (4 - h) = 4;$

slope of the tangent line at $(-2,\ f(-2))$

4. $f(x) = 3x^2$

(A) Average rate of change $= \dfrac{f(5) - f(2)}{5 - 2} = \dfrac{3(5)^2 - 3(2)^2}{5 - 2}$

$= \dfrac{75 - 12}{3} = \dfrac{63}{3} = 21$

(B) Slope of secant line $= \dfrac{f(5) - f(2)}{5 - 2} = \dfrac{75 - 12}{3} = 21$

(C) Slope of secant line $= \dfrac{3(2 + h)^2 - 3(2)^2}{2 + h - 2} = \dfrac{3(4 + 4h + h^2) - 12}{h}$

$= \dfrac{12 + 12h + 3h^2 - 12}{h}$

$= \dfrac{12h + 3h^2}{h} = 12 + 3h$

(D) In view of part (C), slope of the graph at
$(2,\ f(2)) = \lim_{h \to 0} (12 + 3h) = 12.$

(E) Instantaneous rate of change at $x = 2$ is
$\lim_{h \to 0} \dfrac{f(2 + h) - f(2)}{h}$ if the limit exists.
In view of parts (C) and (D), we have
$\lim_{h \to 0} \dfrac{f(2 + h) - f(2)}{h} = 12.$

(F) The slope of the tangent line at $(2,\ f(2))$ is the limit of the slope
of the secant line through $(2,\ f(2))$ and $(2 + h,\ f(2 + h))$ as $h \to 0$.
From part (C), the slope of the tangent line at
$(2,\ f(2)) = \lim_{h \to 0} \dfrac{f(2 + h) - f(2)}{2 + h - 2} = \lim_{h \to 0} (12 + 3h) = 12.$

(G) The equation of the tangent line at $(2,\ f(2)) = (2,\ 12)$ is:
$y - 12 = 12(x - 2)$
or $y - 12 = 12x - 24$
$y = 12x - 12.$

6. $f(x) = 9$

    <u>Step 1</u>. Find $f(x + h)$.

          $f(x + h) = 9$

    <u>Step 2</u>. Find $f(x + h) - f(x)$.

          $f(x + h) - f(x) = 9 - 9 = 0$

    <u>Step 3</u>. Find $\dfrac{f(x + h) - f(x)}{h}$.

$$\frac{f(x + h) - f(x)}{h} = \frac{0}{h} = 0$$

    <u>Step 4</u>. Find $f'(x) = \lim\limits_{h \to 0} \dfrac{f(x + h) - f(x)}{h} = \lim\limits_{h \to 0}(0) = 0$

          Thus, if $f(x) = 9$, then $f'(x) = 0$; $f'(1) = 0$, $f'(2) = 0$, $f'(3) = 0$.

8. $f(x) = 4 - 6x$

    <u>Step 1</u>. $f(x + h) = 4 - 6(x + h) = 4 - 6x - 6h$

    <u>Step 2</u>. $f(x + h) - f(x) = (4 - 6x - 6h) - (4 - 6x)$

$$= 4 - 6x - 6h - 4 + 6x = -6h$$

    <u>Step 3</u>. $\dfrac{f(x + h) - f(x)}{h} = \dfrac{-6h}{h} = -6$

    <u>Step 4</u>. $f'(x) = \lim\limits_{h \to 0} \dfrac{f(x + h) - f(x)}{h} = \lim\limits_{h \to 0}(-6) = -6$

          $f'(1) = -6$, $f'(2) = -6$, $f'(3) = -6$

10. $f(x) = 2x^2 + 8$

    <u>Step 1</u>. $f(x + h) = 2(x + h)^2 + 8 = 2(x^2 + 2xh + h^2) + 8$

$$= 2x^2 + 4xh + 2h^2 + 8$$

    <u>Step 2</u>. $f(x + h) - f(x) = (2x^2 + 4xh + 2h^2 + 8) - (2x^2 + 8)$

$$= 2x^2 + 4xh + 2h^2 + 8 - 2x^2 - 8$$
$$= 4xh + 2h^2$$

    <u>Step 3</u>. $\dfrac{f(x + h) - f(x)}{h} = \dfrac{4xh + 2h^2}{h} = 4x + 2h$

    <u>Step 4</u>. $f'(x) = \lim\limits_{h \to 0} \dfrac{f(x + h) - f(x)}{h} = \lim\limits_{h \to 0}(4x + 2h) = 4x$

          $f'(1) = 4$, $f'(2) = 8$, $f'(3) = 12$

12. $f(x) = x^2 + 4x + 7$

    <u>Step 1</u>. $f(x + h) = (x + h)^2 + 4(x + h) + 7 = x^2 + 2xh + h^2 + 4x + 4h + 7$

    <u>Step 2</u>. $f(x + h) - f(x) = (x^2 + 2xh + h^2 + 4x + 4h + 7) - (x^2 + 4x + 7)$

$$= 2xh + 4h + h^2 = h(2x + 4 + h)$$

Step 3. $\dfrac{f(x + h) - f(x)}{h} = \dfrac{h(2x + 4 + h)}{h} = 2x + 4 + h$

Step 4. $f'(x) = \lim\limits_{h \to 0} \dfrac{f(x + h) - f(x)}{h} = \lim\limits_{h \to 0}(2x + 4 + h) = 2x + 4$

$\qquad f'(1) = 6, \ f'(2) = 8, \ f'(3) = 10$

14. $f(x) = 2x^2 + 5x + 1$

Step 1. $f(x + h) = 2(x + h)^2 + 5(x + h) + 1$

$\qquad\qquad\qquad = 2(x^2 + 2xh + h^2) + 5x + 5h + 1$

$\qquad\qquad\qquad = 2x^2 + 4xh + 2h^2 + 5x + 5h + 1$

Step 2. $f(x + h) - f(x) = (2x^2 + 4xh + 2h^2 + 5x + 5h + 1) - (2x^2 + 5x + 1)$

$\qquad\qquad\qquad\qquad = h(4x + 5 + 2h)$

Step 3. $\dfrac{f(x + h) - f(x)}{h} = \dfrac{h(4x + 5 + 2h)}{h} = 4x + 5 + 2h$

Step 4. $f'(x) = \lim\limits_{h \to 0} \dfrac{f(x + h) - f(x)}{h} = \lim\limits_{h \to 0}(4x + 5 + 2h) = 4x + 5$

$\qquad f'(1) = 9, \ f'(2) = 13, \ f'(3) = 17$

16. $f(x) = -x^2 + 9x - 2$

Step 1. $f(x + h) = -(x + h)^2 + 9(x + h) - 2$

$\qquad\qquad\qquad = -(x^2 + 2xh + h^2) + 9x + 9h - 2$

$\qquad\qquad\qquad = -x^2 - 2xh - h^2 + 9x + 9h - 2$

Step 2. $f(x + h) - f(x) = (-x^2 - 2xh - h^2 + 9x + 9h - 2) - (-x^2 + 9x - 2)$

$\qquad\qquad\qquad\qquad = -2xh + 9h - h^2 = h(-2x + 9 - h)$

Step 3. $\dfrac{f(x + h) - f(x)}{h} = \dfrac{h(-2x + 9 - h)}{h} = -2x + 9 - h$

Step 4. $f'(x) = \lim\limits_{h \to 0} \dfrac{f(x + h) - f(x)}{h} = \lim\limits_{h \to 0}(-2x + 9 - h) = -2x + 9$

$\qquad f'(1) = 7, \ f'(2) = 5, \ f'(3) = 3$

18. $f(x) = -2x^3 + 5$

Step 1. $f(x + h) = -2(x + h)^3 + 5 = -2(x^3 + 3x^2h + 3xh^2 + h^3) + 5$

$\qquad\qquad\qquad\qquad\qquad = -2x^3 - 6x^2h - 6xh^2 - 2h^3 + 5$

Step 2. $f(x + h) - f(x) = -2x^3 - 6x^2h - 6xh^2 - 2h^3 + 5 - (-2x^3 + 5)$

$\qquad\qquad\qquad\qquad = -6x^2h - 6xh^2 - 2h^3$

$\qquad\qquad\qquad\qquad = -2h(3x^2 + 3xh + h^2)$

Step 3. $\dfrac{f(x + h) - f(x)}{h} = \dfrac{-2h(3x^2 + 3xh + h^2)}{h} = -2(3x^2 + 3xh + h^2)$

Step 4. $f'(x) = \lim\limits_{h \to 0} \dfrac{f(x + h) - f(x)}{h} = \lim\limits_{h \to 0}\{-2(3x^2 + 3xh + h^2)\} = -6x^2$

$\qquad f'(1) = -6, \ f'(2) = -24, \ f'(3) = -54$

20. $f(x) = \dfrac{6}{x} - 2$

Step 1. $f(x + h) = \dfrac{6}{x + h} - 2$

Step 2. $f(x + h) - f(x) = \left(\dfrac{6}{x + h} - 2\right) - \left(\dfrac{6}{x} - 2\right)$

$$= \dfrac{6}{x + h} - \dfrac{6}{x} = \dfrac{6x - 6x - 6h}{x(x + h)} = \dfrac{-6h}{x(x + h)}$$

Step 3. $\dfrac{f(x + h) - f(x)}{h} = \dfrac{\dfrac{-6h}{x(x + h)}}{h} = -\dfrac{6}{x(x + h)}$

Step 4. $f'(x) = \lim\limits_{h \to 0} \dfrac{f(x + h) - f(x)}{h} = \lim\limits_{h \to 0} \dfrac{-6}{x(x + h)} = -\dfrac{6}{x^2}$

$f'(1) = -6, \quad f'(2) = -\dfrac{6}{4} = -\dfrac{3}{2}, \quad f'(3) = -\dfrac{6}{9} = -\dfrac{2}{3}$

22. $f(x) = 3 - 7\sqrt{x}$

Step 1. $f(x + h) = 3 - 7\sqrt{x + h}$

Step 2. $f(x + h) - f(x) = (3 - 7\sqrt{x + h}) - (3 - 7\sqrt{x}) = 7(\sqrt{x} - \sqrt{x + h})$

Step 3. $\dfrac{f(x + h) - f(x)}{h} = \dfrac{7(\sqrt{x} - \sqrt{x + h})}{h} = \dfrac{7(\sqrt{x} - \sqrt{x + h})}{h} \cdot \dfrac{(\sqrt{x} + \sqrt{x + h})}{(\sqrt{x} + \sqrt{x + h})}$

$$= \dfrac{7(x - (x + h))}{h(\sqrt{x} + \sqrt{x + h})} = \dfrac{7(x - x - h)}{h(\sqrt{x} + \sqrt{x + h})}$$

$$= \dfrac{-7h}{h(\sqrt{x} + \sqrt{x + h})} = \dfrac{-7}{\sqrt{x} + \sqrt{x + h}}$$

Step 4. $f'(x) = \lim\limits_{h \to 0} \dfrac{f(x + h) - f(x)}{h} = \lim\limits_{h \to 0} \left(\dfrac{-7}{\sqrt{x} + \sqrt{x + h}}\right) = \dfrac{-7}{2\sqrt{x}}$

$f'(1) = -\dfrac{7}{2}, \quad f'(2) = -\dfrac{7}{2\sqrt{2}} = -\dfrac{7\sqrt{2}}{4}, \quad f'(3) = -\dfrac{7}{2\sqrt{3}} = -\dfrac{7\sqrt{3}}{6}$

24. $f(x) = 16\sqrt{x + 9}$

Step 1. $f(x + h) = 16\sqrt{x + h + 9}$

Step 2. $f(x + h) - f(x) = 16\sqrt{x + h + 9} - 16\sqrt{x + 9}$

$$= 16(\sqrt{x + h + 9} - \sqrt{x + 9})$$

Step 3. $\dfrac{f(x + h) - f(x)}{h} = \dfrac{16(\sqrt{x + h + 9} - \sqrt{x + 9})}{h}$

$$= \dfrac{16(\sqrt{x + h + 9} - \sqrt{x + 9})}{h} \cdot \dfrac{(\sqrt{x + h + 9} + \sqrt{x + 9})}{(\sqrt{x + h + 9} + \sqrt{x + 9})}$$

$$= \dfrac{16((x + h + 9) - (x + 9))}{h(\sqrt{x + h + 9} + \sqrt{x + 9})}$$

$$= \dfrac{16h}{h(\sqrt{x + h + 9} + \sqrt{x + 9})} = \dfrac{16}{\sqrt{x + h + 9} + \sqrt{x + 9}}$$

Step 4. $f'(x) = \lim\limits_{h \to 0} \dfrac{f(x + h) - f(x)}{h} = \lim\limits_{h \to 0} \dfrac{16}{\sqrt{x + h + 9} + \sqrt{x + 9}}$

$$= \dfrac{16}{2\sqrt{x + 9}} = \dfrac{8}{\sqrt{x + 9}}$$

$f'(1) = \dfrac{8}{\sqrt{10}} = \dfrac{4\sqrt{10}}{5}$, $f'(2) = \dfrac{8}{\sqrt{11}} = \dfrac{8\sqrt{11}}{11}$, $f'(3) = \dfrac{8}{\sqrt{12}} = \dfrac{4\sqrt{3}}{3}$

26. $f(x) = \dfrac{5x}{3 + x}$

Step 1. $f(x + h) = \dfrac{5(x + h)}{3 + (x + h)} = \dfrac{5x + 5h}{3 + x + h}$

Step 2. $f(x + h) - f(x) = \dfrac{5x + 5h}{3 + x + h} - \dfrac{5x}{3 + x}$

$$= \dfrac{(5x + 5h)(3 + x) - 5x(3 + x + h)}{(3 + x + h)(3 + x)}$$

$$= \dfrac{5x(3 + x) + 5h(3 + x) - 5x(3 + x) - 5xh}{(3 + x + h)(3 + x)}$$

$$= \dfrac{15h}{(3 + x + h)(3 + x)}$$

Step 3. $\dfrac{f(x + h) - f(x)}{h} = \dfrac{\dfrac{15h}{(3 + x + h)(3 + x)}}{h} = \dfrac{15}{(3 + x + h)(3 + x)}$

Step 4. $f'(x) = \lim\limits_{h \to 0} \dfrac{f(x + h) - f(x)}{h} = \lim\limits_{h \to 0} \dfrac{15}{(3 + x + h)(3 + x)} = \dfrac{15}{(3 + x)^2}$

$f'(1) = \dfrac{15}{16}$, $f'(2) = \dfrac{15}{25} = \dfrac{3}{5}$, $f'(3) = \dfrac{15}{36} = \dfrac{5}{12}$

28. $y = f(x) = x^2 + x$

(A) $f(2) = 2^2 + 2 = 6$, $f(4) = 4^2 + 4 = 20$

Slope of secant line: $\dfrac{f(4) - f(2)}{4 - 2} = \dfrac{20 - 6}{2} = \dfrac{14}{2} = 7$

(B) $f(2) = 6$, $f(2 + h) = (2 + h)^2 + (2 + h) = 4 + 4h + h^2 + 2 + h$

$$= 6 + 5h + h^2$$

Slope of secant line: $\dfrac{f(2 + h) - f(2)}{h} = \dfrac{6 + 5h + h^2 - 6}{h}$

$$= \dfrac{5h + h^2}{h} = 5 + h$$

(C) Slope of tangent line at $(2, f(2))$:

$\lim\limits_{h \to 0} \dfrac{f(2 + h) - f(2)}{h} = \lim\limits_{h \to 0}(5 + h) = 5$

(D) Equation of tangent line at $(2, f(2))$:

$y - f(2) = f'(2)(x - 2)$ or $y - 6 = 5(x - 2)$ and $y = 5x - 4$.

30. $f(x) = x^2 + x$

    (A) Average velocity: $\dfrac{f(4) - f(2)}{4 - 2} = \dfrac{(4)^2 + 4 - ((2)^2 + 2)}{2} = \dfrac{16 + 4 - 6}{2}$

                                         = 7 meters per second

    (B) Average velocity: $\dfrac{f(2 + h) - f(2)}{h} = \dfrac{(2 + h)^2 + (2 + h) - 6}{h}$

$$= \dfrac{4 + 4h + h^2 + 2 + h - 6}{h}$$

$$= \dfrac{5h + h^2}{h} = 5 + h \text{ meters per second}$$

    (C) Instantaneous velocity: $\lim\limits_{h \to 0} \dfrac{f(2 + h) - f(2)}{h} = \lim\limits_{h \to 0} (5 + h)$

$$= 5 \text{ meters per second}$$

32. $F'(x)$ does exist at $x = b$.   **34.** $F'(x)$ does not exist at $x = d$.

36. $F'(x)$ does not exist at $x = f$.   **38.** $F'(x)$ does exist at $x = h$.

40. $f(x) = x^2 + 2x$

    (A) <u>Step 1</u>. Simplify $\dfrac{f(x + h) - f(x)}{h}$.

$$\dfrac{f(x + h) - f(x)}{h} = \dfrac{(x + h)^2 + 2(x + h) - (x^2 + 2x)}{h}$$

$$= \dfrac{x^2 + 2xh + h^2 + 2x + 2h - x^2 - 2x}{h}$$

$$= \dfrac{2xh + h^2 + 2h}{h} = 2x + 2 + h$$

    <u>Step 2</u>. Evaluate $\lim\limits_{h \to 0} \dfrac{f(x + h) - f(x)}{h}$.

$$\lim\limits_{h \to 0} \dfrac{f(x + h) - f(x)}{h} = \lim\limits_{h \to 0} (2x + 2 + h) = 2x + 2$$

    Therefore, $f'(x) = 2x + 2$.

    (B) $f'(-2) = -2$, $f'(-1) = 0$,   (C)
        $f'(1) = 4$

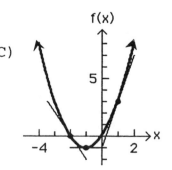

42. To find $v = f'(x)$, use the two-step process for the given distance function, $f(x) = 8x^2 - 4x$.

Step 1. $\dfrac{f(x + h) - f(x)}{h} = \dfrac{8(x + h)^2 - 4(x + h) - (8x^2 - 4x)}{h}$

$$= \dfrac{8(x^2 + 2xh + h^2) - 4x - 4h - 8x^2 + 4x}{h}$$

$$= \dfrac{8x^2 + 16xh + 8h^2 - 4x - 4h - 8x^2 + 4x}{h}$$

$$= \dfrac{16xh - 4h + 8h^2}{h} = 16x - 4 + 8h$$

Step 2. $\displaystyle\lim_{h \to 0} \dfrac{f(x + h) - f(x)}{h} = \lim_{h \to 0} (16x - 4 + 8h) = 16x - 4$

Thus, the velocity, $v = f'(x) = 16x - 4$
$$f'(1) = 12 \text{ feet per second}$$
$$f'(3) = 44 \text{ feet per second}$$
$$f'(5) = 76 \text{ feet per second}$$

44. (A) The graphs of g and h are vertical translations of the graph of f. All Three functions should have the same derivatives; they differ from each other by a constant.

(B) $m(x) = -x^2 + c$

Step 1. $m(x + h) = -(x + h)^2 + c = -x^2 - 2xh - h^2 + c$

Step 2. $m(x + h) - m(x) = (-x^2 - 2xh - h^2 + c) - (-x^2 + c)$
$$= -x^2 - 2xh - h^2 + c + x^2 - c$$
$$= -2xh - h^2$$

Step 3. $\dfrac{m(x + h) - m(x)}{h} = \dfrac{-2xh - h^2}{h} = -2x - h$

Step 4. $m'(x) = \displaystyle\lim_{h \to 0} \dfrac{m(x + h) - m(x)}{h} = \lim_{h \to 0} (-2x - h) = -2x$

46. (A) For any point on the graph of f, the slope of the graph is m.

(B) $f(x) = mx + b$

Step 1. $f(x + h) = m(x + h) + b = mx + mh + b$

Step 2. $f(x + h) - f(x) = (mx + mh + b) - (mx + b) = mh$

Step 3. $\dfrac{f(x + h) - f(x)}{h} = \dfrac{mh}{h} = m$

Step 4. $f'(x) = \displaystyle\lim_{h \to 0} \dfrac{f(x + h) - f(x)}{h} = \lim_{h \to 0} m = m$

48. The graph of $f(x) = \begin{cases} 2x & \text{if } x < 2 \\ 6 - x & \text{if } x \geq 2 \end{cases}$ is:

f is not differentiable at $x = 2$ because the graph of f has a sharp corner at this point.

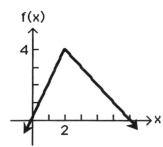

50. $f(x) = \begin{cases} 2 - x^2 & \text{if } x \leq 0 \\ 2 & \text{if } x > 0 \end{cases}$

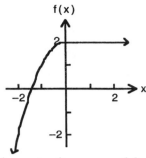

It is clear that $f'(x) = \begin{cases} -2x & \text{if } x < 0 \\ 0 & \text{if } x > 2 \end{cases}$

Thus, the only question is $f'(0)$.
Since $\lim\limits_{x \to 0^-} f'(x) = \lim\limits_{x \to 0^-} (-2x) = 0$ and

$\lim\limits_{x \to 0^+} f'(x) = \lim\limits_{x \to 0^+} (0) = 0$, f is differentiable at 0 as well;
f is differentiable for all real numbers.

52. $f(x) = 1 - |x|$

$$\lim_{h \to 0} \frac{f(0 + h) - f(0)}{h} = \lim_{h \to 0} \frac{1 - |0 + h| - (1 - |0|)}{h} = \lim_{h \to 0} \frac{|h|}{h}$$

The limit does not exist. Thus, f is not differentiable at $x = 0$.

54. $f(x) = x^{2/3}$

$$\lim_{h \to 0} \frac{f(0 + h) - f(0)}{h} = \lim_{h \to 0} \frac{(0 + h)^{2/3} - 0^{2/3}}{h} = \lim_{h \to 0} \frac{h^{2/3}}{h} = \lim_{h \to 0} \frac{1}{h^{1/3}}$$

The limit does not exist. Thus, f is not differentiable at $x = 0$.

56. $f(x) = \sqrt{1 + x^2}$

$$\lim_{h \to 0} \frac{f(0 + h) - f(0)}{h} = \lim_{h \to 0} \frac{\sqrt{1 + (0 + h)^2} - \sqrt{1 + 0^2}}{h} = \lim_{h \to 0} \frac{\sqrt{1 + h^2} - 1}{h}$$

$$= \lim_{h \to 0} \frac{\sqrt{1 + h^2} - 1}{h} \cdot \frac{\sqrt{1 + h^2} + 1}{\sqrt{1 + h^2} + 1}$$

$$= \lim_{h \to 0} \frac{1 + h^2 - 1}{h\left[\sqrt{1 + h^2} + 1\right]}$$

$$= \lim_{h \to 0} \frac{h}{\sqrt{1 + h^2} + 1} = \frac{0}{2} = 0$$

f is differentiable at $x = 0$ and $f'(0) = 0$.

58. $y = 16x^2$
Now, if $y = 1{,}024$ ft, then

$$16x^2 = 1{,}024$$
$$x^2 = \frac{1{,}024}{16} = 64$$
$$x = 8 \text{ sec.}$$

$y' = 32x$ and at $x = 8$, $y' = 32 \times 8 = 256$ ft/sec.

60. $P(x) = 45x - 0.025x^2 - 5,000, \ 0 \le x \le 2,400.$

(A) Average change $= \dfrac{P(850) - P(800)}{850 - 800}$

$$= \frac{[45(850) - 0.025(850)^2 - 5,000] - [45(800) - 0.025(800)^2 - 5,000]}{50}$$

$$= \frac{45(850) - 0.025(850)^2 - 45(800) - 0.025(800)^2}{50}$$

$$= \frac{54,250 - 54,062.5}{50} = \frac{187.5}{50} = \$3.75$$

(B) $P(x) = 45x - 0.025x^2 - 5,000$

<u>Step 1</u>. $P(x + h) = 45(x + h) - 0.025(x + h)^2 - 5,000$

$\qquad\qquad\quad = 45x + 45h - 0.025x^2 - 0.05xh - 0.025h^2 - 5,000$

<u>Step 2</u>. $P(x + h) - P(x)$

$\qquad = (45x + 45h - 0.025x^2 - 0.05xh - 0.025h^2 - 5,000)$

$\qquad\qquad\qquad\qquad\qquad\qquad\qquad - (45x - 0.025x^2 - 5,000)$

$\qquad = 45h - 0.05xh - 0.025h^2$

<u>Step 3</u>. $\dfrac{P(x + h) - P(x)}{h} = \dfrac{45h - 0.05xh - 0.025h^2}{h} = 45 - 0.05x - 0.025h$

<u>Step 4</u>. $P'(x) = \lim\limits_{h \to 0} \dfrac{P(x + h) - P(x)}{h} = \lim\limits_{h \to 0}(45 - 0.05x - 0.025h)$

$\qquad\qquad\qquad\qquad\qquad\qquad\qquad\qquad = 45 - 0.05x$

(C) $P(800) = 45(800) - 0.025(800)^2 - 5,000 = 15,000$

$\quad\ P'(800) = 45 - 0.05(800) = 5;$

At a production level of 800 car seats, the profit is \$15,000 and is increasing at the rate of \$5 per seat.

62. $S(t) = 2\sqrt{t + 6}$

<u>Step 1</u>. $S(t + h) = 2\sqrt{t + h + 6}$

<u>Step 2</u>. $S(t + h) - S(t) = 2[\sqrt{t + h + 6} - \sqrt{t + 6}]$

$\qquad\qquad\qquad\qquad\quad = 2[\sqrt{t + h + 6} - \sqrt{t + 6}] \cdot \dfrac{\sqrt{t + h + 6} + \sqrt{t + 6}}{\sqrt{t + h + 6} + \sqrt{t + 6}}$

$\qquad\qquad\qquad\qquad\quad = \dfrac{2[(t + h + 6) - (t + 6)]}{\sqrt{t + h + 6} + \sqrt{t + 6}} = \dfrac{2h}{\sqrt{t + h + 6} + \sqrt{t + 6}}$

<u>Step 3</u>. $\dfrac{S(t + h) - S(t)}{h} = \dfrac{\frac{2h}{\sqrt{t + h + 6} + \sqrt{t + 6}}}{h} = \dfrac{2}{\sqrt{t + h + 6} + \sqrt{t + 6}}$

<u>Step 4</u>. $S'(t) = \lim\limits_{h \to 0}\dfrac{S(t + h) - S(t)}{h} = \lim\limits_{h \to 0}\dfrac{2}{\sqrt{t + h + 6} + \sqrt{t + 6}}$

$\qquad\qquad\qquad\qquad\qquad\qquad = \dfrac{2}{2\sqrt{t + 6}} = \dfrac{1}{\sqrt{t + 6}}$

(B) $S(10) = 2\sqrt{10 + 6} = 2\sqrt{16} = 2(4) = 8$;

$$S'(10) = \frac{1}{\sqrt{10 + 6}} = \frac{1}{\sqrt{16}} = \frac{1}{4} = 0.25$$

After 10 months, the total sales are $8 million and are INCREASING at the rate of $0.25 million = $250,000 per month.

(C) The estimated total sales are $8.2 million after 11 months and $8.5 million after 12 months.

64. (A) $p(t) = 27t^2 - 75t + 6,015$

Step 1. $p(t + h) = 27(t + h)^2 - 75(t + h) + 6,015$
$$= 27t^2 + 54th + 27h^2 - 75t - 75h + 6,015$$

Step 2. $p(t + h) - p(t) = (27t^2 + 54th + 27h^2 - 75t - 75h + 6,015)$
$$- (27t^2 - 75t + 6,015)$$
$$= 54th + 27h^2 - 75h$$

Step 3. $\dfrac{p(t + h) - p(t)}{h} = \dfrac{54th + 27h^2 - 75h}{h} = 54t + 27h - 75$

Step 4. $p'(t) = \lim\limits_{h \to 0} \dfrac{p(t + h) - p(t)}{h} = \lim\limits_{h \to 0}(54t + 27h - 75) = 54t - 75$

(B) 2010 corresponds to $t = 20$, thus
$$p(20) = 27(20)^2 - 75(20) + 6,105 = 15,315$$
$$p'(20) = 54(20) - 75 = 1,005.$$

In 2010, 15,315 thousand tons of copper are consumed and this quantity is increasing at the rate of 1,005 thousand tons per year.

66. (A)
```
QuadReg
y=ax²+bx+c
a=1.541666667
b=14.38560606
c=743.6272727
```

(B) Let $y = C(x)$ denote the regression equation in (A). Then, using a graphing utility, $C(20) = 1,648.0$ and $C'(20) = 76.1$ (one decimal place accuracy). In 2010, commercial sales will be 1,648 billion kilowatt hours and will be INCREASING at the rate of 76.1 billion kilowatt hours per year.

68. (A) $F(t) = 98 + \dfrac{4}{t + 1}$

Step 1. $F(t + h) = 98 + \dfrac{4}{t + h + 1}$

Step 2. $F(t + h) - F(t) = \left(98 + \dfrac{4}{t + h + 1}\right) - \left(98 + \dfrac{4}{t + 1}\right)$

$$= \frac{4}{t + h + 1} - \frac{4}{t + 1} = 4\left[\frac{(t + 1) - (t + h + 1)}{(t + h + 1)(t + 1)}\right]$$

$$= \frac{-4h}{(t + h + 1)(t + 1)}$$

Step 3. $\dfrac{F(t + h) - F(t)}{h} = \dfrac{\dfrac{-4h}{(t + h + 1)(t + 1)}}{h} = \dfrac{-4}{(t + h + 1)(t + 1)}$

Step 4. $F'(t) = \lim\limits_{h \to 0} \dfrac{F(t + h) - F(t)}{h} = \lim\limits_{h \to 0} \left(\dfrac{-4}{(t + h + 1)(t + 1)} \right) = \dfrac{-4}{(t + 1)^2}$

(B) $F(3) = 99$; $F'(3) = -0.25$

After 3 hours, the body temperature is 99° and is DECREASING at the rate of 0.25° per hour.

70. (A) $f(t) = 0.008t^2 - 0.74t + 23$

Step 1. $f(t + h) = 0.008(t + h) - 0.74(t + h) + 23$
$\qquad\qquad = 0.008t^2 + 0.016th + 0.008h^2 - 0.74t - 0.74h + 23$

Step 2. $f(t + h) - f(t) = (0.008t^2 + 0.016th + 0.008h^2 - 0.74t$
$\qquad\qquad\qquad\qquad\qquad\qquad - 0.74h + 23) - (0.008t^2 - 0.74t + 23)$
$\qquad\qquad\qquad\qquad = 0.016th + 0.008h^2 - 0.74h$

Step 3. $\dfrac{f(t + h) - f(t)}{h} = \dfrac{0.016th + 0.008h^2 - 0.74h}{h}$
$\qquad\qquad\qquad\qquad = 0.016t + 0.008h - 0.74$

Step 4. $f'(t) = \lim\limits_{h \to 0} \dfrac{f(t + h) - f(t)}{h} = \lim\limits_{h \to 0} (0.016t + 0.008h - 0.74)$
$\qquad\qquad\qquad\qquad\qquad\qquad = 0.016t - 0.74$

(B) 2000 corresponds to $t = 40$. Thus,
$\qquad f(40) = 0.008(40)^2 - 0.74(40) + 23 = 6.2;$
$\qquad f'(40) = 0.016(40) - 0.74 = -0.1.$

In 2000, the number of female infant deaths per 100,000 births was 6.2 and was decreasing at the rate of -0.1 deaths per 100,000 births per year.

EXERCISE 3-4

2. $\dfrac{d}{dx} 3 = 0$ (Derivative of a constant rule)

4. $y = x^6$
$\qquad y' = 6x^{6-1}$ (Power rule)
$\qquad\quad = 6x^5$

6. $g(x) = x^5$
$\qquad g'(x) = 5x^{5-1}$ (Power rule)
$\qquad\qquad = 5x^4$

8. $y = x^{-8}$
$\qquad \dfrac{dy}{dx} = -8x^{-8-1}$ (Power rule)
$\qquad\qquad = -8x^{-9}$

10. $f(x) = x^{9/2}$
$\qquad f'(x) = \dfrac{9}{2} x^{(9/2)-1}$ (Power rule)
$\qquad\qquad = \dfrac{9}{2} x^{7/2}$

12. $y = \dfrac{1}{x^{12}} = x^{-12}$
$\qquad y' = -12x^{-12-1}$ (Power rule)
$\qquad\quad = -12x^{-13}$

14. $\dfrac{d}{dx}(-2x^3) = -2(3x^2)$ (constant times a function rule)

$$= -6x^2$$

16. $f(x) = .8x^4$

$f'(x) = (.8)(4x^3) = 3 \cdot 2x^3$

18. $y = \dfrac{x^5}{25}$

$$y' = \dfrac{1}{25}(5x^4) = \dfrac{x^4}{5}$$

20. $h(x) = 5g(x);\ h'(2) = 5g'(2) = 5(-1) = -5$

22. $h(x) = g(x) - f(x);\ h'(2) = g'(2) - f'(2) = -1 - 3 = -4$

24. $h(x) = -4f(x) + 5g(x) - 9;\ h'(2) = -4f'(2) + 5g'(2)$

$$= -4(3) + 5(-1) = -17$$

26. $\dfrac{d}{dx}(-4x + 9) = \dfrac{d}{dx}(-4x) + \dfrac{d}{dx}(9) = -4 + 0 = -4$

28. $y = 2 + 5t - 8t^3$

$\dfrac{dy}{dt} = 0 + 5 - 24t^2 = 5 - 24t^2$

30. $g(x) = 5x^{-7} - 2x^{-4}$

$g'(x) = (5) \cdot (-7)x^{-8} - (2) \cdot (-4)x^{-5}$

$$= -35x^{-8} + 8x^{-5}$$

32. $\dfrac{d}{du}(2u^{4.5} - 3.1u + 13.2) = (2) \cdot (4.5)u^{3.5} - 3.1 + 0$

$$= 9u^{3.5} - 3.1$$

34. $F(t) = 0.2t^3 - 3.1t + 13.2$

$F'(t) = (0.2) \cdot (3)t^2 - 3.1 + 0 = 0.6t^2 - 3.1$

36. $w = \dfrac{7}{5u^2} = \dfrac{7}{5}u^{-2}$

$w' = \left(\dfrac{7}{5}\right) \cdot (-2)u^{-3} = -\dfrac{14}{5}u^{-3}$

38. $\dfrac{d}{dx}\left(\dfrac{5x^3}{4} - \dfrac{2}{5x^3}\right) = \dfrac{d}{dx}\left(\left(\dfrac{5}{4}\right)x^3 - \left(\dfrac{2}{5}\right)x^{-3}\right)$

$$= \left(\dfrac{5}{4}\right) \cdot (3)x^2 - \left(\dfrac{2}{5}\right) \cdot (-3)x^{-4}$$

$$= \dfrac{15}{4}x^2 + \dfrac{6}{5}x^{-4}$$

40. $H(w) = \dfrac{5}{w^6} - 2\sqrt{w} = 5w^{-6} - 2w^{1/2}$

$H'(w) = (5) \cdot (-6)w^{-7} - (2) \cdot \left(\dfrac{1}{2}\right)w^{-1/2} = -30w^{-7} - w^{-1/2}$

42. $\dfrac{d}{du}(8u^{3/4} + 4u^{-1/4}) = (8) \cdot \left(\dfrac{3}{4}\right)u^{-1/4} + (4) \cdot \left(-\dfrac{1}{4}\right)u^{-5/4}$

$$= 6u^{-1/4} - u^{-5/4}$$

44. $F(t) = \dfrac{5}{t^{1/5}} - \dfrac{8}{t^{3/2}} = 5t^{-1/5} - 8t^{-3/2}$

$F'(t) = (5) \cdot \left(-\dfrac{1}{5}\right)t^{-6/5} - (8) \cdot \left(-\dfrac{3}{2}\right)t^{-5/2}$

$$= -t^{-6/5} + 12t^{-5/2}$$

46. $w = \dfrac{10}{\sqrt[5]{u}} = 10u^{-1/5}$

$w' = (10) \cdot \left(-\dfrac{1}{5}\right)u^{-6/5} = -2u^{-6/5}$

48. $\dfrac{d}{dx}\left(2.8x^{-3} - \dfrac{0.6}{\sqrt[3]{x^2}} + 7\right) = \dfrac{d}{dx}(2.8x^{-3} - 0.6x^{-2/3} + 7)$

$$= (2.8) \cdot (-3)x^{-4} - (0.6) \cdot \left(-\dfrac{2}{3}\right)x^{-5/3} + 0$$

$$= -8.4x^{-4} + 0.4x^{-5/3}$$

50. $f(x) = 2x^2 + 8x$

(A) $f'(x) = 4x + 8$

(B) Slope of the graph of f at $x = 2$: $f'(2) = 4(2) + 8 = 16$
Slope of the graph of f at $x = 4$: $f'(4) = 4(4) + 8 = 24$

(C) Tangent line at $x = 2$: $y - y_1 = m(x - x_1)$
$x_1 = 2$
$y_1 = f(2) = 2(2)^2 + 8(2) = 24$
$m = f'(2) = 16$
Thus, $y - 24 = 16(x - 2)$ or $y = 16x - 8$
Tangent line at $x = 4$: $y - y_1 = m(x - x_1)$
$x_1 = 4$
$y_1 = f(4) = 2(4)^2 + 8(4) = 64$
$m = f'(4) = 24$
Thus, $y - 64 = 24(x - 4)$ or $y = 24x - 32$

(D) The tangent line is horizontal at the values $x = c$ such that
$f'(c) = 0$. Thus, we must solve the following:
$f'(x) = 4x + 8 = 0$
$4x = -8$
$x = -2$

52. $f(x) = x^4 - 32x^2 + 10$

(A) $f'(x) = 4x^3 - 64x$

(B) Slope of the graph of f at $x = 2$: $f'(2) = 4(2)^3 - 64(2) = -96$
Slope of the graph of f at $x = 4$: $f'(4) = 4(4)^3 - 64(4) = 0$

(C) Tangent line at $x = 2$: $y - y_1 = m(x - x_1)$, where

$x_1 = 2$, $y_1 = f(2) = (2)^4 - 32(2)^2 + 10 = -102$, $m = -96$

$y + 102 = -96(x - 2)$ or $y = -96x + 90$
Tangent line at $x = 4$ is a horizontal line since the slope $m = 0$.
The equation of the tangent line at $x = 4$ then is
$y = f(4) = (4)^4 - 32(4)^2 + 10 = -246$

(D) Solve $f'(x) = 0$ for x:
$$4x^3 - 64x = 0$$
$$4x(x^2 - 16) = 0$$
$$4x(x + 4)(x - 4) = 0$$
$$x = -4, \ x = 0, \ x = 4$$

54. $f(x) = 80x - 10x^2$

(A) $v = f'(x) = 80 - 20x$

(B) $v\big|_{x=0} = f'(0) = 80$ ft/sec.

$v\big|_{x=3} = f'(3) = 80 - 20(3) = 20$ ft/sec.

(C) Solve $v = f'(x) = 0$ for x:
$$80 - 20x = 0$$
$$20x = 80$$
$$x = 4 \text{ seconds}$$

56. $f(x) = x^3 - 9x^2 + 24x$

(A) $v = f'(x) = 3x^2 - 18x + 24$

(B) $v\big|_{x=0} = f'(0) = 24$ ft/sec.

$v\big|_{x=3} = f'(3) = 3(3)^2 - 18(3) + 24 = -3$ ft/sec.

(C) Solve $v = f'(x) = 0$ for x:
$$3x^2 - 18x + 24 = 0 \quad \text{or} \quad x^2 - 6x + 8 = 0$$
$$(x - 2)(x - 4) = 0$$
$$x = 2, \ x = 4 \text{ seconds}$$

58. $x = 1.5247$ **60.** $x = 2.3247$

62. $x = -3.7626, \ 0.5742, \ 5.4384$ **64.** $x = 1.2391, \ 1.6400, \ 4.9209$

66. The tangent line to the graph of a parabola at the vertex is a
horizontal line. Therefore, to find the x coordinate of the vertex,
we solve $f'(x) = 0$ for x.

68. No. The derivative is a quadratic function which can have at most two zeros.

70. $y = (2x - 5)^2$
$y' = (2)(2x - 5)(2) = 8x - 20$

72. $y = \dfrac{x^2 + 25}{x^2} = 1 + \dfrac{25}{x^2} = 1 + 25x^{-2}$

$\dfrac{dy}{dx} = 0 + (25) \cdot (-2)x^{-3} = -50x^{-3}$

74. $\dfrac{d}{dx}\left(\dfrac{5x - 3}{15x^6}\right) = \dfrac{d}{dx}\left(\dfrac{5x}{15x^6} - \dfrac{3}{15x^6}\right)$

$\qquad\qquad = \dfrac{d}{dx}\left(\dfrac{1}{3}x^{-5} - \dfrac{1}{5}x^{-6}\right)$

$\qquad\qquad = \left(\dfrac{1}{3}\right) \cdot (-5)x^{-6} - \left(\dfrac{1}{5}\right) \cdot (-6)x^{-7}$

$\qquad\qquad = -\dfrac{5}{3}x^{-6} + \dfrac{6}{5}x^{-7}$

76. $f(x) = \dfrac{2x^5 - 4x^3 + 2x}{x^3} = \dfrac{2x^5}{x^3} - \dfrac{4x^3}{x^3} + \dfrac{2x}{x^3}$

$\qquad\qquad = 2x^2 - 4 + 2x^{-2}$

$f'(x) = 4x - 4x^{-3}$

78. $f(x) = x^4$

$\underline{\text{Step 1}}.\ f(x + h) = (x + h)^4 = [(x + h)^2]^2$

$\qquad\qquad = [x^2 + 2xh + h^2]$

$\qquad\qquad = x^4 + 4x^2h^2 + h^4 + 4x^3h + 2x^2h^2 + 4xh^3$

$\underline{\text{Step 2}}.\ f(x + h) - f(x) = x^4 + 4x^2h^2 + h^4 + 4x^3h + 2x^2h^2 + 4xh^3 - x^4$

$\qquad\qquad = h(4x^2h + h^3 + 4x^3 + 2x^2h + 4xh^2)$

$\underline{\text{Step 3}}.\ \dfrac{f(x + h) - f(x)}{h} = \dfrac{h(4x^2h + h^3 + 4x^3 + 2x^2h + 4xh^2)}{h}$

$\qquad\qquad = 4x^2h + h^3 + 4x^3 + 2x^2h + 4xh^2$

$\underline{\text{Step 4}}.\ f'(x) = \lim\limits_{h \to 0}\dfrac{f(x + h) - f(x)}{h} = \lim\limits_{h \to 0}(4x^2h + h^3 + 4x^3 + 2x^2h + 4xh^2)$

$\qquad\qquad = 4x^3$

$\text{So, } \dfrac{d}{dx}x^4 = 4x^3.$

80. $f(x) = x^{2/3};\ f'(x) = \dfrac{2}{3}x^{-1/3} = \dfrac{2}{3x^{1/3}}$

The domain of $f'(x)$ is all real numbers except $x = 0$. At $x = 0$, the graph of $y = f(x)$ has a sharp point and a vertical tangent.

82. $S(t) = 0.015t^4 + 0.4t^3 + 3.4t^2 + 10t - 3$

(A) $S'(t) = (0.015) \cdot (4)t^3 + (0.4) \cdot (3)t^2 + (3.4)(2)t + 10 - 0$
$= 0.06t^3 + 1.2t^2 + 6.8t + 10$

(B) $S(4) = 0.015(4)^4 + 0.4(4)^3 + 3.4(4)^2 + 10(4) - 3 = 120.84$,
$S'(4) = 0.06(4)^3 + 1.2(4)^2 + 6.8(4) + 10 = 60.24$.

After 4 months, sales are \$120.84 million and are increasing at the rate of \$60.24 million per month.

(C) $S(8) = 0.015(8)^4 + 0.4(8)^3 + 3.4(8)^2 + 10(8) - 3 = 560.84$,
$S'(8) = 0.06(8)^3 + 1.2(8)^2 + 6.8(8) + 10 = 171.92$.

After 8 months, sales are \$560.84 million and are increasing at the rate of \$171.92 million per month.

84. $x = 10 + \dfrac{180}{p}$, $2 \leq p \leq 10$

For $p = 5$, $x = 10 + \dfrac{180}{5} = 10 + 36 = 46$

$x = 10 + \dfrac{180}{p} = 10 + 180p^{-1}$

$\dfrac{dx}{dp} = -180p^{-2} = -\dfrac{180}{p^2}$

For $p = 5$, $\dfrac{dx}{dp}\bigg|_{p=5} = -\dfrac{180}{25} = -7.2$

At the \$5 price level, the demand is 46 pounds and is decreasing at the rate of 7.2 pounds per dollar increase in price.

86. (A)

```
QuadReg
y=ax²+bx+c
a=-9
b=683
c=875
■
```

(B) Let $y = L(x)$ denote the regression equation found in (A). Then $L(18) = -9(18)^2 + 683(18) + 875 \approx 10,300$ (rounded to the nearest hundred) and $L'(18) = -2(9)(18) + 683 = 400$ (rounded to the nearest hundred). Thus, in 1998, 10,300 limousine operators were registered and the number of registered limousine operators was increasing at the rate of 400 operators per year.

88. $C(x) = \dfrac{0.1}{x^2} = 0.1x^{-2}$

$C'(x) = -0.2x^{-3} = -\dfrac{0.2}{x^3}$, the instantaneous rate of change of concentration at x miles.

(A) At $x = 1$, $C'(1) = -0.2$ parts per million per mile.

(B) At $x = 2$, $C'(2) = -\dfrac{0.2}{8} = -0.025$ parts per million per mile.

90. $y = 21\sqrt[3]{x^2}$, $0 \le x \le 8$.

First, find $y' = (21\sqrt[3]{x^2})' = (21x^{2/3})' = 21\left(\dfrac{2}{3} x^{-1/3}\right)$

$$= 14x^{-1/3} = \dfrac{14}{x^{1/3}} = \dfrac{14}{\sqrt[3]{x}},$$

the rate of learning at the end of x hours.

(A) Rate of learning at the end of 1 hour:

$\dfrac{14}{\sqrt[3]{1}} = 14$ items per hour.

(B) Rate of learning at the end of 8 hours:

$\dfrac{14}{\sqrt[3]{8}} = \dfrac{14}{2} = 7$ items per hour.

EXERCISE 3-5

2. $f(x) = 5x^2(x^3 + 2)$

$f'(x) = (5x^2)'(x^3 + 2) + 5x^2(x^3 + 2)'$ (using product rule)

$\quad = 10x(x^3 + 2) + 5x^2(3x^2)$

$\quad = 10x^4 + 20x + 15x^4 = 25x^4 + 20x$

4. $f(x) = (3x + 2)(4x - 5)$

$f'(x) = (3x + 2)'(4x - 5) + (3x + 2)(4x - 5)'$ (using product rule)

$\quad = 3(4x - 5) + (3x + 2)(4)$

$\quad = 12x - 15 + 12x + 8 = 24x - 7$

6. $f(x) = \dfrac{3x}{2x + 1}$

$f'(x) = \dfrac{(3x)'(2x + 1) - (2x + 1)'(3x)}{(2x + 1)^2}$ (using quotient rule)

$\quad = \dfrac{3(2x + 1) - (2)(3x)}{(2x + 1)^2} = \dfrac{6x + 3 - 6x}{(2x + 1)^2} = \dfrac{3}{(2x + 1)^2}$

8. $f(x) = \dfrac{3x - 4}{2x + 3}$

$f'(x) = \dfrac{(3x - 4)'(2x + 3) - (2x + 3)'(3x - 4)}{(2x + 3)^2}$ (using quotient rule)

$\quad = \dfrac{3(2x + 3) - (3x - 4)}{(2x + 3)^2} = \dfrac{6x + 9 - 6x + 8}{(2x + 3)^2} = \dfrac{17}{(2x + 3)^2}$

10. $f(x) = (3x + 5)(x^2 - 3)$

$f'(x) = (3x + 5)'(x^2 - 3) + (3x + 5)(x^2 - 3)'$ (using product rule)

$\quad = 3(x^2 - 3) + (3x + 5)(2x) = 3x^2 - 9 + 6x^2 + 10x$

$\qquad\qquad\qquad\qquad\qquad = 9x^2 + 10x - 9$

12. $f(x) = (0.5x - 4)(0.2x + 1)$

$f'(x) = (0.5x - 4)'(0.2x + 1) + (0.5x - 4)(0.2x + 1)'$ (using product rule)

$\qquad = 0.5(0.2x + 1) + (0.5x - 4)(0.2)$

$\qquad = 0.10x + 0.5 + 0.10x - 0.8 = 0.20x - 0.30$

14. $f(x) = \dfrac{3x + 5}{x^2 - 3}$

$f'(x) = \dfrac{(3x + 5)'(x^2 - 3) - (x^2 - 3)'(3x + 5)}{(x^2 - 3)^2}$ (using quotient rule)

$\qquad = \dfrac{(3x^2 - 3) - (2x) - (3x + 5)}{(x^2 - 3)^2} = \dfrac{3x^2 - 9 - 6x^2 - 10x}{(x^2 - 3)^2}$

$\qquad\qquad\qquad = \dfrac{-3x^2 - 10x - 9}{(x^2 - 3)^2}$

16. $f(x) = (x^2 - 4)(x^2 + 5)$

$f'(x) = (x^2 - 4)'(x^2 + 5) + (x^2 - 4)(x^2 + 5)'$ (using product rule)

$\qquad = 2x(x^2 + 5) + (x^2 - 4)(2x)$

$\qquad = 2x^3 + 10x + 2x^3 - 8x = 4x^3 + 2x$

18. $f(x) = \dfrac{x^2 - 4}{x^2 + 5}$

$f'(x) = \dfrac{(x^2 - 4)'(x^2 + 5) - (x^2 + 5)'(x^2 - 4)}{(x^2 + 5)^2}$ (using quotient rule)

$\qquad = \dfrac{2x(x^2 + 5) - (2x)(x^2 - 4)}{(x^2 + 5)^2} = \dfrac{2x^3 + 10x - 2x^3 + 8x}{(x^2 + 5)^2}$

$\qquad\qquad\qquad = \dfrac{18x}{(x^2 + 5)^2}$

20. $h(x) = x^2 f(x)$

$h'(x) = 2x f(x) + x^2 f'(x)$ (Product Rule)

22. $h(x) = \dfrac{f(x)}{x}$

$h'(x) = \dfrac{x f'(x) - f(x)}{x^2}$ (Quotient Rule)

24. $h(x) = \dfrac{f(x)}{x^3}$

$h'(x) = \dfrac{x^3 f'(x) - 3x^2 f(x)}{x^6}$ (Quotient Rule)

26. $h(x) = \dfrac{x^2}{f(x)}$

$h'(x) = \dfrac{2x f(x) - x^2 f'(x)}{(f(x))^2}$ (Quotient Rule)

28. $y = (x^3 + 2x^2)(3x - 1)$

$y' = (x^3 + 2x^2)'(3x - 1) + (x^3 + 2x^2)(3x - 1)'$

$ = (3x^2 + 4x)(3x - 1) + (x^3 + 2x^2)(3)$

$ = 9x^3 + 12x^2 - 3x^2 - 4x + 3x^3 + 6x^2$

$ = 12x^3 + 15x^2 - 4x$

30. $\dfrac{d}{dt}[(3 - 0.4t^3)(0.5t^2 - 2t)]$

$= \left[\dfrac{d}{dt}(3 - 0.4t^3)\right](0.5t^2 - 2t) + (3 - 0.4t^3)\left[\dfrac{d}{dt}(0.5t^2 - 2t)\right]$

$= -1.2t^2(0.5t^2 - 2t) + (3 - 0.4t^3)(t - 2)$

$= -0.6t^4 + 2.4t^3 + 3t - 6 - 0.4t^4 + 0.8t^3$

$= -t^4 + 3.2t^3 + 3t - 6$

32. $f(x) = \dfrac{3x^2}{2x - 1}$

$f'(x) = \dfrac{(3x^2)'(2x - 1) - (2x - 1)'(3x^2)}{(2x - 1)^2}$

$ = \dfrac{6x(2x - 1) - 2(3x^2)}{(2x - 1)^2} = \dfrac{12x^2 - 6x - 6x^2}{(2x - 1)^2} = \dfrac{6x^2 - 6x}{(2x - 1)^2}$

34. $y = \dfrac{w^4 - w^3}{3w - 1}$

$\dfrac{dy}{dw} = \dfrac{\left[\dfrac{d}{dw}(w^4 - w^3)\right](3w - 1) - \left[\dfrac{d}{dw}(3w - 1)\right](w^4 - w^3)}{(3w - 1)^2}$

$\phantom{\dfrac{dy}{dw}} = \dfrac{(4w^3 - 3w^2)(3w - 1) - (3)(w^4 - w^3)}{(3w - 1)^2}$

$\phantom{\dfrac{dy}{dw}} = \dfrac{12w^4 - 4w^3 - 9w^3 + 3w^2 - 3w^4 + 3w^3}{(3w - 1)^2}$

$\phantom{\dfrac{dy}{dw}} = \dfrac{9w^4 - 10w^3 + 3w^2}{(3w - 1)^2}$

36. $f(x) = (7 - 3x)(1 + 2x)$

First find $f'(x)$:

$f'(x) = (7 - 3x)'(1 + 2x) + (7 - 3x)(1 + 2x)'$

$ = -3(1 + 2x) + (7 - 3x)(2)$

$ = -3 - 6x + 14 - 6x = -12x + 11$

An equation for the tangent line at $x = 2$ is:

$\quad y - y_1 = m(x - x_1)$

where $x_1 = 2$, $y_1 = f(2) = 5$, and $m = f'(x_1) = f'(2) = -13$.

Thus, we have:

$\quad y - 5 = -13(x - 2) \quad$ or $\quad y = -13x + 31$

38. $f(x) = \dfrac{2x - 5}{2x - 3}$

First find $f'(x)$:

$$f'(x) = \frac{(2x - 5)'(2x - 3) - (2x - 3)'(2x - 5)}{(2x - 3)^2}$$

$$= \frac{2(2x - 3) - 2(2x - 5)}{(2x - 3)^2} = \frac{4x - 6 - 4x + 10}{(2x - 3)^2} = \frac{4}{(2x - 3)^2}$$

An equation for the tangent line at $x = 2$ is:

$\quad y - y_1 = m(x - x_1)$

where $x_1 = 2$, $y_1 = f(2) = -1$, and $m = f'(x_1) = f'(2) = 4$.

Thus, we have:

$\quad\quad y + 1 = 4(x - 2)$ or $y = 4x - 9$

40. $f(x) = (2x - 3)(x^2 - 6)$

$\quad f'(x) = (2x - 3)'(x^2 - 6) + (2x - 3)(x^2 - 6)'$

$\quad\quad\quad = 2(x^2 - 6) + (2x - 3)(2x)$

$\quad\quad\quad = 2x^2 - 12 + 4x^2 - 6x = 6x^2 - 6x - 12$

To find the value(s) of x where $f'(x) = 0$, set

$\quad f'(x) = 6x^2 - 6x - 12 = 0$

$\quad\quad\quad$ or $x^2 - x - 2 = 0$

$\quad\quad\quad (x + 1)(x - 2) = 0$

Thus, $x = -1$, $x = 2$.

42. $f(x) = \dfrac{x}{x^2 + 9}$

$$f'(x) = \frac{(x)'(x^2 + 9) - (x^2 + 9)'(x)}{(x^2 + 9)^2}$$

$$= \frac{x^2 + 9 - (2x)(x)}{(x^2 + 9)^2} = \frac{x^2 + 9 - 2x^2}{(x^2 + 9)^2} = \frac{9 - x^2}{(x^2 + 9)^2}$$

To find the value(s) of x where $f'(x) = 0$, set

$$f'(x) = \frac{9 - x^2}{(x^2 + 9)^2} = 0 \quad \text{or} \quad 9 - x^2 = 0,$$

$\quad (3 - x)(3 + x) = 0.$

Thus, $x = -3$, $x = 3$.

44. $f(x) = x^4(x^3 - 1)$

First, we use the product rule:

$\quad f'(x) = (x^4)'(x^3 - 1) + x^4(x^3 - 1)'$

$\quad\quad\quad = 4x^3(x^3 - 1) + x^4(3x^2)$

$\quad\quad\quad = 4x^6 - 4x^3 + 3x^6 = 7x^6 - 4x^3$

Next, simplifying $f(x)$, we have $f(x) = x^7 - x^4$.

Thus, $f'(x) = 7x^6 - 4x^3$.

46. $f(x) = \dfrac{x^4 + 4}{x^4}$

First, we use the quotient rule:

$f'(x) = \dfrac{(x^4 + 4)'(x^4) - (x^4)'(x^4 + 4)}{(x^4)^2} = \dfrac{4x^3(x^4) - (4x^3)(x^4 + 4)}{x^8}$

$\quad = \dfrac{4x^7 - 4x^7 - 16x^3}{x^8} = \dfrac{-16x^3}{x^8} = -\dfrac{16}{x^5}$

Next, simplifying $f(x)$, we have $f(x) = 1 + \dfrac{4}{x^4} = 1 + 4x^{-4}$.

Thus, $f'(x) = 4(-4x^{-5}) = -16x^{-5} = -\dfrac{16}{x^5}$.

48. $g(w) = (5 - 2w^3)^2$

$g'(w) = 2(5 - 2w^3)(-6w^2) = -12w^2(5 - 2w^3)$

$\qquad\qquad\qquad\qquad\quad = -60w^2 + 24w^5$

$\qquad\qquad\qquad\qquad\quad = 24w^5 - 60w^2$

50. $y = \dfrac{x^3 - 3x + 4}{2x^2 + 3x - 2}$

$y' = \dfrac{(x^3 - 3x + 4)'(2x^2 + 3x - 2) - (2x^2 + 3x - 2)'(x^3 - 3x + 4)}{(2x^2 + 3x - 2)^2}$

$\quad = \dfrac{(3x^2 - 3)(2x^2 + 3x - 2) - (4x + 3)(x^3 - 3x + 4)}{(2x^2 + 3x - 2)^2}$

$\quad = \dfrac{6x^4 + 9x^3 - 6x^2 - 6x^2 - 9x + 6 - 4x^4 + 12x - 16x - 3x^3 + 9x - 12}{(2x^2 + 3x - 2)^2}$

$\quad = \dfrac{2x^4 + 6x^3 - 16x - 6}{(2x^2 + 3x - 2)^2}$

52. $\dfrac{d}{dx}[(4x^{1/2} - 1)(3x^{1/3} + 2)]$

$\quad = \left[\dfrac{d}{dx}(4x^{1/2} - 1)\right](3x^{1/3} + 2) + (4x^{1/2} - 1)\left[\dfrac{d}{dx}(3x^{1/3} + 2)\right]$

$\quad = (2x^{-1/2})(3x^{1/3} + 2) + (4x^{1/2} - 1)(x^{-2/3})$

$\quad = 6x^{-1/6} + 4x^{-1/2} + 4x^{-1/6} - x^{-2/3}$

$\quad = 10x^{-1/6} + 4x^{-1/2} - x^{-2/3}$

$\quad = \dfrac{10}{x^{1/6}} + \dfrac{4}{x^{1/2}} - \dfrac{1}{x^{2/3}}$

$\quad = \dfrac{10x + 4x^{2/3} - x^{1/2}}{x^{7/6}}$

54. $y = \dfrac{2\sqrt{x}}{x^2 - 3x + 1} = \dfrac{2x^{1/2}}{x^2 - 3x + 1}$

$y' = \dfrac{(2x^{1/2})'\,(x^2 - 3x + 1) - (x^2 - 3x + 1)'\,(2x^{1/2})}{(x^2 - 3x + 1)^2}$

$\quad = \dfrac{x^{-1/2}(x^2 - 3x + 1) - 2(2x - 3)x^{1/2}}{(x^2 - 3x + 1)^2} = \dfrac{(x^2 - 3x + 1) - 2x(2x - 3)}{(x^2 - 3x + 1)^2 x^{1/2}}$

$\quad = \dfrac{x^2 - 3x + 1 - 4x^2 + 6x}{(x^2 - 3x + 1)^2 x^{1/2}} = \dfrac{-3x^2 + 3x + 1}{(x^2 - 3x + 1)^2 x^{1/2}}$

56. $h(t) = \dfrac{-0.05t^2}{2t + 1}$

$h'(t) = \dfrac{(-0.1t)\,(2t + 1) - (2)\,(-0.05t^2)}{(2t + 1)^2}$ \qquad (Quotient Rule)

$\quad = \dfrac{-0.2t^2 - 0.1t + 0.1t^2}{(2t + 1)^2} = \dfrac{-0.1t^2 - 0.1t}{(2t + 1)^2}$

58. $y = \dfrac{x^2 - 3x + 1}{\sqrt[4]{x}} = \dfrac{x^2 - 3x + 1}{x^{1/4}}$

$\dfrac{dy}{dx} = \dfrac{\left[\dfrac{d}{dx}(x^2 - 3x + 1)\right]x^{1/4} - \left[\dfrac{d}{dx}(x^{1/4})\right](x^2 - 3x + 1)}{x^{1/2}}$

$\quad = \dfrac{(2x - 3)x^{1/4} - \left(\dfrac{1}{4}x^{-3/4}\right)(x^2 - 3x + 1)}{x^{1/2}}$

$\quad = \dfrac{(2x - 3)x - \dfrac{1}{4}(x^2 - 3x + 1)}{(x^{1/2})(x^{3/4})}$

$\quad = \dfrac{4(2x - 3)x - (x^2 - 3x + 1)}{4x^{5/4}} = \dfrac{8x^2 - 12x - x^2 + 3x - 1}{4x^{5/4}}$

$\quad = \dfrac{7x^2 - 9x - 1}{4x^{5/4}}$

60. $y = \dfrac{2x - 1}{(x^3 + 2)\,(x^2 - 3)}$

$y' = \dfrac{(2x - 1)'\,(x^3 + 2)\,(x^2 - 3) - [\,(x^3 + 2)\,(x^2 - 3)\,]'\,(2x - 1)}{[\,(x^3 + 2)\,(x^2 - 3)\,]^2}$

$\quad = \dfrac{2(x^3 + 2)\,(x^2 - 3) - [\,(x^3 + 2)'\,(x^2 - 3) + (x^3 + 2)\,(x^2 - 3)'\,]\,(2x - 1)}{[\,(x^3 + 2)\,(x^2 - 3)\,]^2}$

$\quad = \dfrac{2(x^5 - 3x^3 + 2x^2 - 6) - [\,(3x^2)\,(x^2 - 3) + (x^3 + 2)\,(2x)\,]\,(2x - 1)}{[\,(x^3 + 2)\,(x^2 - 3)\,]^2}$

$$= \frac{2x^5 - 6x^3 + 4x^2 - 12 - [3x^4 - 9x^2 + 2x^4 + 4x](2x - 1)}{(x^3 + 2)^2(x^2 - 3)^2}$$

$$= \frac{2x^5 - 6x^3 + 4x^2 - 12 - 6x^5 + 3x^4 + 18x^3 - 9x^2 - 4x^5 + 2x^4 - 8x^2 + 4x}{(x^3 + 2)^2(x^2 - 3)^2}$$

$$= \frac{-8x^5 + 5x^4 + 12x^3 - 13x^2 + 4x - 12}{(x^3 + 2)^2(x^2 - 3)^2}$$

62. $f(x) = (x^2 + 3)(x^2 + 4x)$

$f'(x) = (x^2 + 3)'(x^2 + 4x) + (x^2 + 3)(x^2 + 4x)'$

$\quad = (2x)(x^2 + 4x) + (x^2 + 3)(2x + 4)$

$\quad = 2x^3 + 8x^2 + 2x^3 + 4x^2 + 6x + 12$

$\quad = 4x^3 + 12x^2 + 6x + 12$

Set $f'(x) = 4x^3 + 12x^2 + 6x + 12 = 0$ and solve using a root-approximation routine on a graphing utility:
$f'(x) = 0$ at $x = -2.8435$.

64. $f(x) = \dfrac{x^3 + 15x - 1}{x^2 + 1}$

$f'(x) = \dfrac{(x^3 + 15x - 1)'(x^2 + 1) - (x^2 + 1)'(x^3 + 15x - 1)}{(x^2 + 1)^2}$

$\quad = \dfrac{(3x^2 + 15)(x^2 + 1) - 2x(x^3 + 15x - 1)}{(x^2 + 1)^2}$

$\quad = \dfrac{3x^4 + 3x^2 + 15x^2 + 15 - 2x^4 - 30x^2 + 2x}{(x^2 + 1)^2}$

$\quad = \dfrac{x^4 - 12x^2 + 2x + 15}{(x^2 + 1)^2}$

$f'(x) = 0$ implies $x^4 - 12x^2 + 2x + 15 = 0$.
Solve using a root-approximation routine on a graphing utility:
$f'(x) = 0$ at $x = -3.3562$, $x = -1.0889$, $x = 1.3086$, $x = 3.1365$.

66. $N(t) = \dfrac{180t}{t + 4}$

(A) $N'(t) = \dfrac{180(t + 4) - 180t}{(t + 4)^2} = \dfrac{180t + 720 - 180t}{(t + 4)^2} = \dfrac{720}{(t + 4)^2}$

(B) $N(16) = \dfrac{180(16)}{16 + 20} = 144$; $N'(16) = \dfrac{720}{(16 + 4)^2} = 1.8$;

after 16 months, the total number of subscribers is 144,000 and is increasing at a rate of 1,800 subscribers per month.

(C) The total subscribers after 17 months will be approximately 145,800.

68. $x = \dfrac{100p}{0.1p + 1}$, $10 \le p \le 70$

(A) $\dfrac{dx}{dp} = \dfrac{100(0.1p + 1) - 0.1(100p)}{(0.1p + 1)^2} = \dfrac{10p + 100 - 10p}{(0.1p + 1)^2} = \dfrac{100}{(0.1p + 1)^2}$

(B) $x(40) = \dfrac{100(40)}{0.1(40) + 1} = \dfrac{4,000}{5} = 800$;

$\left.\dfrac{dx}{dp}\right|_{40} = \dfrac{100}{(0.1(40) + 1)^2} = \dfrac{100}{25} = 4$

At a price level of \$40, the supply is 800 CD players and is increasing at the rate of 4 players per dollar.

(C) At a price of \$41, the demand will be approximately 804 CD players.

70. $T(x) = x^2\left(1 - \dfrac{x}{9}\right)$, $0 \le x \le 7$

(A) $T'(x) = 2x\left(1 - \dfrac{x}{9}\right) + x^2\left(-\dfrac{1}{9}\right) = 2x - \dfrac{2}{9}x^2 = \dfrac{1}{9}x^2 = 2x - \dfrac{1}{3}x^2$;

(B) $T'(1) = 2(1) - \dfrac{1}{3}(1)^2 = 2 - \dfrac{1}{3} = \left(\dfrac{5}{3}\right)^0$ per mg of drug;

$T'(3) = 2(3) - \dfrac{1}{3}(3)^2 = 6 - 3 = 3^0$ per mg of drug;

$T'(6) = 2(6) - \dfrac{1}{3}(6)^2 = 12 - 12 = 0^0$ per mg of drug.

EXERCISE 3-6

2. (-2); $\dfrac{d}{dx}(5 - 2x)^6 = 6(5 - 2x)^5(-2) = -12(6 - 2x)^5$

4. $6x$; $\dfrac{d}{dx}(3x^2 + 7)^5 = 5(3x^2 + 7)^4(6x) = 30x(3x^2 + 7)^4$

6. $(-3 - 4x)$; $\dfrac{d}{dx}(4 - 3x - 2x^2)^8 = 8(4 - 3x - 2x^2)^7(-3 - 4x)$

$= -8(3 + 4x)(4 - 3x - 2x^2)^7$

8. $f(x) = (3x - 7)^5$

$f'(x) = 5(3x - 7)^4(3x - 7)' = 5(3x - 7)^4(3) = 15(3x - 7)^4$

10. $f(x) = (9 - 5x)^2$

$f'(x) = 2(9 - 5x)(9 - 5x)' = 2(9 - 5x)(-5) = -10(9 - 5x)$

12. $f(x) = (6 - 0.5x)^4$

$f'(x) = 4(6 - 0.5x)^3(6 - 0.5x)' = 4(6 - 0.5x)^3(-0.5)$

$= -2(6 - 0.5x)^3$

14. $f(x) = (5x^2 - 3)^6$

$f'(x) = 6(5x^2 - 3)^5(5x^2 - 3)' = 6(5x^2 - 3)^5(10x)$
$$= 60x(5x^2 - 3)^5$$

16. $f(x) = (2x^2 + x + 1)^7$

$f'(x) = 7(2x^2 + x + 1)^6(2x^2 + x + 1)' = 7(2x^2 + x + 1)^6(4x + 1)$
$$= 7(4x + 1)(2x^2 + x + 1)^6$$

18. $f(x) = (4x + 3)^{1/2}$

$f'(x) = \dfrac{1}{2}(4x + 3)^{-1/2}(4x + 3)' = \dfrac{1}{2}(4x + 3)^{-1/2}(4)$
$$= 2(4x + 3)^{-1/2} = \dfrac{2}{(4x + 3)^{1/2}}$$

20. $f(x) = (x^5 + 2)^{-3}$

$f'(x) = (-3)(x^5 + 2)^{-4}(x^5 + 2)' = (-3)(x^5 + 2)^{-4}(5x^4)$
$$= -15x^4(x^5 + 2)^{-4}$$
$$= -\dfrac{15x^4}{(x^5 + 2)^4}$$

22. $f(x) = (3x - 1)^4$

$f'(x) = 4(3x - 1)^3(3) = 12(3x - 1)^3$

Tangent line at $x = 1$: $y - y_1 = m(x - x_1)$ where $x_1 = 1$,

$y_1 = f(1) = (3(1) - 1)^4 = 16$, $m = f'(1) = 12(3(1) - 1)^3 = 96$.

Thus, $y - 16 = 96(x - 1)$ or $y = 96x - 80$.

The tangent line is horizontal at the value(s) of x such that $f'(x) = 0$:
$$12(3x - 1)^3 = 0$$
$$3x - 1 = 0$$
$$x = \dfrac{1}{3}$$

24. $f(x) = (2x + 8)^{1/2}$

$f'(x) = \dfrac{1}{2}(2x + 8)^{-1/2}(2) = (2x + 8)^{-1/2} = \dfrac{1}{(2x + 8)^{1/2}}$

Tangent line at $x = 4$: $y - y_1 = m(x - x_1)$ where $x_1 = 4$,

$y_1 = f(4) = [2(4) + 8]^{1/2} = 4$, $m = f'(4) = \dfrac{1}{[2(4) + 8]^{1/2}} = \dfrac{1}{4}$.

Thus, $y - 4 = \dfrac{1}{4}(x - 4)$ or $y = \dfrac{1}{4}x + 3$.

The tangent line is horizontal at the value(s) of x such that $f'(x) = 0$.
$f'(x) = \dfrac{1}{(2x + 8)^{1/2}} \neq 0$, so there is none.

26. $y = 2(x^3 + 6)^5$

$y' = 2(5)(x^3 + 6)^4(3x^2) = 30x^2(x^3 + 6)^4$

28. $\dfrac{d}{dt}[3(t^3 + t^2)^{-2}] = 3(-2)(t^3 + t^2)^{-3}(3t^2 + 2t)$

$$= \dfrac{-6(3t^2 + 2t)}{(t^3 + t^2)^3}$$

30. $g(w) = \sqrt[3]{3w - 7} = (3w - 7)^{1/3}$

$\dfrac{dg}{dw} = \dfrac{1}{3}(3w - 7)^{-2/3}(3) = (3w - 7)^{-2/3} = \dfrac{1}{\sqrt[3]{(3w - 7)^2}}$

32. $h(x) = \sqrt{2x - 5} = (2x - 5)^{1/2}$

$h'(x) = \dfrac{1}{2}(2x - 5)^{-1/2}(2) = (2x - 5)^{-1/2} = \dfrac{1}{\sqrt{2x - 5}}$

34. $\dfrac{d}{dx}[\sqrt[5]{1.6x - 4.6}] = \dfrac{d}{dx}[(1.6x - 4.6)^{1/5}]$

$$= \dfrac{1}{5}(1.6x - 4.6)^{-4/5}(1.6)$$

$$= 0.32(1.6x - 4.6)^{-4/5} = \dfrac{0.32}{\sqrt[5]{(1.6x - 4.6)^4}}$$

36. $G(t) = (2t^2 + 2t - 3)^{1/2}$

$G'(t) = \dfrac{1}{2}(2t^2 + 2t - 3)^{-1/2}(4t + 2) = \dfrac{2t + 1}{\sqrt{2t^2 + 2t - 3}}$

38. $y = \dfrac{1}{3x - 7} = (3x - 7)^{-1}$

$y' = (-1) \cdot (3x - 7)^{-2}(3) = -3(3x - 7)^{-2} = \dfrac{-3}{(3x - 7)^2}$

40. $\dfrac{d}{dw}\left[\dfrac{1}{(w^2 - 2)^6}\right] = \dfrac{d}{dw}[(w^2 - 2)^{-6}]$

$$= (-6) \cdot (w^2 - 2)^{-7}(2w)$$

$$= -12w(w^2 - 2)^{-7} = \dfrac{-12w}{(w^2 - 2)^7}$$

42. $y = \left(\dfrac{1}{x^2} - 5\right)^{-2} = (x^{-2} - 5)^{-2}$

$\dfrac{dy}{dx} = (-2) \cdot (x^{-2} - 5)^{-3}(-2x^{-3})$

$$= 4x^{-3}(x^{-2} - 5)^{-3} = \dfrac{4}{x^3\left(\dfrac{1}{x^2} - 5\right)^3}$$

44. $g(t) = \dfrac{3}{\sqrt[3]{t - t^2}} = 3(t - t^2)^{-1/3}$

$g'(t) = (3) \cdot \left(-\dfrac{1}{3}\right) \cdot (t - t^2)^{-4/3}(1 - 2t)$

$\qquad = -(1 - 2t)(t - t^2)^{-4/3} = \dfrac{2t - 1}{\sqrt[3]{(t - t^2)^4}}$

46. $f(x) = x^2(1 - x)^4$

$f'(x) = (x^2)'(1 - x)^4 + x^2[(1 - x)^4]'$

$\qquad = 2x(1 - x)^4 + x^2[4(1 - x)^3(-1)]$

$\qquad = 2x(1 - x)^4 - 4x^2(1 - x)^3 = 2x(1 - x)^3[(1 - x) - 2x]$

$\qquad\qquad\qquad\qquad\qquad\qquad = 2x(1 - x)^3(1 - 3x)$

$\qquad\qquad\qquad\qquad\qquad\qquad = 2x(1 - 3x)(1 - x)^3$

An equation for the tangent line to the graph of f at $x = 2$ is:
$y - y_1 = m(x - x_1)$ where $x_1 = 2$,

$y_1 = f(2) = (2)^2(1 - 2)^4 = 4$, $m = f'(2) = 2(2)[1 - 3(2)](1 - 2)^3 = 20$.

Thus, $y - 4 = 20(x - 2)$ or $y = 20x - 36$

48. $f(x) = \dfrac{x^4}{(3x - 8)^2}$

$f'(x) = \dfrac{(x^4)'(3x - 8)^2 - [(3x - 8)^2]'(x^4)}{(3x - 8)^4}$

$\qquad = \dfrac{4x^3(3x - 8)^2 - [2(3x - 8)(3)]x^4}{(3x - 8)^4}$

$\qquad = \dfrac{4x^3(3x - 8)^2 - 6x^4(3x - 8)}{(3x - 8)^4}$

$\qquad = \dfrac{2x^3(3x - 8)[2(3x - 8) - 3x]}{(3x - 8)^4} = \dfrac{2x^3[6x - 16 - 3x]}{(3x - 8)^3}$

$\qquad\qquad\qquad\qquad\qquad\qquad = \dfrac{2x^3(3x - 16)}{(3x - 8)^3}$

An equation for the tangent line to the graph of f at $x = 4$ is:
$y - y_1 = m(x - x_1)$ where $x_1 = 4$,

$y_1 = f(4) = \dfrac{(4)^4}{[3(4) - 8]^2} = \dfrac{4^4}{4^2} = 4^2 = 16$,

$m = f'(4) = \dfrac{2(4)^3[3(4) - 16]}{[3(4) - 8]^3} = \dfrac{-8(4)^3}{(4)^3} = -8$.

Thus, $y - 16 = -8(x - 4)$ or $y = -8x + 48$.

50. $f(x) = x\sqrt{x - 6} = x(x - 6)^{1/2}$

$f'(x) = (x)'(x - 6)^{1/2} + x[(x - 6)^{1/2}]'$

$\quad = (x - 6)^{1/2} + x\left[\dfrac{1}{2}(x - 6)^{-1/2}(1)\right]$

$\quad = (x - 6)^{1/2} + \dfrac{1}{2}x(x - 6)^{-1/2} = \dfrac{2(x - 6) + x}{2(x - 6)^{1/2}}$

$\quad\quad\quad\quad\quad\quad\quad\quad\quad\quad\quad\quad = \dfrac{3x - 12}{2(x - 6)^{1/2}} = \dfrac{3(x - 4)}{2(x - 6)^{1/2}}$

An equation for the tangent line to the graph of f at $x = 7$ is:
$y - y_1 = m(x - x_1)$ where $x_1 = 7$,

$y_1 = f(7) = 7\sqrt{7 - 6} = 7$, $\quad m = f'(7) = \dfrac{3(7 - 4)}{2(7 - 6)^{1/2}} = \dfrac{9}{2}$.

Thus, $y - 7 = \dfrac{9}{2}(x - 7)$ or $y = \dfrac{9}{2}x - \dfrac{49}{2}$.

52. $f(x) = x^3(x - 7)^4$

$f'(x) = (x^3)'(x - 7)^4 + x^3[(x - 7)^4]'$

$\quad = 3x^2(x - 7)^4 + x^3[4(x - 7)^3(1)]$

$\quad = 3x^2(x - 7)^4 + 4x^3(x - 7)^3$

$\quad = x^2(x - 7)^3[3(x - 7) + 4x]$

$\quad = x^2(x - 7)^3[3x - 21 + 4x] = x^2(x - 7)^3(7x - 21)$

$\quad = 7x^2(x - 3)(x - 7)^3$

The tangent line to the graph of f is horizontal at the value(s) of x such that $f'(x) = 0$. Thus, we set $7x^2(x - 3)(x - 7)^3 = 0$ and $x = 0$, $x = 3$, $x = 7$.

54. $f(x) = \dfrac{x - 1}{(x - 3)^3}$

$f'(x) = \dfrac{(x - 1)'(x - 3)^3 - [(x - 3)^3]'(x - 1)}{(x - 3)^6}$

$\quad = \dfrac{(x - 3)^3 - [3(x - 3)^2(1)](x - 1)}{(x - 3)^6}$

$\quad = \dfrac{(x - 3)^3 - 3(x - 3)^2(x - 1)}{(x - 3)^6} = \dfrac{(x - 3)^2[(x - 3) - 3(x - 1)]}{(x - 3)^6}$

$\quad = \dfrac{[x - 3 - 3x + 3]}{(x - 3)^4} = \dfrac{-2x}{(x - 3)^4}$

The tangent line to the graph of f is horizontal at the value(s) of x such that $f'(x) = 0$. Thus, we set $-2x = 0$ and $x = 0$.

56. $f(x) = \sqrt{x^2 + 4x + 5} = (x^2 + 4x + 5)^{1/2}$

$f'(x) = \dfrac{1}{2}(x^2 + 4x + 5)^{-1/2}(2x + 4)$

$\qquad = \dfrac{x + 2}{(x^2 + 4x + 5)^{1/2}}$

The tangent line to the graph of f is horizontal at the value(s) of x such that $f'(x) = 0$. Thus, we set

$\dfrac{x + 2}{(x^2 + 4x + 5)^{1/2}} = 0$

$\qquad\qquad x + 2 = 0$

and $\qquad\qquad x = -2$

58. $f(x) = x(x - 2)(x + 3)(x - 4) = (x^2 - 2x)(x^2 - x - 12)$

$f'(x) = (x^2 - 2x)'(x^2 - x - 12) + (x^2 - 2x)(x^2 - x - 12)'$

$\qquad = (2x - 2)(x^2 - x - 12) + (x^2 - 2x)(2x - 1)$

$\qquad = 2x^3 - 2x^2 - 24x - 2x^2 + 2x + 24 + 2x^3 - x^2 - 4x^2 + 2x$

$\qquad = 4x^3 - 9x^2 - 20x + 24$

$f'(x) = 0$ implies $4x^3 - 9x^2 - 20x + 24 = 0$.

Using a root-approximation routine on a graphing utility:
$x = -1.9354$, $x = 0.9617$, $x = 3.2237$.

60. $f(x) = (x^3 + 3x^2)(x^2 + 4)$

$f'(x) = (x^3 + 3x^2)'(x^2 + 4) + (x^3 + 3x^2)(x^2 + 4)'$

$\qquad = (3x^2 + 6x)(x^2 + 4) + (x^3 + 3x^2)(2x)$

$\qquad = 3x^4 + 12x^2 + 6x^3 + 24x + 2x^4 + 6x^3$

$\qquad = 5x^4 + 12x^3 + 12x^2 + 24x$

$\qquad = x(5x^3 + 12x^2 + 12x + 24)$

$f'(x) = 0$ implies $x = 0$, $5x^3 + 12x^2 + 12x + 24 = 0$.

Using a root-approximation routine on a graphing utility:
$x = -2.2731$, $x = 0.0000$.

62. $f(x) = \sqrt{x^4 - 4x^3 + 4x + 20} = (x^4 - 4x^3 + 4x + 20)^{1/2}$

$f'(x) = \dfrac{1}{2}(x^4 - 4x^3 + 4x + 20)^{-1/2}(4x^3 - 12x^2 + 4)$

$\qquad = \dfrac{2x^3 - 6x^2 + 2}{(x^4 - 4x^3 + 4x + 20)^{1/2}}$

$f'(x) = 0$ implies $2x^3 - 6x^2 + 2 = 0$ or $x^3 - 3x^2 + 1 = 0$

Using a root-approximation routine on a graphing utility:
$x = -0.5321$, $x = 0.6527$, $x = 2.8794$.

64. $\dfrac{d}{dx}[2x^2(x^3-3)^4] = \left[\dfrac{d}{dx}(2x^2)\right](x^3-3)^4 + 2x^2\left[\dfrac{d}{dx}(x^3-3)^4\right]$

$\qquad\qquad = 4x(x^3-3)^4 + 2x^2[4(x^3-3)^3(3x^2)]$

$\qquad\qquad = 4x(x^3-3)^4 + 24x^4(x^3-3)^3$

$\qquad\qquad = 4x(x^3-3)^3[(x^3-3)+6x^3]$

$\qquad\qquad = 4x(x^3-3)^3(7x^3-3)$

66. $\dfrac{d}{dx}\left[\dfrac{3x^2}{(x^2+5)^3}\right] = \dfrac{\left[\dfrac{d}{dx}(3x^2)\right](x^2+5)^3 - \left[\dfrac{d}{dx}(x^2+5)^3\right](3x^2)}{(x^2+5)^6}$

$\qquad\qquad = \dfrac{6x(x^2+5)^3 - [3(x^2+5)^2(2x)](3x^2)}{(x^2+5)^6}$

$\qquad\qquad = \dfrac{6x(x^2+5)^3 - 18x^3(x^2+5)^2}{(x^2+5)^6}$

$\qquad\qquad = \dfrac{6x(x^2+5)^2[(x^2+5)-3x^2]}{(x^2+5)^6}$

$\qquad\qquad = \dfrac{6x(5-2x^2)}{(x^2+5)^4} = \dfrac{30x-12x^3}{(x^2+5)^4}$

68. $\dfrac{d}{dx}[(x^2-1)^3(x^2-2)^2]$

$\qquad = \left[\dfrac{d}{dx}(x^2-1)^3\right](x^2-2)^2 + (x^2-1)^3\left[\dfrac{d}{dx}(x^2-2)^2\right]$

$\qquad\quad = 3(x^2-1)^2(2x)(x^2-2)^2 + (x^2-1)^3[2(x^2-2)(2x)]$

$\qquad\quad = 6x(x^2-1)^2(x^2-2)^2 + 4x(x^2-1)^3(x^2-2)$

$\qquad\quad = 2x(x^2-1)^2(x^2-2)[3(x^2-2)+2(x^2-1)]$

$\qquad\quad = 2x(x^2-1)^2(x^2-2)[3x^2-6+2x^2-2]$

$\qquad\quad = 2x(x^2-1)^2(x^2-2)(5x^2-8)$

70. $\dfrac{d}{dx}\left(3x\sqrt{2x^2+3}\right) = \dfrac{d}{dx}(3x(2x^2+3)^{1/2})$

$\qquad\quad = \left[\dfrac{d}{dx}(3x)\right](2x^2+3)^{1/2} + 3x\left[\dfrac{d}{dx}(2x^2+3)^{1/2}\right]$

$\qquad\quad = 3(2x^2+3)^{1/2} + 3x\left[\dfrac{1}{2}(2x^2+3)^{-1/2}(4x)\right]$

$\qquad\quad = 3(2x^2+3)^{1/2} + 6x^2(2x^2+3)^{-1/2}$

$\qquad\quad = \dfrac{3(2x^2+3)+6x^2}{(2x^2+3)^{1/2}} = \dfrac{12x^2+9}{(2x^2+3)^{1/2}}$

72. $\dfrac{d}{dx} \dfrac{x^2}{\sqrt{x^2 + 1}} = \dfrac{d}{dx} \dfrac{x^2}{(x^2 + 1)^{1/2}}$

$$= \frac{\left[\dfrac{d}{dx}(x^2)\right](x^2 + 1)^{1/2} - \left[\dfrac{d}{dx}(x^2 + 1)^{1/2}\right](x^2)}{(x^2 + 1)}$$

$$= \frac{2x(x^2 + 1)^{1/2} - \left[\dfrac{1}{2}(x^2 + 1)^{-1/2}(2x)\right](x^2)}{(x^2 + 1)}$$

$$= \frac{2x(x^2 + 1)^{1/2} - x^3(x^2 + 1)^{-1/2}}{(x^2 + 1)} \cdot \frac{(x^2 + 1)^{1/2}}{(x^2 + 1)^{1/2}}$$

$$= \frac{2x(x^2 + 1) - x^3}{(x^2 + 1)^{3/2}} = \frac{x^3 + 2x}{(x^2 + 1)^{3/2}}$$

74. $\dfrac{d}{dx}\sqrt{\dfrac{4x + 1}{2x^2 + 1}} = \dfrac{d}{dx}\dfrac{(4x + 1)^{1/2}}{(2x^2 + 1)^{1/2}}$

$$= \frac{\left[\dfrac{d}{dx}(4x + 1)^{1/2}\right](2x^2 + 1)^{1/2} - \left[\dfrac{d}{dx}(2x^2 + 1)^{1/2}\right](4x + 1)^{1/2}}{(2x^2 + 1)}$$

$$= \frac{\left[\dfrac{1}{2}(4x + 1)^{-1/2}(4)\right](2x^2 + 1)^{1/2} - \left[\dfrac{1}{2}(2x^2 + 1)^{-1/2}(4x)\right](4x + 1)^{1/2}}{(2x^2 + 1)}$$

$$= \frac{2(4x + 1)^{-1/2}(2x^2 + 1)^{1/2} - 2x(2x^2 + 1)^{-1/2}(4x + 1)^{1/2}}{(2x^2 + 1)}$$

$$= \frac{2(2x^2 + 1) - 2x(4x + 1)}{(4x + 1)^{1/2}(2x^2 + 1)^{3/2}}$$

$$= \frac{-4x^2 - 2x + 2}{(4x + 1)^{1/2}(2x^2 + 1)^{3/2}}$$

76. $C(x) = 6 + \sqrt{4x + 4} = 6 + (4x + 4)^{1/2}, \quad 0 \le x \le 30$

(A) $C'(x) = \dfrac{1}{2}(4x + 4)^{-1/2}(4) = 2(4x + 4)^{-1/2} = \dfrac{2}{(4x + 4)^{1/2}}$

(B) $C'(15) = \dfrac{2}{[4(15) + 4]^{1/2}} = \dfrac{2}{8} = \dfrac{1}{4} = 0.25$ or 25.

At a production level of 15 cameras, total costs are increasing at the rate of $25 per camera; also, the cost of producing the 16th camera is approximately $25.

$C'(24) = \dfrac{2}{[4(24) + 4]^{1/2}} = \dfrac{2}{10} = 0.2$ or 20.

At a production level of 24 cameras, total costs are increasing at the rate of $20 per camera; also, the cost of producing the 25th camera is approximately $20.

78. $x = 1,000 - 60\sqrt{p + 25} = 1,000 - 60(p + 25)^{1/2}$, $20 \leq p \leq 100$.

(A) $\dfrac{dx}{dp} = -60\left(\dfrac{1}{2}\right)(p + 25)^{-1/2} = \dfrac{-30}{(p + 25)^{1/2}}$

(B) $x(75) = 1,000 - 60(75 + 25)^{1/2} = 1,000 - 600 = 400$

$\dfrac{dx}{dp}\bigg|_{75} = \dfrac{-30}{(75 + 25)^{1/2}} = \dfrac{-30}{10} = -3$

At a price of \$75, the demand is 400 speakers and is decreasing at the rate of 3 speakers per dollar.

80. $A = 100\left(1 + \dfrac{1}{2}r\right)^{10}$

$\dfrac{dA}{dr} = 100(10)\left(1 + \dfrac{1}{2}r\right)^{9}\left(\dfrac{1}{2}\right) = 500\left(1 + \dfrac{1}{2}r\right)^{9}$

82. $C(t) = 500(8 - t)^2$, $0 \leq t \leq 7$

(A) $C'(t) = 500(2)(8 - t)(-1) = -1,000(8 - t) = 1,000t - 8,000$;

(B) $C'(1) = 1,000 - 8,000 = -7,000$. The number of bacteria per cm^3 is decreasing at the rate of 7,000 per day after one day.

$C'(6) = 6,000 - 8,000 = -2,000$. The number of bacteria per cm^3 is decreasing at the rate of 2,000 per day after six days.

EXERCISE 3-7

---

2. $C(x) = 1,000 + 100x - 0.25x^2$

(A) The exact cost of producing the 51st guitar is:
$C(51) - C(50)$

$= 1,000 + 100(51) - 0.25(51)^2 - [1,000 + 100(50) - 0.25(50)^2]$
$= 100 - 0.25(51)^2 + 0.25(50)^2 = 74.75$ or \$74.75

(B) $C'(x) = 100 - 0.5x$
$C'(50) = 100 - 0.5(50) = 75$ or \$75.

4. $C(x) = 20,000 + 10x$

(A) $\overline{C}(x) = \dfrac{20,000 + 10x}{x} = \dfrac{20,000}{x} + 10 = 20,000x^{-1} + 10$

$\overline{C}(1,000) = \dfrac{20,000 + 10(1,000)}{1,000} = \dfrac{30,000}{1,000} = 30$ or \$30

(B) $\overline{C}'(x) = -20,000x^{-2} = \dfrac{-20,000}{x^2}$

$\overline{C}'(1,000) = \dfrac{-20,000}{(1,000)^2} = -0.02$ or -2¢

At a production level of 1,000 dictionaries, average cost is decreasing at the rate of 2¢ per dictionary.

(C) The average cost per dictionary if 1,001 are produced is approximately \$74.75 - \$0.02 = \$74.73.

6. $P(x) = 22x - 0.2x^2 - 400, \ 0 \le x \le 100$

(A) The exact profit from the sale of the 41st stereo is
$$P(41) - P(40) = 22(41) - 0.2(41)^2 - 400 - [22(40) - 0.2(40)^2 - 400]$$
$$= 22 - 0.2(41)^2 + 0.2(40)^2 = 5.80 \text{ or } \$5.80$$

(B) $P'(x) = 22 - 0.4x$
$P'(40) = 22 - 0.4(40) = 22 - 16 = 6 \text{ or } \$6$

8. $P(x) = 12x - 0.02x^2 - 1,000, \ 0 \le x \le 600$
$P'(x) = 12 - 0.04x$

(A) $P'(200) = 12 - 0.04(200) = 12 - 8 = 4 \text{ or } \$4;$
at a production level of 200 cameras, profit is increasing at the rate of $4 per camera.

(B) $P'(350) = 12 - 0.04(350) = 12 - 14 = -2 \text{ or } -\$2;$
at a production level of 350 cameras, profit is decreasing at the rate of $2 per camera.

10. $P(x) = 20x - 0.02x^2 - 320, \ 0 \le x \le 1,000$

Average profit: $\overline{P}(x) = \dfrac{P(x)}{x} = 20 - 0.02x - \dfrac{320}{x} = 20 - 0.02x - 320x^{-1}$

(A) At $x = 40$, $\overline{P}(40) = 20 - 0.02(40) - \dfrac{320}{40} = 11.20 \text{ or } \$11.20.$

(B) $\overline{P}'(x) = -0.02 + 320x^{-2} = -0.02 + \dfrac{320}{x^2}$

$\overline{P}'(40) = -0.02 + \dfrac{320}{(40)^2} = 0.18 \text{ or } \$0.18;$

at a production level of 40 grills, the average profit per grill is increasing at the rate of $0.18 per grill.

(C) The average profit per grill if 41 grills are produced is approximately $11.20 + $0.18 = $11.38.

12. $x = 1,000 - 20p$

(A) $20p = 1,000 - x, \ p = 50 - 0.05x, \ 0 \le x \le 1,000$

(B) $R(x) = x(50 - 0.05x) = 50x - 0.05x^2, \ 0 \le x \le 1,000$

(C) $R'(x) = 50 - 0.10x$
$R'(400) = 50 - 0.10(400) = 50 - 40 = 10;$
at a production level of 400 steam irons, revenue is increasing at the rate of $10 per steam iron.

(D) $R'(650) = 50 - 0.10(650) = 50 - 65 = -15;$
at a production level of 650 steam irons, revenue is decreasing at the rate of $15 per steam iron.

14. $x = 9,000 - 30p$ and $C(x) = 150,000 + 30x$

(A) $30p = 9,000 - x$, $p = 300 - \dfrac{1}{30}x$, $0 \le x \le 9,000$

(B) $C'(x) = 30$

(C) $R(x) = x\left(300 - \dfrac{1}{30}x\right) = 300x - \dfrac{1}{30}x^2$, $0 \le x \le 9,000$

(D) $R'(x) = 300 - \dfrac{1}{15}x$

(E) $R'(3,000) = 300 - \dfrac{1}{15}(3,000) = 100$; at a production level of

3,000 sets, revenue is increasing at the rate of $100 per set.

$R'(6000) = 300 - \dfrac{1}{15}(6,000) = 300 - 400 = -100$; at a production

level of 6,000 sets, revenue is decreasing at the rate of $100 per set.

(F) The graphs of $C(x)$ and $R(x)$ are shown at the right.

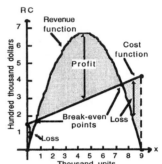

To find the break-even points, set $C(x) = R(x)$:
$$150,000 + 30x = 300x - \dfrac{1}{30}x^2$$

$$x^2 - 8,100x + 4,500,000 = 0$$
$$(x - 600)(x - 7,500) = 0$$
$$x = 600 \quad \text{or} \quad x = 7,500$$

Now, $C(600) = 150,000 + 30(600) = 168,000$;

$\qquad C(7,500) = 150,000 + 30(7,500) = 375,000$

Thus, the break-even points are:
(600, 168,000) and (7,500, 375,000).

(G) $P(x) = R(x) - C(x) = 300x - \dfrac{1}{30}x^2 - (150,000 + 30x)$

$\qquad\qquad = -\dfrac{1}{30}x^2 + 270x - 150,000$

(H) $P'(x) = -\dfrac{1}{15}x + 270$

(I) $P'(1,500) = -\dfrac{1}{15}(1,500) + 270 = 170$; at a production level of 1,500

sets, profit is increasing at the rate of $170 per set.

$P'(4,500) = -\dfrac{1}{15}(4,500) + 270 = -30$; at a production level of 4,500

sets, profit is decreasing at the rate of $30 per set.

16. (A) We are given $p = 25$ when $x = 300$ and $p = 20$ when $x = 400$. Thus, we have the pair of equations:

$25 = 300m + b$

$20 = 400\,m + b$

Subtracting the second equation from the first, we get $-100m = 5$. Thus, $m = -\dfrac{1}{20}$.

Substituting this into either equation yields $b = 40$. Therefore,

$p = -\dfrac{1}{20}x + 40 = 40 - \dfrac{x}{20}$, $0 \le x \le 800$

(B) $R(x) = x\left(40 - \dfrac{x}{20}\right) = 40x - \dfrac{x^2}{20}$, $0 \le x \le 800$

(C) From the research department's estimates, $m = 5$ and $b = 5{,}000$. Thus, $C(x) = 5x + 5{,}000$

(D) The graphs of $R(x)$ and $C(x)$ are shown at the right.

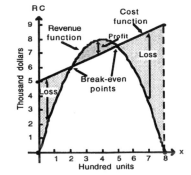

To find the break-even points, set $C(x) = R(x)$:

$$5x + 5{,}000 = 40x - \dfrac{x^2}{20}$$

$$x^2 - 700x + 100{,}000 = 0$$

$$(x - 200)(x - 500) = 0$$

$$x = 200 \quad \text{or} \quad x = 500$$

Now, $C(200) = 5(200) + 5{,}000 = 6{,}000$ and

$C(500) = 5(500) + 5{,}000 = 7{,}500$

Thus, the break-even points are: $(200, 6{,}000)$ and $(500, 7{,}500)$.

(E) $P(x) = R(x) - C(x) = 40x - \dfrac{x^2}{20} - (5x + 5{,}000)$

$$= 35x - \dfrac{x^2}{20} - 5{,}000$$

(F) $P'(x) = 35 - \dfrac{x}{10}$

$P'(325) = 35 - \dfrac{325}{10} = 2.5$; at a production level of 325 toasters, profit is increasing at the rate of \$2.50 per toaster.

$P'(425) = 35 - \dfrac{425}{10} = -7.5$; at a production level of 425 toasters, profit is decreasing at the rate of \$7.50 per toaster.

18. Total cost: $C(x) = 5x + 2{,}340$

Total revenue: $R(x) = 40x - 0.1x^2$, $0 \le x \le 400$

(A) $R'(x) = 40 - 0.2x$

The graph of R has a horizontal tangent line at the value(s) of x where $R'(x) = 0$, i.e.

$$40 - 0.2x = 0$$
$$\text{or} \quad x = 200$$

(B) $P(x) = R(x) - C(x) = 40x - 0.1x^2 - (5x + 2{,}340)$
$$= 35x - 0.1x^2 - 2{,}340$$

(C) $P'(x) = 35 - 0.2x$. Setting $P'(x) = 0$, we have

$$35 - 0.2x = 0$$
$$\text{or} \quad x = 175$$

(D) The graphs of $C(x)$, $R(x)$ and $P(x)$ are shown at the right.

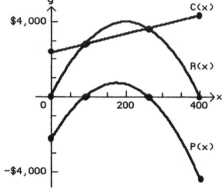

Break-even points: $R(x) = C(x)$

$$40x - 0.1x^2 = 5x + 2{,}340$$
$$x^2 - 350x + 23{,}400 = 0$$
$$(x - 90)(x - 260) = 0$$
$$x = 90 \quad \text{or} \quad x = 260$$

Thus, the break-even points are:
(90, 2,790) and (260, 3,640).

x intercepts for P: $-0.1x^2 + 35x - 2{,}340 = 0$ or
$$x^2 - 350x + 23{,}400 = 0$$
which is the same as the above equation. Thus, $x = 90$ and $x = 260$ are x intercepts of P.

20. Demand equation: $p = 60 - 2\sqrt{x} = 60 - 2x^{1/2}$

Cost equation: $C(x) = 3{,}000 + 5x$

(A) Revenue $R(x) = xp = x(60 - 2x^{1/2})$
$$= 60x - 2x^{3/2}$$

(B) The graphs for R and C for $0 \le x \le 900$ are shown below:

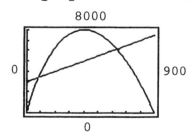

Break-even points: (81, 3,405), (631, 6,155)

22. (A)

```
LinReg
y=ax+b
a=-.1985715253
b=1996.678966
r=-.982877241
```

(B) Fixed costs: $2,832,085; variable cost: $292

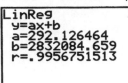

```
LinReg
y=ax+b
a=292.126464
b=2832084.659
r=.9956751513
```

(C) Let $y = p(x)$ be the linear regression equation found in part (A) and let $y = C(x)$ be the linear regression equation found in part (B). Then revenue $R(x) = xp(x)$, and the break-even points are $R(x) = C(x)$.
Break-even points: (2,253, 3,490,130), (6,331, 4,681,675).

(D) The company will make a profit when $2,253 \leq x \leq 6,331$. From part (A), $p(2,253) = 740$ and $p(6,331) = 1,549$. Thus, the company will make a profit for the price range $\$740 \leq p \leq \$1,549$.

4 GRAPHING AND OPTIMIZATION

2. (b, c); (c, d); (f, g)　　　　**4.** (a, b); (d, f); (g, h)

6. $x = b, g$　　　　　　　　　**8.** $x = d, g$

10. f has a local maximum at $x = d$, and a local minimum at $x = b$; f does not have a local extremum at $x = a$ or at $x = c$.

12. (b)　　　**14.** (h)　　　**16.** (g)　　　**18.** (a)

20. $f(x) = -3x^2 - 12x$

$f'(x) = -6x - 12$

f' is continuous for all x and

$f'(x) = -6x - 12 = 0$

$\qquad\qquad\qquad x = -2$

Thus, $x = -2$ is a partition number for f':

Next we construct a sign chart for f'.

Test Numbers	
x	$f'(x)$
0	−12 (−)
−3	6 (+)

```
f'(x)  + + + +  ! - - - -
       +-+-+-+--●-+-+-+-+--->x
f(x)    -3 -2 ! 0
       Increasing ! Decreasing
```

Therefore, f is increasing on $(-\infty, -2)$ and decreasing on $(-2, \infty)$; f has a local maximum at $x = -2$, which is $f(-2) = 12$.

22. $f(x) = -3x^2 + 12x - 5$

$f'(x) = -6x + 12$

f' is continuous for all x and

$f'(x) = -6x + 12 = 0$

$\qquad\qquad\qquad x = 2$

Thus, $x = 2$ is a partition number for f'.

Next we construct a sign chart for f'.

Test Numbers	
x	$f'(x)$
0	12 (+)
3	−6 (−)

```
f'(x)  + + +  ! - - -
       +-+-+--●-+-+-+-+-+--->x
f(x)    0  2 3
       Increasing ! Decreasing
```

Therefore, f is increasing on $(-\infty, 2)$ and increasing on $(2, \infty)$; f has a local maximum at $x = 2$.

24. $f(x) = -x^3 - 4x + 8$

$f'(x) = -3x^2 - 4$

f' is continuous for all x and $f'(x) = -(3x^2 + 4) < 0$.

Thus, f is decreasing for all x; no local extrema.

26. $f(x) = -x^3 + 12x - 5$

$f'(x) = -3x^2 + 12$ which is continuous for all x.

$f'(x) = -3x^2 + 12 = -3(x - 2)(x + 2) = 0$

$$x = -2, 2$$

Thus, $x = -2$ and $x = 2$ are partition numbers for f'.

Next, we construct a sign chart for f':

Test Numbers	
x	$f'(x)$
-3	$-15\ (-)$
0	$12\ (+)$
3	$-15\ (-)$

Therefore, f is decreasing on $(-\infty, -2)$ and $(2, \infty)$; increasing on $(-2, 2)$; f has a local minimum at $x = -2$ ($f(-2) = -21$) and a local maximum at $x = 2$ ($f(2) = 11$).

28. $f(x) = -2x^3 + 3x^2 + 120x$

$f'(x) = -6x^2 + 6x + 120$ which is continuous for all x.

$f'(x) = -6(x^2 - x - 20) = -6(x + 4)(x - 5) = 0$

$$x = -4, 5$$

Thus, $x = -4$ and $x = 5$ are partition numbers for f'.
Next, we construct a sign chart for f':

Test Numbers	
x	$f'(x)$
-5	$-60\ (-)$
0	$120\ (+)$
6	$-60\ (-)$

Therefore, f is decreasing on $(-\infty, -4)$ and $(5, \infty)$; increasing on $(-4, 5)$; f has a local minimum at $x = -4$ and a local maximum at $x = 5$.

30. $f(x) = x^4 + 2x^3 + 5$

$f'(x) = 4x^3 + 6x^2$ which is continuous for all x.

$f'(x) = 4x^3 + 6x^2 = 2x^2(2x + 3) = 0$

$$x = -\frac{3}{2}, 0$$

Thus, $x = -\frac{3}{2}$ and $x = 0$ are partition numbers for f'.

Next, we construct a sign chart for f:

Test Numbers	
x	$f'(x)$
-2	$-8\ (-)$
-1	$2\ (+)$
1	$10\ (+)$

Therefore, f is decreasing on $\left(-\infty, -\frac{3}{2}\right)$; increasing on $\left(-\frac{3}{2}, \infty\right)$;

$f(-1.5) = 3.3125$ is a local minimum.

32. $f(x) = x^4 + 4x$

$f'(x) = 4x^3 + 4$

f' is continuous for all x and

$$f'(x) = 4x^3 + 4 = 0$$
$$x = -1$$

Thus, $x = -1$ is a partition number for f'.
We construct a sign chart for f':

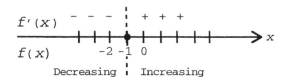

Test Numbers

x	$f'(x)$
-2	$-28\ (-)$
0	$4\ (+)$

Therefore, f is decreasing on $(-\infty, -1)$ and increasing on $(-1, \infty)$; local minimum at $x = -1$.

34. Let $f(x) = x^4 + x^2 - 9x$.
Since $f(x)$ is a polynomial its critical values (if exist) are the zeros of $f'(x)$.

$f'(x) = 4x^3 + 2x - 9$

Using a graphing utility to approximate the zeros of $f'(x)$ we have:
$f'(x) = 0$ for $x \approx 1.18$
Sign chart for f':

Test Numbers

x	$f'(x)$
0	$-9\ (-)$
2	$27\ (+)$

Therefore, f is decreasing on $(-\infty, 1.18)$; increasing on $(1.18, \infty)$; local minimum at $x = 1.18$.

36. $f(x) = x^4 + 5x^3 - 15x$ is a polynomial.

$f'(x) = 4x^3 + 15x^2 - 15$

Using a graphing utility to approximate the zeros of $f'(x)$ we have:
$f'(x) = 0$ for $x_1 \approx -3.43$, $x_2 \approx -1.22$, $x_3 \approx 0.90$.

Sign chart for f':

Test Numbers

x	$f'(x)$
-4	$-131\ (-)$
-2	$13\ (+)$
0	$-15\ (-)$
1	$4\ (+)$

Therefore, f is decreasing on $(-\infty, -3.43)$ and $(-1.22, 0.90)$; increasing on $(-3.43, -1.22)$ and $(0.90, \infty)$; local minima at $x = -3.43$ and $x = 0.90$; local maximum at $x = -1.22$.

38. $f(x) = x^4 + 2x^3 - 4x^2 - 6x$

$f'(x) = 4x^3 + 6x^2 - 8x - 6$

Using a graphing utility to approximate the zeros of $f'(x)$ we have:
$f'(x) = 0$ for $x_1 \approx -2.11$, $x_2 \approx -0.59$, $x_3 \approx 1.20$.

Sign chart for f':

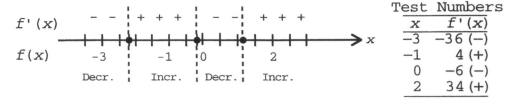

Test Numbers	
x	$f'(x)$
-3	-36 $(-)$
-1	4 $(+)$
0	-6 $(-)$
2	34 $(+)$

Therefore, f is decreasing on $(-\infty, -2.11)$ and $(-0.59, 1.20)$; increasing on $(-2.11, -0.59)$ and $(1.20, \infty)$; local minima at $x = -2.11$ and $x = 1.20$; local maximum at $x = -0.59$.

40. $f(x) = 2x^2 - 8x + 9$

$f'(x) = 4x - 8$

f' is continuous for all x and

$f'(x) = 4x - 8 = 0$

$\qquad\qquad x = 2$

Thus, $x = 2$ is a partition number for f'.

The sign chart for f' is:

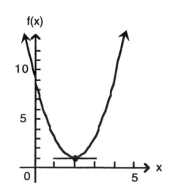

Test Numbers	
x	$f'(x)$
0	-8 $(-)$
3	4 $(+)$

Therefore, f is decreasing on $(-\infty, 2)$ and increasing on $(2, \infty)$; f has a local minimum at $x = 2$.

x	$f'(x)$	f	GRAPH OF f
$(-\infty, 2)$	$-$	Decreasing	Falling
$x = 2$	0	Local minimum	Horizontal tangent
$(2, \infty)$	$+$	Increasing	Rising

x	$f(x)$
0	9
2	1

42. $f(x) = x^3 - 12x + 2$

$f'(x) = 3x^2 - 12$

f' is continuous for all x and

$f'(x) = 3x^2 - 12 = 0$

$\qquad\qquad x = -2, \ 2$

Thus, $x = -2$ and $x = 2$ are partition numbers for f'.

The sign chart for f' is:

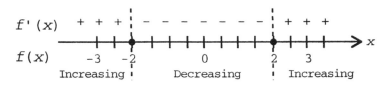

Test Numbers

x	$f'(x)$
-3	15 (+)
0	-12 (−)
3	15 (+)

Therefore, f is increasing on $(-\infty, -2)$ and on $(2, \infty)$, f is decreasing on $(-2, 2)$; f has a local maximum at $x = -2$ and a local minimum at $x = 2$.

x	$f'(x)$	f	GRAPH OF f
$(-\infty, -2)$	+	Increasing	Rising
$x = -2$	0	Local maximum	Horizontal tangent
$(-2, 2)$	−	Decreasing	Falling
$x = 2$	0	Local minimum	Horizontal tangent
$(2, \infty)$	+	Increasing	Rising

x	$f(x)$
-2	18
0	2
2	-12

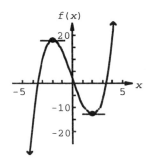

44. $f(x) = x^3 + 3x^2 + 3x$

$f'(x) = 3x^2 + 6x + 3$

f' is continuous for all x and

$f'(x) = 3x^2 + 6x + 3$

$\qquad = 3(x^2 + 2x + 1) = 3(x + 1)^2 = 0$

$\qquad\qquad\qquad\qquad\qquad x = -1$

Thus, $x = -1$ is a partition number for f'.

The sign chart for f' is:

Test Numbers

x	$f'(x)$
-2	3 (+)
0	3 (+)

Therefore, f is increasing for all x, i.e., on $(-\infty, \infty)$, and there is a horizontal tangent line at $x = -1$.

x	$f'(x)$	f	GRAPH of f
$(-\infty, -1)$	+	Increasing	Rising
-1	0		Horizontal tangent
$(-1, \infty)$	+	Increasing	Rising

x	$f(x)$
-1	-1
0	0

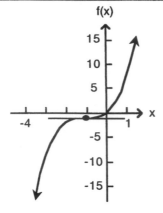

46. $f(x) = -x^4 + 50x^2$

$f'(x) = -4x^3 + 100x$ which is continuous for all x.

$f'(x) = -4x^3 + 100x = -4x(x - 5)(x + 5) = 0$
$$x = -5,\ 0,\ 5$$

Thus, $x = -5$, $x = 0$, and $x = 5$ are partition numbers.

The sign chart for f' is:

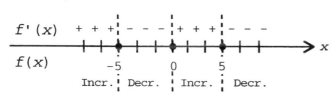

Test Numbers	
x	$f'(x)$
-6	264 (+)
-1	-96 $(-)$
1	96 (+)
6	-264 $(-)$

Therefore, f is increasing on $(-\infty, -5)$ and $(0, 5)$; decreasing on $(-5, 0)$ and $(5, \infty)$. There are 3 horizontal tangent lines at $x = -5$, $x = 0$, and $x = 5$.

x	$f'(x)$	f	GRAPH of f
$(-\infty, -5)$	+	Increasing	Rising
-5	0		Horizontal tangent
$(-5, 0)$	$-$	Decreasing	Falling
0	0		Horizontal tangent
$(0, 5)$	+	Increasing	Rising
5	0		Horizontal tangent
$(5, \infty)$	$-$	Decreasing	Falling

x	$f(x)$
-5	625
0	0
5	625

48.

x	f'(x)	f(x)	GRAPH of f
$(-\infty, -1)$	+	Increasing	Rising
$x = -1$	0	Local maximum	Horizontal tangent
$(-1, 1)$	–	Decreasing	Falling
$x = 1$	0	Neither local maximum nor local minimum	Horizontal tangent
$(1, \infty)$	–	Decreasing	Falling

Using this information together with the points $(-2, 1)$, $(-1, 3)$, $(0, 2)$, $(1, 1)$, $(2, -1)$ on the graph, we have

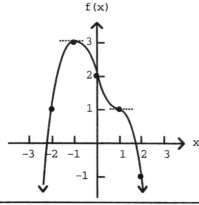

50.

x	f'(x)	f(x)	Graph of f(x)
$(-\infty, -1)$	+	Increasing	Rising
$x = -1$	Not defined	Neither local maximum nor local minimum	Vertical tangent
$(-1, 0)$	+	Increasing	Rising
$x = 0$	0	Local maximum	Horizontal tangent
$(0, 2)$	–	Decreasing	Falling
$x = 2$	0	Local minimum	Horizontal tangent
$(2, \infty)$	+	Increasing	Rising

Using this information together with the points $(-2, -3)$, $(-1, 0)$, $(0, 2)$, $(2, -1)$, $(3, 0)$ on the graph, we have

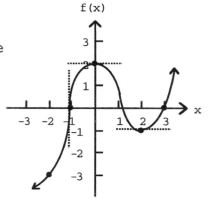

52.

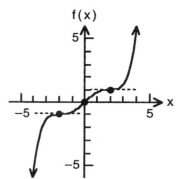

x	-2	0	2
f(x)	-1	0	1

54.

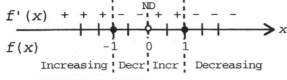

x	-1	0	1
$f(x)$	2	0	2

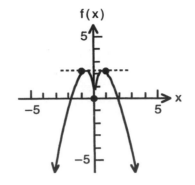

56. $f_2' = g_1$ **58.** $f_4' = g_3$ **60.** $f_6' = g_5$

62. Increasing on $(-\infty, -3)$ and $(1, \infty)$; decreasing on $(-3, 1)$; local maximum at $x = -3$; local minimum at $x = 1$.

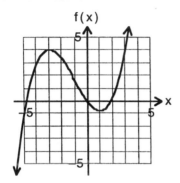

64. Increasing on $(-\infty, -2)$; decreasing on $(-2, 1)$ and $(1, \infty)$; local maximum at $x = -2$.

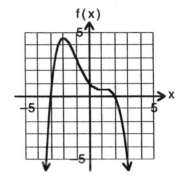

66. Increasing on $(-\infty, -3)$ and $(-1, 2)$; decreasing on $(-3, -1)$ and $(2, \infty)$; local maxima at $x = -3$ and $x = 2$; local minimum at $x = -1$.

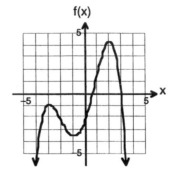

68. $f'(x) > 0$ on $(-2, 2)$; $f'(x) < 0$ on $(-\infty, -2)$ and $(2, \infty)$; $f'(x) = 0$ at $x = -2$ and $x = 2$.

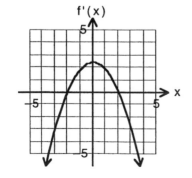

70. $f'(x) > 0$ on $(-\infty, -3)$ and $(1, 3)$; $f'(x) < 0$ on $(-3, 1)$ and $(3, \infty)$; $f'(x) = 0$ at $x = -3$, $x = 1$, and $x = 3$.

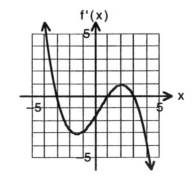

72. $f(x) = \dfrac{9}{x} + x$ [<u>Note</u>: f is not defined at $x = 0$.]

$f'(x) = -\dfrac{9}{x^2} + 1$

Critical values: $x = 0$ is *not* a critical value of f since 0 is not in the domain of f, but $x = 0$ is a partition number for f'.

$f'(x) = -\dfrac{9}{x^2} + 1 = 0$

$\qquad -9 + x^2 = 0$

$\quad (x + 3)(x - 3) = 0$

Thus, the critical values are $x = -3$ and $x = 3$; $x = -3$ and $x = 3$ are also partition numbers for f'.

The sign chart for f' is:

Test Numbers	
x	$f'(x)$
-4	$\frac{7}{16}$ (+)
-1	-8 (−)
1	-8 (−)
4	$\frac{7}{16}$ (+)

$f'(x)$ + + + | − − | − − | + + +

$f(x)$ −4 −3   −1 | 1   3 4

Increasing | Decr | Decr | Increasing

Therefore, f is increasing on $(-\infty, -3)$ and on $(3, \infty)$, f is decreasing on $(-3, 0)$ and on $(0, \infty)$; f has a local maximum at $x = -3$ and a local minimum at $x = 3$.

74. $f(x) = 3 - \dfrac{4}{x} - \dfrac{2}{x^2}$ [<u>Note</u>: f is not defined at $x = 0$.]

$f'(x) = \dfrac{4}{x^2} + \dfrac{4}{x^3}$

Critical values: $x = 0$ is not a critical value of f since 0 is not in the domain of f; $x = 0$ is a partition number for f'.

$f'(x) = \dfrac{4}{x^2} + \dfrac{4}{x^3} = 0$

$\qquad x + 1 = 0$

$\qquad\quad x = -1$

Thus, the critical value is $x = -1$; -1 is also a partition number for f'.

The sign chart for f' is:

Test Numbers	
x	$f'(x)$
-2	$\frac{1}{2}$ (+)
$-\frac{1}{2}$	-16 (−)
1	8 (+)

$f'(x)$ + + + + | − − − | + + + +

$f(x)$ −2   −1 −$\frac{1}{2}$ 0   1   2

Increasing | Decr. | Increasing

Therefore, f is increasing on $(-\infty, -1)$ and $(0, \infty)$; decreasing on $(-1, 0)$; local maximum at $x = -1$.

76. $f(x) = \dfrac{x^2}{x+1}$ [Note: f is not defined at $x = -1$.]

$f'(x) = \dfrac{2x(x+1) - x^2}{(x+1)^2} = \dfrac{2x^2 + 2x - x^2}{(x+1)^2} = \dfrac{x^2 + 2x}{(x+1)^2}$

Critical values: $x = -1$ is *not* a critical value of f since -1 is not in the domain of f; $x = -1$ is a partition number for f'.

$f'(x) = \dfrac{x^2 + 2x}{(x+1)^2} = 0$

$x^2 + 2x = 0$

$x(x + 2) = 0$

$x = 0,\ -2$

Thus, the critical values are $x = -2$ and $x = 0$; -2 and 0 are also partition numbers for f'.

The sign chart for f' is:

Test Numbers	
x	$f'(x)$
-3	$\frac{3}{4}$ (+)
$-\frac{3}{2}$	-3 (−)
$-\frac{1}{2}$	-3 (−)
1	$\frac{3}{4}$ (+)

Therefore, f is increasing on $(-\infty, -2)$ and on $(0, \infty)$, f is decreasing on $(-2, -1)$ and on $(-1, 0)$; f has a local maximum at $x = -2$ and a local minimum at $x = 0$.

78. $f(x) = x^3(x-5)^2$

$f'(x) = 3x^2(x-5)^2 + 2(x-5)x^3$

$= x^2(x-5)[3(x-5) + 2x]$

$= x^2(x-5)[3x - 15 + 2x] = x^2(x-5)(5x - 15)$

$= 5x^2(x-5)(x-3)$

Thus, the critical values of f are $x = 0$, $x = 3$, and $x = 5$.

Now we construct the sign chart for f' ($x = 0$, $x = 3$, $x = 5$ are partition numbers).

Test Numbers	
x	$f'(x)$
-1	120 (+)
1	40 (+)
4	-80 (−)
6	540 (+)

Therefore, f is increasing on $(-\infty, 0)$, $(0, 3)$ and $(5, \infty)$, decreasing on $(3, 5)$; local maximum at $x = 3$; local minimum at $x = 5$.

80. $f(x) = 6(4 - x)^{2/3} + 4$

$f'(x) = 6\left(\dfrac{2}{3}\right)(-1)(4 - x)^{-1/3} = -\dfrac{4}{(4 - x)^{1/3}}$

Critical values: f' is not defined at $x = 4$. [Note: $f(4)$ is defined, $f(4) = 4$.] $f'(x) \neq 0$ for all x. Thus, the critical value for f is $x = 4$; $x = 4$ is also a partition number for f'.

Test Numbers

x	$f'(x)$
1	$-\dfrac{4}{\sqrt[3]{3}}$ (−)
5	4 (+)

Therefore, f is decreasing on $(-\infty, 4)$; increasing on $(4, \infty)$; local maximum at $x = 4$.

82. $f(x) = \dfrac{-3x}{x^2 + 4}$

$f'(x) = \dfrac{-3(x^2 + 4) - 2x(-3x)}{(x^2 + 4)^2} = \dfrac{-3x^2 - 12 + 6x^2}{(x^2 + 4)^2} = \dfrac{3x^2 - 12}{(x^2 + 4)^2}$

Critical values:

$f'(x) = \dfrac{3x^2 - 12}{(x^2 + 4)^2} = 0$

$3x^2 - 12 = 0$

$3(x^2 - 4) = 3(x + 2)(x - 2) = 0$

Thus, the critical values are $x = -2$ and $x = 2$; -2 and 2 are also partition numbers for f'.

The sign chart for f' is:

Test Numbers

x	$f'(x)$
-3	$\dfrac{15}{169}$ (+)
0	$-\dfrac{3}{4}$ (−)
3	$\dfrac{15}{169}$ (+)

Therefore, f is increasing on $(-\infty, -2)$ and on $(2, \infty)$; decreasing on $(-2, 2)$; f has a local maximum at $x = -2$ ($f(-2) = 0.75$) and a local minimum at $x = 2$ ($f(2) = -0.75$).

84. Let $f(x) = x^4 + kx^2$

(A) $k > 0$

$f'(x) = 4x^3 + 2kx = 2x(2x^2 + k) = 0$

$x = 0$ [Note: $2x^2 + k > 0$]

The only critical value is $x = 0$.

f is decreasing on $(-\infty, 0)$; increasing on $(0, \infty)$; local minimum at $x = 0$.

(B) $k < 0$

$$f'(x) = 2x(2x^2 + k) = 0$$
$$x = 0, \pm\sqrt{-\frac{k}{2}}$$

Critical values: $x = -\sqrt{-\frac{k}{2}}$, $x = 0$, $x = \sqrt{-\frac{k}{2}}$;

$f'(x)$ $-$ $-$ $+$ $+$ $+$ $-$ $-$ $-$ $+$ $+$

$f(x)$ $-\sqrt{-\frac{k}{2}}$ 0 $\sqrt{-\frac{k}{2}}$

f is decreasing on $\left(-\infty, -\sqrt{-\frac{k}{2}}\right)$ and $\left(0, \sqrt{-\frac{k}{2}}\right)$; f is increasing

on $\left(-\sqrt{-\frac{k}{2}}, 0\right)$ and $\left(\sqrt{-\frac{k}{2}}, \infty\right)$; f has local minima at $x = -\sqrt{-\frac{k}{2}}$ and

$x = \sqrt{-\frac{k}{2}}$; local maximum at $x = 0$.

(C) $k = 0$

$$f'(x) = 4x^3$$

$f'(x) < 0$ for $x < 0$; $f'(x) = 0$ for $x = 0$; $f'(x) > 0$ for $x > 0$.
Thus, the only critical value is $x = 0$. The function is decreasing
on $(-\infty, 0)$ and increasing on $(0, \infty)$; local minimum at $x = 0$.

86. (A) The marginal revenue function, R', is positive on $(0, 500)$, zero at $x = 500$, and negative on $(500, 1,000)$.

(B)

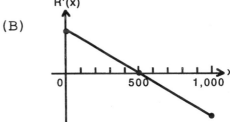

88. (A) The price function, $E(t)$, decreases for the first 10 months to a local minimum, increases for the next 40 months to a local maximum, and then decreases for the remaining 20 months.

(B)

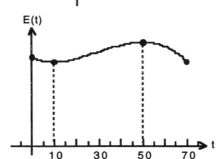

90. $C(x) = 0.08x^2 + 30x + 450$

(A) $\overline{C}(x) = \dfrac{C(x)}{x} = 0.08x + 30 + \dfrac{450}{x}$

(B) Critical values:

$$\overline{C}'(x) = 0.08 - \frac{450}{x^2} = 0$$
$$0.08x^2 - 450 = 0$$
$$x^2 - 5625 = 0$$
$$(x - 75)(x + 75) = 0$$

Thus, the critical value of $\overline{C}$ on the interval $(0, 200)$ is $x = 75$.
$x = 75$ is a partition number for $\overline{C}'$.

Sign chart for $\overline{C}'$ is:

Test Numbers	
x	$\overline{C}'(x)$
50	$-0.1\,(-)$
100	$0.026\,(+)$

Therefore, $\overline{C}$ is decreasing for $0 < x < 75$ and increasing for $75 < x < 200$; $\overline{C}$ has local minimum at $x = 75$.

92. $P(x) = R(x) - C(x)$

$P'(x) = R'(x) - C'(x)$

Thus, if $R'(x) < C'(x)$ on the interval (a, b),

then $P'(x) = R'(x) - C'(x) < 0$ on this interval and P is decreasing.

94. $C(t) = \dfrac{0.3t}{t^2 + 6t + 9}$, $0 < t < 12$

$$C'(t) = \frac{0.3(t^2 + 6t + 9) - (2t + 6)(0.3t)}{(t^2 + 6t + 9)^2}$$

$$= \frac{0.3(t + 3)^2 - 2(t + 3)(0.3t)}{(t + 3)^4}$$

$$= \frac{0.3(t + 3)[(t + 3) - 2t]}{(t + 3)^4}$$

$$= \frac{0.3(3 - t)}{(t + 3)^3} \quad \text{which is continuous for all } t$$
$$\text{in the interval } (0, 12)$$

$$= 0$$

$$t = 3$$

Thus, the critical value for C' on the interval $(0, 12)$ is $t = 3$. $t = 3$ is a partition number for C'.

Sign chart for C' is:

Test Numbers	
t	$C'(t)$
1	$\frac{3}{320}\,(+)$
4	$\frac{-3}{3430}\,(-)$

Therefore, C is increasing on $(0, 3)$ and decreasing on $(3, 12)$; C has a local minimum at $t = 3$ $(C(3) = 0.025)$.

EXERCISE 4-2

2. (A) (b, d), (e, f), (f, h) (B) (a, b), (d, e)
    (C) (a, b), (d, e) (D) (b, d), (e, f), (f, h)
    (E) (c, f) and (g, h) (F) (a, c) and (f, g)
    (G) b, d, e (H) b, d, e

4. $f'(x) > 0$, $f''(x) < 0$; (a)   **6.** $f'(x) < 0$, $f''(x) < 0$; (b)

8. $g(x) = -x^3 + 2x^2 - 3x + 9$
$g'(x) = -3x^2 + 4x - 3$
$g''(x) = -6x + 4$

10. $k(x) = -6x^{-2} + 12x^{-3}$
$k'(x) = 12x^{-3} - 36x^{-4}$
$k''(x) = -36x^{-4} + 144x^{-5}$

12. $y = x^3 - 24x^{1/3}$
$\dfrac{dy}{dx} = 3x^2 - 8x^{-2/3}$
$\dfrac{d^2y}{dx^2} = 6x + \dfrac{16}{3}x^{-5/3}$

14. $y = (x^2 - 16)^5$
$y' = 5(2x)(x^2 - 16)^4 = 10x(x^2 - 16)^4$
$y'' = 10(x^2 - 16)^4 + 4(2x)(x^2 - 16)^3(10x)$
$= 10(x^2 - 16)^3[(x^2 - 16) + 8x^2]$
$= 10(x^2 - 16)^3(9x^2 - 16)$

16. $f(x) = x^4 + 6x$
$f'(x) = 4x^3 + 6$
$f''(x) = 12x^2 \geq 0$ for all x.
Thus, f is concave upward for all x; there are no inflection points.

18. $f(x) = -x^3 - 5x^2 + 4x - 3$
$f'(x) = -3x^2 - 10x + 4$
$f''(x) = -6x - 10 = -2(3x + 5)$
Now, $f''(x) = -2(3x + 5) = 0$

$$x = -\frac{5}{3}$$

Sign chart for f'' $\left(\text{partition number for } f'' \text{ is } -\dfrac{5}{3}\right)$ is:

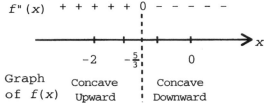

Test Numbers	
x	$f''(x)$
-2	$2\ (+)$
0	$-10\ (-)$

Therefore, the graph of f is concave upward on $\left(-\infty, -\dfrac{5}{3}\right)$ and concave downward on $\left(-\dfrac{5}{3}, \infty\right)$; there is an inflection point at $x = -\dfrac{5}{3}$.

20. $f(x) = x^4 - 2x^3 - 36x + 12$
$f'(x) = 4x^3 - 6x^2 - 36$
$f''(x) = 12x^2 - 12x = 12x(x - 1)$
Now, $f''(x) = 12x(x - 1) = 0$
$x = 0, 1$
The sign chart for f'' (0 and 1 are partition numbers for f'') is:

$f''(x)$ $+ + + \ 0 \ - \ 0 \ + + +$

Graph of f: Concave Upward on $(-1, 0)$; Concave Downward; Concave Upward
$-1 \quad 0 \ \tfrac{1}{2} \ 1 \quad 2$

Test Numbers	
x	$f''(x)$
-1	$24\ (+)$
$\tfrac{1}{2}$	$-3\ (-)$
2	$24\ (+)$

Therefore, the graph of f is concave upward on $(-\infty, 0)$ and $(1, \infty)$; concave downward on $(0, 1)$; there are inflection points at $x = 0$ and $x = 1$.

22.

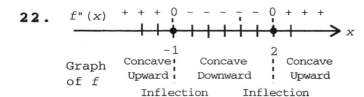

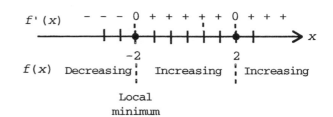

Using this information together with the points $(-4, 0)$, $(-2, -2)$, $(-1, -1)$, $(0, 0)$, $(2, 1)$, $(4, 3)$ on the graph, we have

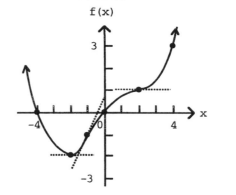

24.

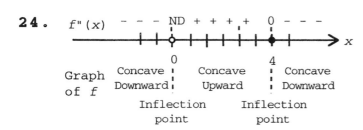

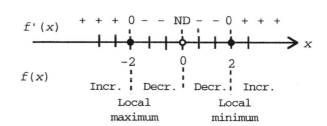

Using this information together with the points $(-4, 0)$, $(-2, 3)$, $(0, 0)$, $(2, -2)$, $(4, 0)$, $(6, 3)$ on the graph, we have

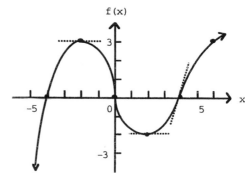

26.

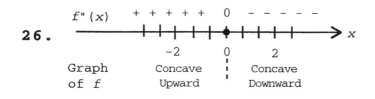

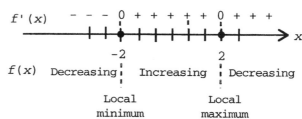

x	-2	0	2
$f(x)$	-2	1	4

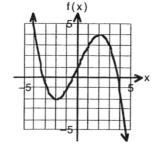

28.

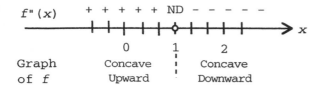

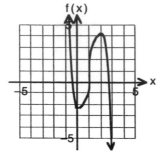

x	0	1	2
$f(x)$	-2	0	4

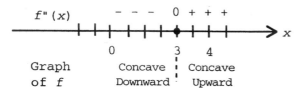

30. $f(x) = x^3 - 9x^2 + 15x + 10$

$f'(x) = 3x^2 - 18x + 15 = 3(x^2 - 6x + 5) = 3(x - 1)(x - 5)$

$f''(x) = 6x - 18 = 6(x - 3)$

Critical values: $x = 1, 5$

$f''(1) = -12 < 0$. Therefore, f has a local maximum at $x = 1$.

$f''(5) = 12 > 0$. Therefore, f has a local minimum at $x = 5$.

$f''(x) = 6(x - 3) = 0$

$\qquad\qquad x = 3$ (a partition number for f'')

The sign chart for f'' is:

Test Numbers

x	$f''(x)$
0	-18 (-)
4	6 (+)

The graph of f has an inflection point at $x = 3$. The graph of f is:

x	$f(x)$
0	10
1	17
5	-15

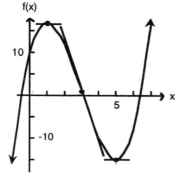

32. $f(x) = 1 - 3x - x^3$

$f'(x) = -3 - 3x^2 = -3(1 + x^2)$

$f''(x) = -6x$

Since $f'(x) = -3(1 + x^2) < 0$ for all x, f does not have any critical values. Now, $f''(x) = -6x = 0$

$\qquad\qquad x = 0$

The sign chart for f'' (partition number is 0) is:

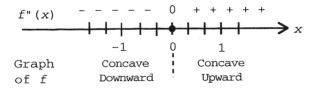

x	$f''(x)$
−1	6 (+)
1	−6 (−)

Test Numbers

The graph of f has an inflection point at $x = 0$.
The graph of f is:

x	$f(x)$
−1	5
0	1
1	−3

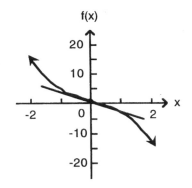

34. $f(x) = 0.25x^4 - 2x^3$

$f'(x) = x^3 - 6x^2 = x^2(x - 6)$

$f''(x) = 3x^2 - 12x = 3x(x - 4)$

Critical values: $x = 0, 6$

$f''(0) = 0$. Therefore, f may have an inflection point at $x = 0$.

$f''(6) = 36 > 0$. Therefore, f has a local minimum at $x = 6$.

$f''(x) = 3x(x - 4) = 0$

$x = 0, 4$ (partition numbers for f'')

The sign chart for f'' is:

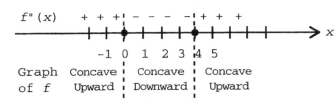

x	$f''(x)$
−1	9 (+)
1	−3 (−)
5	15 (+)

Test Numbers

The graph of f has two inflection points at $x = 0$ and $x = 4$.
The graph of f is:

x	$f(x)$
−1	4.25
0	3
1	2.25
2	−1

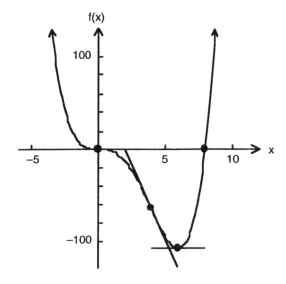

36. $f(x) = -4x(x + 2)^3$; Domain: All real numbers; y-intercept: 0; x-intercepts: 0, -2.

$$f'(x) = -4(x + 2)^3 - 12x(x + 2)^2 = -4(x + 2)^2[(x + 2) + 3x]$$
$$= -4(x + 2)^2(4x + 2)$$
$$= -8(x + 2)^2(2x + 1)$$

$$f''(x) = -8\{2(x + 2)(2x + 1) + 2(x + 2)^2\} = -16(x + 2)[(2x + 1) + (x + 2)]$$
$$= -16(x + 2)[3x + 3]$$
$$= -48(x + 2)(x + 1)$$

Critical values: $x = -2, -\dfrac{1}{2}$; f increasing on $(-\infty, -0.5)$ and decreasing on $(-0.5, \infty)$.

$f''(-2) = 0$. Therefore, f may have an inflection point at $x = -2$.

$f''\left(-\dfrac{1}{2}\right) = -36 < 0$. Therefore, f has a local maximum at $x = -\dfrac{1}{2}$.

$f''(x) = -48(x + 2)(x + 1) = 0$
$$x = -2, -1 \quad \text{(partition numbers for } f'')$$

The sign chart for f'' is:

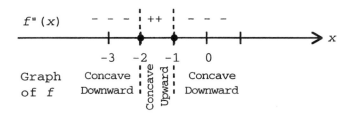

Test Numbers	
x	$f''(x)$
-3	$-96\ (-)$
$-\dfrac{3}{2}$	$12\ (+)$
0	$-96\ (-)$

The graph of f has two inflection points at $x = -2$ and $x = -1$. The graph of f is:

x	$f(x)$
-3	-12
-2	0
-1	4
0	0

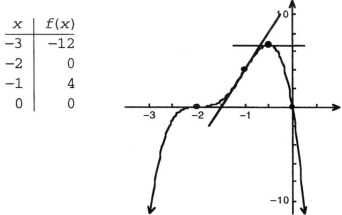

38. $f(x) = (x^2 + 3)(x^2 - 1)$

<u>Step 1. Analyze $f(x)$</u>:

(A) Domain: All real numbers, $(-\infty, \infty)$.

(B) Intercepts: y-intercept: $f(0) = -3$

x-intercepts: $(x^2 + 3)(x^2 - 1) = 0$
$$(x^2 + 3)(x - 1)(x + 1) = 0$$
$$x = -1, 1$$

(C) Asymptotes: There are no asymptotes.

Step 2. Analyze $f'(x)$:

$$f'(x) = 2x(x^2 - 1) + 2x(x^2 + 3)$$
$$= 2x(x^2 - 1 + x^2 + 3) = 2x(2x^2 + 2) = 4x(x^2 + 1) = 0$$
$$x = 0$$

Critical values: $x = 0$
Partition numbers: $x = 0$
Sign chart for f':

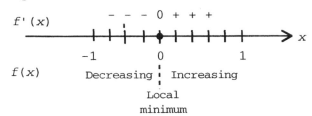

Test Numbers	
x	$f'(x)$
-1	-8 (-)
1	8 (+)

Step 3. Analyze $f''(x)$:

$f''(x) = 12x^2 + 4 > 0$ for all x. Thus, the graph of f is concave upward on $(-\infty, \infty)$.

Step 4. Sketch the graph of f:

x	$f(x)$
-1	0
0	-3
1	0

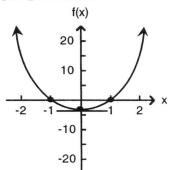

40. $f(x) = (x^2 - 1)(x^2 - 5)$

Step 1. Analyze $f(x)$:

(A) Domain: All real numbers, $(-\infty, \infty)$.

(B) Intercepts: y-intercept: $f(0) = 5$

x-intercepts: $(x^2 - 1)(x^2 - 5) = 0$
$(x - 1)(x + 1)(x - \sqrt{5})(x + \sqrt{5}) = 0$
$x = -\sqrt{5}, -1, 1, \sqrt{5}$

(C) Asymptotes: There are no asymptotes.

Step 2. Analyze $f'(x)$:

$$f'(x) = 2x(x^2 - 5) + 2x(x^2 - 1)$$
$$= 2x(x^2 - 5 + x^2 - 1) = 4x(x^2 - 3) = 0$$
$$x = 0, \pm\sqrt{3}$$

Critical values: $x = -\sqrt{3}, 0, \sqrt{3}$
Partition numbers: Same as critical values.
Sign chart for f':

Test Numbers	
x	$f'(x)$
-2	-8 (-)
-1	8 (+)
1	-8 (-)
2	8 (+)

Step 3. Analyze $f''(x)$:

$f''(x) = 12x^2 - 12 = 12(x - 1)(x + 1)$

Partition numbers for f'': $x = -1$, $x = 1$

Sign chart for f'':

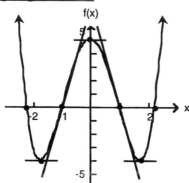

Test Numbers	
x	$f''(x)$
-2	$36 (+)$
0	$-12 (-)$
2	$36 (+)$

Thus, the graph of f is concave upward on $(-\infty, -1)$ and on $(1, \infty)$; the graph of f is concave downward on $(-1, 1)$; the graph has inflection points at $x = -1$ and $x = 1$.

Step 4. Sketch the graph of f:

x	$f(x)$
$-\sqrt{5}$	0
$-\sqrt{3}$	-4
-1	0
0	5
1	0
$\sqrt{3}$	-4
$\sqrt{5}$	0

42. $f(x) = 3x^5 - 5x^4$

Step 1. Analyze $f(x)$:

(A) Domain: All real numbers, $(-\infty, \infty)$.

(B) Intercepts: y-intercept: $f(0) = 0$

x-intercepts: $3x^5 - 5x^4 = x^4(3x - 5) = 0$

$$x = 0, \frac{5}{3}$$

(C) Asymptotes: There are no asymptotes.

Step 2. Analyze $f'(x)$:

$f'(x) = 15x^4 - 20x^3 = 5x^3(3x - 4) = 0$

$$x = 0, \frac{4}{3}$$

Critical values: $x = 0$, $x = \dfrac{4}{3}$

Partition numbers: Same as critical values.

Sign chart for f':

Test Numbers	
x	$f'(x)$
-1	$35 (+)$
1	$-5 (-)$
2	$80 (+)$

Step 3. Analyze $f''(x)$:

$f''(x) = 60x^3 - 60x^2 = 60x^2(x - 1)$

Partition numbers for f'': $x = 0$, $x = 1$

Sign chart
for f'':

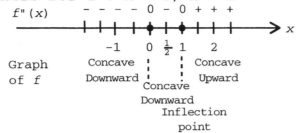

Test Numbers	
x	$f''(x)$
-1	$-120\,(+)$
$\frac{1}{2}$	$-15\,(-)$
2	$60\,(+)$

Thus, the graph of f is concave downward on $(-\infty, 0)$ and on $(0, 1)$; concave upward on $(2, \infty)$; there is an inflection point at $x = 1$.

Step 4. Sketch the graph of f:

x	$f(x)$
0	0
1	-2
$\frac{4}{3}$	-3.16
$\frac{5}{3}$	0

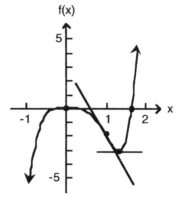

44.

x	$f'(x)$	$f(x)$
$-\infty < x < -3$	Negative and increasing	Decreasing and concave upward
$x = -3$	x-intercept	Local minimum
$-3 < x < -2$	Positive and increasing	Increasing and concave upward
$x = -2$	Local maximum	Inflection point
$-2 < x < 0$	Positive and decreasing	Increasing and concave downward
$x = 0$	Local minimum	Inflection point
$0 < x < \infty$	Positive and increasing	Increasing and concave upward

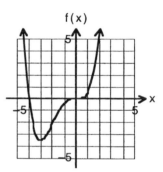

46.

x	$f'(x)$	$f(x)$
$-\infty < x < -2$	Positive and decreasing	Increasing and concave downward
$x = -2$	x-intercept	Local maximum
$-2 < x < 12$	Negative and decreasing	Decreasing and concave downward
$x = 1$	Local minimum	Inflection point
$1 < x < 2$	Negative and increasing	Decreasing and concave upward
$x = 2$	x-intercept	Local minimum
$2 < x < \infty$	Positive and increasing	Increasing and concave upward

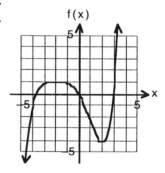

48. $f(x) = x^4 + 2x^3 - 5x^2 - 4x + 4$

Step 1. Analyze $f(x)$:

(A) Domain: all real numbers

(B) Intercepts: y-intercept: $f(0) = 4$

x-intercepts: $x \approx -3.07,\ -1.22,\ 0.65,\ 1.64$

(C) Asymptotes: None

Step 2. Analyze $f'(x)$: $f'(x) = 4x^3 + 6x^2 - 10x - 4$
Critical values: $x = -2.38, -0.35, 1.22$
f is decreasing on $(-\infty, -2.38)$ and $(-0.35, 1.22)$; f is increasing on $(-2.38, -0.35)$ and $(1.22, \infty)$; f has local minima at $x = -2.38$ and 1.22; f has a local maximum at $x = -0.35$.

Step 3. Analyze $f''(x)$: $f''(x) = 12x^2 + 12x - 10$
The graph of f is concave upward on $(-\infty, -1.54)$ and $(0.54, \infty)$; the graph of f is concave downward on $(-1.54, 0.54)$; the graph has inflection points at $x = -1.54$ and 0.54.

50. $f(x) = x^4 - 12x^3 + 28x^2 + 76x - 50$

Step 1. Analyze $f(x)$:

(A) Domain: All real numbers

(B) Intercepts: y-intercept: $f(0) = -50$
x-intercepts: $x \approx -1.89, 0.57$

(C) Asymptotes: None

Step 2. Analyze $f'(x)$: $f'(x) = 4x^3 - 36x^2 + 56x + 76$
Critical values: $x \approx -0.85, 3.55, 6.30$

f is decreasing on $(-\infty, -0.85)$ and $(3.55, 6.30)$;
f is increasing on $(-0.85, 3.55)$ and $(6.30, \infty)$;
f has local minima at $x = -0.85$ and 6.30; f has a local maximum at $x = 3.55$.

Step 3. Analyze $f''(x)$: $f''(x) = 12x^2 - 72x + 56$

The graph of f is concave upward on $(-\infty, 0.92)$ and $(5.08, \infty)$; the graph of f is concave downward on $(0.92, 5.08)$; the graph has inflection points at $x = 0.92$ and $x = 5.08$.

52. $f(x) = -x^4 + x^3 + x^2 + 6$
Step 1. Analyze $f(x)$:

(A) Domain: all real numbers

(B) Intercepts: y-intercept: $f(0) = 6$
x-intercepts: $x \approx -1.49, 2.11$

(C) Asymptotes: None

Step 2. Analyze $f'(x)$: $f'(x) = -4x^3 + 3x^2 + 2x$
Critical values: $x \approx -0.43, 0, 1.18$
f is increasing on $(-\infty, -0.43)$ and $(0, 1.18)$; f is decreasing on $(-0.43, 0)$ and $(1.18, \infty)$; f has local maxima at $x = -0.43$ and 1.18; f has a local minimum at $x = 0$.

Step 3. Analyze $f''(x)$: $f''(x) = -12x^2 + 6x + 2$
The graph of f is concave downward on $(-\infty, -0.23)$ and $(0.73, \infty)$; the graph of f is concave upward on $(-0.23, 0.73)$; the graph has inflection points at $x = -0.23$ and $x = 0.73$.

54. $f(x) = x^5 + 4x^4 - 7x^3 - 20x^2 + 20x - 20$

Step 1. Analyze $f(x)$:

(A) Domain: all real numbers

(B) Intercepts: y-intercept: $f(0) = -20$

   x-intercepts: $x \approx -4.20$, -2.87, 2.22

(C) Asymptotes: None

Step 2. Analyze $f'(x)$:

$f'(x) = 5x^4 + 16x^3 - 21x^2 - 40x + 20$
Critical values: $x \approx -3.67$, -1.56, 0.44, 1.59
f is increasing on $(-\infty, -3.67)$, $(-1.56, 0.44)$, and $(1.59, \infty)$; f is decreasing on $(-3.67, -1.56)$ and $(0.44, 1.59)$; f has local maxima at $x = -3.67$ and 0.44; f has local minima at $x = -1.56$ and 1.59.

Step 3. Analyze $f''(x)$:

The graph of f is concave downward on $(-\infty, -2.89)$ and $(-0.62, 1.11)$; the graph of f is concave upward on $(-2.89, -0.62)$ and $(1.11, \infty)$; the graph has inflection points at $x = -2.89$, -0.61 and 1.11.

56. If the graph of $y = f(x)$ is concave up on an interval, then $f'(x)$ is increasing on that interval. And if the graph of $y = f(x)$ is concave down on an interval, then $f'(x)$ is decreasing on that interval.

58. Let $x = c$ be an x-intercept for the graph of $y = f'(x)$. If $f'(x)$ is decreasing on an open interval containing c, then $f(x)$ has a local maximum at $x = c$. If $f'(x)$ is increasing on an open interval containing c, then $f(x)$ has a local minimum at $x = c$.

60. The graph of the PPI is concave downward.

62. The graph of $C'(x)$ is positive and increasing. Since the marginal costs are increasing, the production process is becoming less efficient as production increases. Initially, marginal costs are higher at Plant A, but as production levels increase, marginal costs at Plant B eventually exceed those at Plant A.

64. $P(x) = R(x) - C(x)$

$= 1,296x - 0.12x^3 - (830 + 396x)$

$= 1,296x - 0.12x^3 - 830 - 396x$

$= x - 0.12x^3 - 830$

$P'(x) = 900 - 0.36x^2 = 0.36(2,500 - x^2)$

$= 0.36(50 - x)(50 + x)$

$P''(x) = -0.72x$

Critical values: $P'(x) = 0$, $x = \pm 50$
Thus, $x = 50$ is the only critical value in the interval $(0, 80)$.
$P''(50) = -0.72(50) = -36 < 0$

(A) P has a local maximum at $x = 50$.
(B) Since $P''(x) = -0.72x < 0$ for $0 < x < 80$, P is concave downward on the whole interval $(0, 80)$.

66. $T(x) = -0.25x^4 + 6x^3, \quad 0 \le x \le 18$

$T'(x) = -x^3 + 18x^2 = -x^2(x - 18)$

$T''(x) = -3x^2 + 36x = -3x(x - 12)$

The sign chart for T'' (partition number is 12):

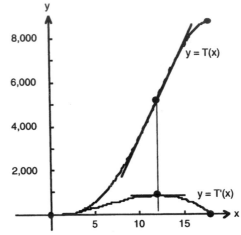

Test Numbers	
x	$T''(x)$
1	33 (+)
13	-39 (-)

Thus, T' is increasing on (0, 12) and decreasing on (12, 18).
$T''(x) = -3x(x - 12)$.

The point of diminishing returns is $x = 12$ and the maximum rate of change is $T'(12) = 864$. Note that $T'(x)$ has a local maximum and $T(x)$ has an inflection point at $x = 12$.

68. $N(x) = -0.25x^4 + 13x^3 - 180x^2 + 10,000, \quad 15 \le x \le 24$

$N'(x) = -x^3 + 39x^2 - 360x$

$N''(x) = -3x^2 + 78x - 360 = -3(x^2 - 26x + 120) = -3(x - 6)(x - 20)$

The sign chart for N'' (partition number is 20):

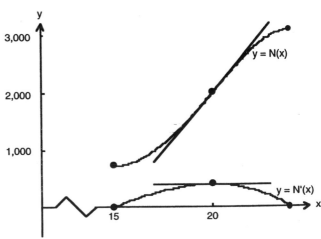

Test Numbers	
x	$N''(x)$
19	39 (+)
21	-45 (-)

Thus, N' is increasing on (15, 20) and decreasing on (20, 24).
$N''(x) = -3(x - 6)(x - 20)$.

The point of diminishing returns is $x = 20$ and the maximum rate of change is $N'(20) = 400$. Note that $N'(x)$ has a local maximum and $N(x)$ has an inflection point at $x = 20$.

70. (A)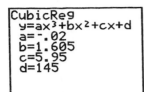

CubicReg
y=ax³+bx²+cx+d
a=⁻.02
b=1.605
c=5.95
d=145

(B) From part (A),
$$y(x) = -0.02x^3 + 1.605x^2 + 5.95x + 145$$
so, $y'(x) = -0.06x^2 + 3.210x + 5.95$

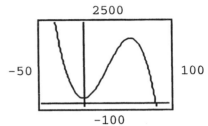

The graph of $y'(x)$ is shown at the right and the maximum value of y' occurs at $x \approx 27$; and $y(27) \approx 1,082$.

The manager should place 27 ads each month to maximize the rate of change of sales; the manager can expect to sell 1,082 CD's.

72. $T(x) = x^2\left(1 - \dfrac{x}{9}\right)$, $0 \le x \le 6$

$$T'(x) = 2x\left(1 - \frac{x}{9}\right) - x^2 = 2x - \frac{2x^2}{9} - \frac{x^2}{9} = 2x - \frac{1}{3}x^2$$
$$= x\left(2 - \frac{x}{3}\right)$$
$$= \frac{1}{3}x(6 - x)$$

$$T''(x) = 2 - \frac{2}{3}x = 0$$
$$x = 3$$

(A) The sign chart for T'' (partition number is 3) is:

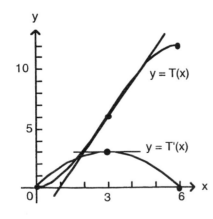

Test Numbers

x	$T''(x)$
0	+
4	−

Thus, T' is increasing on (0, 3) and decreasing on (3, 6).

(B) From the results in (A), the graph of T has an inflection point at $x = 3$.

(C)

(D) Using the result in (A), T' has a local maximum at $x = 3$:
$$T'(3) = \frac{1}{3}(3)(6 - 3) = 3$$

2. (A) (d, ∞) (B) $(-\infty, a)$, (a, c), (c, d)
   (C) $(-\infty, a)$, (a, c), (c, d) (D) (d, ∞)
   (E) $x = d$ (F) no local minima
   (G) (a, b), (c, e) (H) $(-\infty, a)$, (b, c), (e, ∞)
   (I) $(-\infty, a)$, (b, c), (e, ∞) (J) (a, b), (c, e)
   (K) $x = b$, $x = e$ (L) $y = L$
   (M) $x = a$, $x = c$
   (N) x-intercepts: b and f; y-intercept: b

4. $f(x) = \dfrac{3x}{x - 4}$; f is a rational function.

Horizontal asymptote: $\dfrac{a_m x^m}{b_n x^n} = \dfrac{3x}{x} = 3$ and the line $y = 3$ is a horizontal asymptote.

Vertical asymptote: $x = 4$ is the vertical asymptote since $D(4) = 0$ and $N(4) \neq 0$.

[Note: $D(x)$ denotes denominator and $N(x)$ denotes numerator of $f(x)$.]

6. $f(x) = \dfrac{x^2 + 9}{x^2 - 9}$; f is a rational function.

Horizontal asymptote: $\dfrac{a_m x^m}{b_n x^n} = \dfrac{x^2}{x^2} = 1$ and the line $y = 1$ is a horizontal asymptote.

Vertical asymptotes: $D(-3) = D(3) = 0$, $N(-3) \neq 0$, $N(3) \neq 0$, thus the lines $x = -3$ and $x = 3$ are vertical asymptotes.

8. $f(x) = \dfrac{x^3}{x^2 + 1}$; f is a rational function.

Horizontal asymptote: $\dfrac{a_m x^m}{b_n x^n} = \dfrac{x^3}{x^2} = x$; f does not have a horizontal asymptote.

Vertical asymptotes: $D(x) = x^2 + 1 \neq 0$, for all x; f has no vertical asymptotes.

10. $f(x) = \dfrac{3x}{x^2 + 3}$; f is a rational function.

Horizontal asymptote: $\dfrac{a_m x^m}{b_n x^n} = \dfrac{3x}{x^2} = \dfrac{3}{x}$; the x axis ($y = 0$) is a horizontal asymptote.

Vertical asymptotes: Since $D(x) = x^2 + 3 \neq 0$ for all x, there are no vertical asymptotes.

12. $f(x) = \dfrac{5x^2 - 2x + 1}{2x^2 - 5x - 3}$; f is a rational function.

    <u>Horizontal asymptote</u>: $\dfrac{a_m x^m}{b_n x^n} = \dfrac{5x^2}{2x^2} = \dfrac{5}{2}$ and the line $y = \dfrac{5}{2}$ is a

                          horizontal asymptote.

    <u>Vertical asymptotes</u>: $D(x) = 2x^2 - 5x - 3 = 0$; $x = -\dfrac{1}{2}$; $x = 3$ are the

    zeros of $D(x)$; i.e. $D\left(-\dfrac{1}{2}\right) = D(3) = 0$. Since $N\left(-\dfrac{1}{2}\right) \neq 0$ and $N(3) \neq 0$,

    the lines $x = -\dfrac{1}{2}$ and $x = 3$ are the vertical asymptotes.

14. $f(x) = \dfrac{2x^2 + x - 6}{x^2 + 4x + 4}$; f is a rational function.

    <u>Horizontal asymptote</u>: $\dfrac{a_m x^m}{b_n x^n} = \dfrac{2x^2}{x^2} = 2$ and the line $y = 2$ is a

                          horizontal asymptote.

    <u>Vertical asymptotes</u>: $D(x) = x^2 + 4x + 4 = (x + 2)^2$; but $D(-2) = 0$ and $N(-2) = 0$, so we need to rewrite $f(x)$:

$$f(x) = \frac{2x^2 + x - 6}{x^2 + 4x + 4} = \frac{(2x - 3)(x + 2)}{(x + 2)^2} = \frac{2x - 3}{x + 2}, \ x \neq -2.$$

    Now we can see that the line $x = -2$ is a vertical asymptote.

16. <u>Step 1. Analyze $f(x)$</u>:

    (A) Domain: All real numbers, $(-\infty, \infty)$

    (B) Intercepts: y-intercept: $f(0) = 0$

                      x-intercepts: -2, 0, 2

    (C) Asymptotes: Horizontal asymptote: $y = -3$ and $y = 3$

    <u>Step 2. Analyze $f'(x)$</u>:

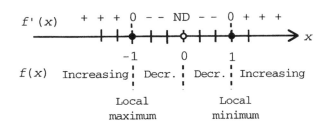

    <u>Step 3. Analyze $f''(x)$</u>:

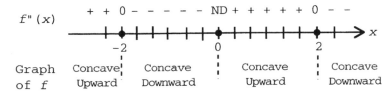

Step 4.   Sketch the graph of f:

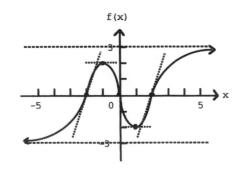

18. Step 1.   Analyze $f(x)$:

(A) Domain: All real numbers except $x = 1$

(B) Intercepts: y-intercept: 0
$\qquad\qquad\qquad$ x-intercepts: -4, 0, 2

(C) Asymptotes: Horizontal asymptote: $y = -2$
$\qquad\qquad\qquad$ Vertical asymptote: $x = 1$

Step 2.   Analyze $f'(x)$:

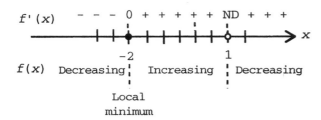

Step 3.   Analyze $f''(x)$:

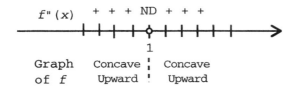

Step 4.   Sketch the graph of f:

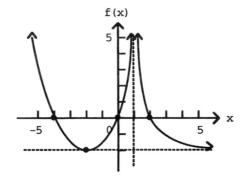

20. Step 1.   Analyze $f(x)$:

(A) Domain: All real numbers except $x = 1$

(B) Intercepts: y-intercept: -2
$\qquad\qquad\qquad$ x-intercept: 2

(C) Asymptotes: Horizontal asymptote: $y = -1$
$\qquad\qquad\qquad$ Vertical asymptote: $x = 1$

Step 2.   Analyze $f'(x)$:

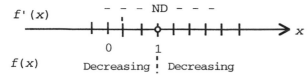

Step 3. Analyze $f''(x)$:

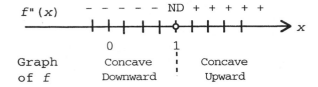

Step 4. Sketch the graph of f:

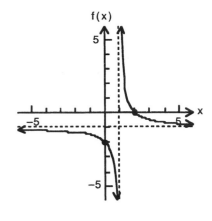

22. Step 1. Analyze $f(x)$:

(A) Domain: All real numbers except $x = -1$, $x = 1$

(B) Intercepts: y-intercept: 0
     x-intercept: 0

(C) Asymptotes: Horizontal asymptote: $y = 0$
     Vertical asymptotes: $x = -1$, $x = 1$

Step 2. Analyze $f'(x)$:

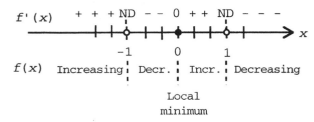

Step 3. Analyze $f''(x)$:

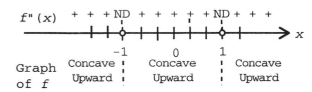

Step 4. Sketch the graph of f:

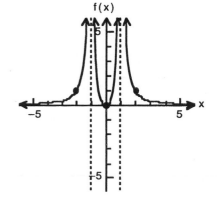

24. $f(x) = \dfrac{2x - 4}{x + 2}$

Step 1. Analyze $f(x)$:
(A) Domain: All real numbers except $x = -2$.
(B) Intercepts: y-intercept: $f(0) = -2$

$\qquad\qquad\qquad$ x-intercepts: $\dfrac{2x - 4}{x + 2} = 0$

$\qquad\qquad\qquad\qquad\qquad\qquad$ $2x - 4 = 0$
$\qquad\qquad\qquad\qquad\qquad\qquad\qquad\quad$ $x = 2$

(C) Asymptotes:

$\quad$ Horizontal asymptote: $\displaystyle\lim_{x\to\infty}\dfrac{2x-4}{x+2} = \lim_{x\to\infty}\dfrac{a_m x^m}{b_n x^n} = \lim_{x\to\infty}\dfrac{2x}{x} = 2$ and the

$\qquad\qquad\qquad\qquad$ line $y = 2$ is a horizontal asymptote.

$\quad$ Vertical asymptote: $D(x) = x + 2 = 0$, $D(-2) = 0$, but $N(-2) \ne 0$,
$\quad$ so the line $x = -2$ is a vertical asymptote.

Step 2. Analyze $f'(x)$:

$f'(x) = \dfrac{2(x + 2) - (2x - 4)}{(x + 2)^2} = \dfrac{2x + 4 - 2x + 4}{(x + 2)^2} = \dfrac{8}{(x + 2)^2} = 8(x + 2)^{-2}$

Critical values: None
Partition number: $x = -2$

Sign chart for f':

$f'(x)$	+ + + ND + + +
	(number line: -3, -2, 0, with open circle at -2) $\to x$
$f(x)$	Increasing ¦ Increasing

Test Numbers

x	$f'(x)$
-3	8 (+)
0	2 (+)

Thus, f is increasing on $(-\infty, -2)$ and on $(-2, \infty)$; there are no local extrema.

Step 3. Analyze $f''(x)$:

$f''(x) = -16(x + 2)^{-3} = -\dfrac{16}{(x + 2)^3}$

Partition number for f'': $x = -2$
Sign chart for f'':

$f''(x)$	+ + + ND - - -
	(number line: -3, -2, 0, with open circle at -2) $\to x$
Graph of f	Concave Upward ¦ Concave Downward

Test Numbers

x	$f''(x)$
-3	16 (+)
0	-2 (−)

Thus, the graph of f is concave upward on $(-\infty, -2)$ and concave downward on $(-2, \infty)$.

Step 4. Sketch the graph of f:

x	$f(x)$
-3	10
0	-2
2	0

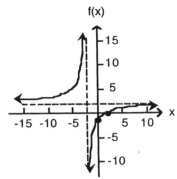

26. $f(x) = \dfrac{2 + x}{3 - x}$

Step 1. Analyze $f(x)$:

(A) Domain: All real numbers except $x = 3$.

(B) Intercepts: y-intercept: $f(0) = \dfrac{2}{3}$

$$x\text{-intercepts: } \frac{2 + x}{3 - x} = 0$$
$$2 + x = 0$$
$$x = -2$$

(C) Asymptotes:

Horizontal asymptote: $\lim\limits_{x \to \infty} \dfrac{2 + x}{3 - x} = \dfrac{1}{-1} = -1$ and the line $y = -1$ is a horizontal asymptote.

Vertical asymptote: $D(x) = 3 - x = 0$, $x = 3$; i.e. $D(3) = 0$, $N(3) \neq 0$, so the line $x = 3$ is a vertical asymptote.

Step 2. Analyze $f'(x)$:

$$f'(x) = \frac{(3 - x) + (2 + x)}{(3 - x)^2} = \frac{3 - x + 2 + x}{(3 - x)^2} = \frac{5}{(3 - x)^2} = 5(3 - x)^{-2}$$

Critical values: None
Partition number: $x = 3$
Sign chart for f':

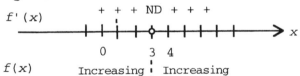

Test Numbers	
x	$f(x)$
0	$\frac{5}{9}$ (+)
4	5 (+)

Thus, f is increasing on $(-\infty, 3)$ and on $(3, \infty)$; there are no local extrema.

Step 3. Analyze $f''(x)$:

$$f''(x) = 10(3 - x)^{-3} = \frac{10}{(3 - x)^3}$$

Partition number for f'': $x = 3$
Sign chart for f'':

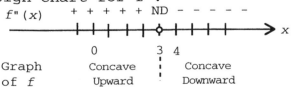

Test Numbers	
x	$f''(x)$
0	$\frac{10}{27}$ (+)
4	-10 (−)

Thus, the graph of f is concave upward on $(-\infty, 3)$ and concave downward on $(3, \infty)$.

Step 4. Sketch the graph of f:

x	$f(x)$
-2	0
0	$\frac{2}{3}$
4	-6

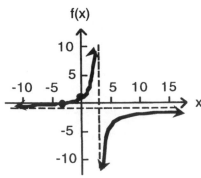

28. $f(x) = \dfrac{1}{x^2 - 4} = \dfrac{1}{(x - 2)(x + 2)}$

Step 1. Analyze $f(x)$:

(A) Domain: All real numbers except $x = -2$, $x = 2$.

(B) Intercepts: y-intercept: $f(0) = -\dfrac{1}{4}$

 x-intercepts: None

(C) Asymptotes:
 <u>Horizontal asymptote</u>: $y = 0$

 <u>Vertical asymptotes</u>: $x = -2$, $x = 2$

Step 2. Analyze $f'(x)$:

$f'(x) = -\dfrac{2x}{(x^2 - 4)^2} = \dfrac{2x}{(x - 2)^2(x + 2)^2}$

$f'(x) = 0$ if $x = 0$
Critical values: $x = 0$
Partition numbers: $x = -2$, $x = 0$, $x = 2$
Sign chart for f':

```
       + + + ND + + + 0 - - - ND - -
f'(x)
      ┼┼┼┼○┼┼┼┼●┼┼┼┼○┼┼┼➤ x
       -3  -2  -1  0  1  2  3
f(x)   Incr.  Incr.   Decr.   Decr.
               Local
             maximum
```

Test Numbers	
x	$f''(x)$
-3	$\frac{6}{25}$ (+)
-1	$\frac{2}{9}$ (+)
1	$-\frac{2}{9}$ (−)
3	$-\frac{6}{25}$ (−)

Thus, f is increasing on $(-\infty, -2)$ and $(-2, 0)$; decreasing on $(0, 2)$ and $(2, \infty)$; f has a local maximum at $x = 0$.

Step 3. Analyze $f''(x)$:

$f''(x) = -2(x^2 - 4)^{-2} - 2x(-4x)(x^2 - 4)^{-3}$

$ = \dfrac{-2}{(x^2 - 4)^2} + \dfrac{8x^2}{(x^2 - 4)^3} = \dfrac{-2(x^2 - 4) + 8x^2}{(x^2 - 4)^3} = \dfrac{6x^2 + 8}{(x - 2)^3(x + 2)^3}$

Partition numbers for f'': $x = -2$, $x = 2$

Sign chart for f'':

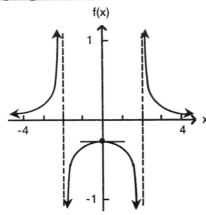

	Test Numbers	
x	$f''(x)$	
-3	$\frac{62}{125}$	$(+)$
0	$-\frac{1}{8}$	$(-)$
3	$\frac{62}{125}$	$(+)$

Thus, the graph of f is concave upward on $(-\infty, -2)$ and on $(2, \infty)$; concave downward on $(-2, 2)$; there are no inflection points.

<u>Step 4. Sketch the graph of f</u>:

x	$f(x)$
-3	$\frac{1}{5}$
-1	$-\frac{1}{3}$
0	$-\frac{1}{4}$
1	$-\frac{1}{3}$
3	$\frac{1}{5}$

30. $f(x) = \dfrac{x^2}{1 + x^2}$

<u>Step 1. Analyze $f(x)$</u>:

(A) Domain: All real numbers, $(-\infty, \infty)$

(B) Intercepts: y-intercept: $f(0) = 0$

$$x\text{-intercepts:} \quad \frac{x^2}{1 + x^2} = 0$$
$$x = 0$$

(C) Asymptotes:

<u>Horizontal asymptote</u>: $y = 1$

<u>Vertical asymptotes</u>: None

<u>Step 2. Analyze $f'(x)$</u>:

$$f'(x) = \frac{(2x)(1 + x^2) - 2x(x^2)}{(1 + x^2)^2} = \frac{2x + 2x^3 - 2x^3}{(1 + x^2)^2} = \frac{2x}{(1 + x^2)^2} = 0$$
$$x = 0$$

Critical value: $x = 0$
Partition number: $x = 0$
Sign chart for f':

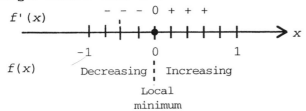

	Test Numbers	
x	$f'(x)$	
-1	$-\frac{1}{2}$	$(-)$
1	$\frac{1}{2}$	$(+)$

Thus, f is decreasing on $(-\infty, 0)$ and increasing on $(0, \infty)$; has a local minimum at $x = 0$.

Step 3. Analyze $f''(x)$:

$$f''(x) = \frac{2(1 + x^2)^2 - 4x(1 + x^2)(2x)}{(1 + x^2)^4}$$

$$= \frac{2(1 + x^2)[(1 + x^2) - 4x^2]}{(1 + x^2)^4} = \frac{2(1 - 3x^2)}{(1 + x^2)^3}$$

$$f''(x) = 0 \quad \text{or} \quad 1 - 3x^2 = 0, \quad x = \pm\frac{1}{\sqrt{3}} = \pm\frac{\sqrt{3}}{3}$$

Partition numbers for f'': $x = -\frac{\sqrt{3}}{3}, \quad x = \frac{\sqrt{3}}{3}$

Sign chart for f'':

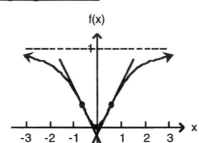

Test Numbers	
x	$f''(x)$
-1	$-\frac{1}{2}$ $(-)$
0	2 $(+)$
1	$-\frac{1}{2}$ $(-)$

Thus, the graph of f is concave downward on $\left(-\infty, -\frac{\sqrt{3}}{3}\right)$ and on $\left(\frac{\sqrt{3}}{3}, \infty\right)$;

concave upward on $\left(-\frac{\sqrt{3}}{3}, \frac{\sqrt{3}}{3}\right)$; f has inflection points at $x = -\frac{\sqrt{3}}{3}$ and

$x = \frac{\sqrt{3}}{3}$.

Step 4. Sketch the graph of f:

x	$f(x)$
-1	$\frac{1}{2}$
$-\frac{\sqrt{3}}{3}$	$\frac{1}{4}$
0	0
$\frac{\sqrt{3}}{3}$	$\frac{1}{4}$
1	$\frac{1}{2}$

32. $f(x) = \dfrac{2x}{x^2 - 9}$

Step 1. Analyze $f(x)$:

(A) Domain: All real numbers except $x = -3$, $x = 3$.

(B) Intercepts: y-intercept: $f(0) = 0$

$\qquad\qquad\quad x$-intercepts: $\dfrac{2x}{x^2 - 9} = 0$

$\qquad\qquad\qquad\qquad\qquad x = 0$

(C) Asymptotes:

<u>Horizontal asymptote</u>: $\displaystyle\lim_{x \to \infty} \frac{2x}{x^2 - 9} = 0$ and the x axis is a
horizontal asymptote.

<u>Vertical asymptotes</u>: $D(x) = x^2 - 9 = 0$, $x = -3$, $x = 3$, $N(-3) \neq 0$,
$N(3) \neq 0$, so the lines $x = -3$ and $x = 3$ are two vertical asymptotes.

Step 2. Analyze $f'(x)$:

$$f'(x) = \frac{2(x^2 - 9) - 2x(2x)}{(x^2 - 9)^2} = \frac{2x^2 - 18 - 4x^2}{(x^2 - 9)^2} = \frac{-2(x^2 + 9)}{(x^2 - 9)^2}$$

Critical values: None

Partition numbers: $x = -3$, $x = 3$

Sign chart for f':

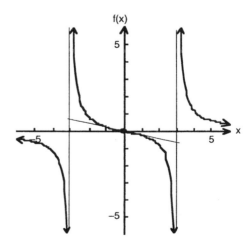

Test Numbers

x	$f'(x)$
-4	$-\frac{50}{49}$ (−)
0	$-\frac{2}{9}$ (−)
4	$-\frac{50}{49}$ (−)

Thus, f is decreasing on $(-\infty, -3)$, on $(-3, 3)$ and on $(3, \infty)$; there are no local extrema.

Step 3. Analyze $f''(x)$:

$$f''(x) = -2\{2x(x^2 - 9)^{-2} - 4x(x^2 - 9)^{-3}(x^2 + 9)\}$$

$$= -2\left\{\frac{2x}{(x^2 - 9)^2} - \frac{4x(x^2 + 9)}{(x^2 - 9)^3}\right\} = -2\left(\frac{2x(x^2 - 9) - 4x(x^2 + 9)}{(x^2 - 9)^3}\right)$$

$$= -2\left(\frac{4x^3 - 18x - 4x^3 - 36x}{(x^2 - 9)^3}\right) = \frac{108x}{(x^2 - 9)^3}$$

Partition numbers for $f''(x)$: $x = -3$, $x = 0$, $x = 3$

Sign chart for f'':

Test Numbers

x	$f''(x)$
-4	$-\frac{432}{343}$ (−)
-1	$\frac{27}{128}$ (+)
1	$-\frac{27}{128}$ (−)
4	$\frac{432}{343}$ (+)

Thus, the graph of f is concave downward on $(-\infty, -3)$ and on $(0, 3)$ and is concave upward on $(-3, 0)$ and on $(0, \infty)$; there is an inflection point at $x = 0$.

Step 4. Sketch the graph of f:

x	$f(x)$
-4	$-\frac{8}{7}$
0	0
4	$\frac{8}{7}$

34. $f(x) = \dfrac{x}{(x-2)^2}$

Step 1. Analyze $f(x)$:

(A) Domain: All real numbers except 2.

(B) Intercepts: y-intercept: $f(0) = 0$

x-intercepts: $\dfrac{x}{(x-2)^2} = 0$

$x = 0$

(C) Asymptotes:

Horizontal asymptote: $\lim\limits_{x \to \infty} \dfrac{x}{(x-2)^2} = 0$ and the x axis is a horizontal asymptote.

Vertical asymptote: $D(x) = (x-2)^2 = 0$, $x = 2$; i.e. $D(2) = 0$, $N(2) \neq 0$, so the line $x = 2$ is a vertical asymptote.

Step 2. Analyze $f'(x)$:

$f'(x) = \dfrac{(x-2)^2 - 2x(x-2)}{(x-2)^4} = \dfrac{x - 2 - 2x}{(x-2)^3} = \dfrac{-(x+2)}{(x-2)^3}$

Critical values: $x = -2$

Partition numbers: $x = -2$, $x = 2$

Sign chart for f':

	Test Numbers	
	x	$f'(x)$
	-3	$-\frac{1}{125}\ (-)$
	0	$\frac{1}{4}\ (+)$
	3	$-5\ (-)$

$f'(x)$: $-\ -\ -\ |\ +\ +\ +\ |\ -\ -\ -$ (0 at $x=-2$, ND at $x=2$)

$f(x)$: $-3\ -2\quad 0\quad 2\ 3$

Decreasing | Incr. | Decreasing

Thus, f is decreasing on $(-\infty, -2)$ and on $(2, \infty)$ and is increasing on $(-2, 2)$; f has a local minimum at $x = -2$.

Step 3. Analyze $f''(x)$:

$f''(x) = -(x-2)^{-3} + 3(x+2)(x-2)^{-4} = \dfrac{-(x-2) + 3(x+2)}{(x-2)^4} = \dfrac{2(x+4)}{(x-2)^4}$

Partition numbers for f'': $x = -4$, $x = 2$

Sign chart for f'':

	Test Numbers	
	x	$f''(x)$
	-5	$-\frac{2}{2401}\ (-)$
	0	$\frac{1}{2}\ (+)$
	3	$14\ (+)$

$f''(x)$: $-\ -\ |\ +\ +\ +\ +\ +\ +\ |\ +\ +$ (0 at $x=-4$, ND at $x=2$)

$-5\ -4\qquad 0\quad 2\ 3$

Graph of f : Concave Downward | Concave Upward | Concave Upward

Thus, the graph of f is concave downward on $(-\infty, -4)$, and concave upward on $(-4, 2)$ and on $(2, \infty)$; there is an inflection point at $x = -4$.

Step 4. Sketch the graph of f:

x	$f(x)$
-4	$-\frac{1}{9}$
0	0
1	1
3	3

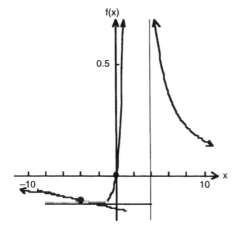

36. $f(x) = \dfrac{3 - 2x}{x^2}$

Step 1. Analyze $f(x)$:

(A) Domain: All real numbers except $x = 0$.

(B) Intercepts: y-intercept: $f(x)$ is not defined at 0.

$$x\text{-intercepts: } \frac{3 - 2x}{x^2} = 0$$

$$x = \frac{3}{2}$$

(C) Asymptotes:

Horizontal asymptote: $\displaystyle\lim_{x \to \infty} \frac{3 - 2x}{x^2} = 0$ and the x axis is a horizontal asymptote.

Vertical asymptote: $D(x) = x^2 = 0$, $x = 0$; i.e. $D(0) = 0$, $N(0) \neq 0$, so the line $x = 0$ (y axis) is a vertical asymptote.

Step 2. Analyze $f'(x)$:

$$f'(x) = \frac{-2x^2 - 2x(3 - 2x)}{x^4} = \frac{-2x^2 - 6x + 4x^2}{x^4} = \frac{2x(x - 3)}{x^4} = \frac{2x(x - 3)}{x^3}$$

Critical values: $x = 3$
Partition numbers: $x = 0$, $x = 3$
Sign chart for f':

Test Numbers	
x	$f'(x)$
-1	$8\ (+)$
1	$-4\ (-)$
4	$\frac{1}{32}\ (+)$

$f'(x)$ $+ \ + $ ND $ - - - - - $ 0 $ + \ +$

$f(x)$ -1 0 1 3 4

Increasing | Decreasing | Increasing

Thus, f is increasing on $(-\infty, 0)$ and on $(3, \infty)$ and decreasing on $(0, 3)$; f has a local minimum at $x = 3$.

Step 3. Analyze $f''(x)$:

$$f''(x) = 2x^{-3} - 6x^{-4}(x - 3) = \frac{2}{x^3} - \frac{6(x - 3)}{x^4} = \frac{2x - 6x + 18}{x^4} = \frac{2(9 - 2x)}{x^4}$$

Partition numbers for f'': $x = 0$, $x = 4.5$

Sign chart for f'':

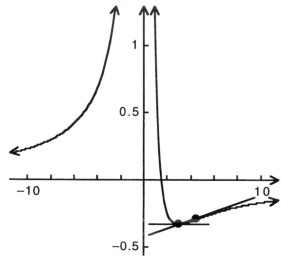

Test Numbers	
x	$f''(x)$
-1	$22\ (+)$
1	$14\ (+)$
5	$-\frac{2}{625}\ (-)$

Thus, the graph of f is concave upward on $(-\infty, 0)$ and $(0, 4.5)$ and concave downward on $(4.5, \infty)$; there is an inflection point at $x = 4.5$.

Step 4. Sketch the graph of f:

x	$f(x)$
-1	5
1	1
5	$-\frac{7}{25}$

38. $f(x) = \dfrac{x^2 - 5x - 6}{x^2}$

Step 1. Analyze $f(x)$:

(A) Domain: All real numbers except $x = 0$.

(B) Intercepts: y-intercept: $f(x)$ is not defined at 0.

$$x\text{-intercept: } \frac{x^2 - 5x - 6}{x^2} = 0$$

$$x^2 - 5x - 6 = (x + 1)(x - 6) = 0$$

$$x = -1,\ x = 6$$

(C) Asymptotes:

Horizontal asymptote: $\displaystyle\lim_{x \to \infty} \frac{x^2 - 5x - 6}{x^2} = 1$ and the line $y = 1$ is a horizontal asymptote.

Vertical asymptote: $D(x) = x^2 = 0$, $x = 0$; i.e. $D(0) = 0$, $N(0) \neq 0$, so the line $x = 0$ (y axis) is a vertical asymptote.

Step 2. Analyze $f'(x)$:

$$f'(x) = \frac{(2x - 5)x^2 - 2x(x^2 - 5x - 6)}{x^4} = \frac{2x^3 - 5x^2 - 2x^3 + 10x^2 + 12x}{x^4}$$

$$= \frac{5x^2 + 12x}{x^4} = \frac{5x + 12}{x^3}$$

Critical values: $x = -\dfrac{12}{5}$

Partition numbers: $x = -\dfrac{12}{5}$, $x = 0$

Sign chart for f':

	Test Numbers	
	x	$f'(x)$
	-3	$\frac{1}{9}$ (+)
	-1	-7 (−)
	1	17 (+)

$f'(x)$ $+$ $+$ $-$ $-$ $-$ $-$ $+$ $+$ x

$f(x)$ -3 $-\frac{12}{5}$ -1 0 1

Increasing | Decreasing | Increasing

Thus, f is increasing on $\left(-\infty, -\dfrac{12}{5}\right)$ and on $(0, \infty)$ and decreasing on $\left(-\dfrac{12}{5}, 0\right)$; f has a local maximum at $x = -\dfrac{12}{5}$.

Step 3. Analyze $f''(x)$:

$$f''(x) = \frac{5x^3 - 3x^2(5x + 12)}{x^6} = \frac{5x - 3(5x + 12)}{x^4} = \frac{5x - 15x - 36}{x^4}$$
$$= \frac{-2(5x + 18)}{x^4}$$

Partition numbers for f'': $x = -\dfrac{18}{5}$, $x = 0$.

Sign chart for f'':

	Test Numbers	
	x	$f''(x)$
	-4	$\frac{1}{64}$ (+)
	-2	-1 (−)
	1	-46 (−)

$f''(x)$ $+$ $+$ $+$ $-$ $-$ $-$ $-$ $-$ $-$ $-$ x

-4 $-\frac{18}{5}$ -2 0 1

Graph | Concave | Concave | Concave
of f | Upward | Downward | Downward

Thus, the graph of f is concave upward on $\left(-\infty, -\dfrac{18}{5}\right)$ and downward on $\left(-\dfrac{18}{5}, 0\right)$ and on $(0, \infty)$; there is an inflection point at $x = -\dfrac{18}{5}$.

Sketch the graph of f:

x	$f(x)$
-4	$\frac{15}{8}$
-2	8
1	-10
6	0

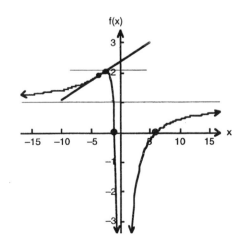

40. $f(x) = \dfrac{x^2}{2 + x}$

Step 1. Analyze $f(x)$:

(A) Domain: All real numbers except $x = -2$.

(B) Intercepts: y-intercept: $f(0) = 0$

$$x\text{-intercepts: } \frac{x^2}{2 + x} = 0$$
$$x = 0$$

(C) Asymptotes:

Horizontal asymptote: $\lim\limits_{x \to \infty} \dfrac{x^2}{2 + x} = \infty$, so there is no horizontal asymptote.

Vertical asymptote: $D(x) = 2 + x = 0$, $x = -2$; i.e. $D(-2) = 0$, $N(-2) \neq 0$, so the line $x = -2$ is a vertical asymptote.

Step 2. Analyze $f'(x)$:

$$f'(x) = \frac{2x(2 + x) - x^2}{(2 + x)^2} = \frac{4x + 2x^2 - x^2}{(2 + x)^2} = \frac{x(4 + x)}{(2 + x)^2}$$

Critical values: $x = -4$, $x = 0$

Partition numbers: $x = -4$, $x = -2$, $x = 0$

Sign chart for f':

Test Numbers	
x	$f'(x)$
-5	$\frac{5}{9}$ (+)
-3	-3 (−)
-1	-3 (−)
1	$\frac{5}{9}$ (+)

Thus, f is increasing on $(-\infty, -4)$ and on $(0, \infty)$ and decreasing on $(-4, -2)$ and on $(-2, 0)$; f has a local maximum at $x = -4$ and a local minimum at $x = 0$.

Step 3. Analyze $f''(x)$:

$$f''(x) = \frac{(4 + 2x)(2 + x)^2 - 2(2 + x)x(4 + x)}{(2 + x)^4} = \frac{(4 + 2x)(2 + x) - 2x(4 + x)}{(2 + x)^3}$$
$$= \frac{8 + 8x + 2x^2 - 8x - 2x^2}{(2 + x)^3}$$
$$= \frac{8}{(2 + x)^3}$$

Partition numbers for f'': $x = -2$

Sign chart for f'':

Test Numbers	
x	$f''(x)$
-3	-8 (−)
1	$\frac{8}{27}$ (+)

Thus, the graph of f is concave downward on $(-\infty, -2)$ and concave upward on $(-2, \infty)$; there are no inflection points.

Step 4. Sketch the graph of f:

x	$f(x)$
-3	-9
0	0
1	$\frac{1}{3}$

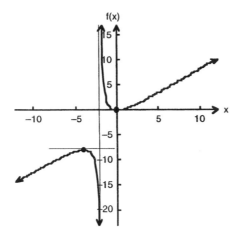

42. $f(x) = \dfrac{2x^2 + 5}{4 - x^2}$

Step 1. Analyze $f(x)$:

(A) Domain: All real numbers except $x = -2$, $x = 2$.

(B) Intercepts: y-intercept: $f(0) = \dfrac{5}{4}$

x-intercepts: None $(2x^2 + 5 > 0)$

(C) Asymptotes:

Horizontal asymptote: $\displaystyle\lim_{x \to \infty} \dfrac{2x^2 + 5}{4 - x^2} = -2$ and the line $y = -2$
is a horizontal asymptote.

Vertical asymptote: $D(x) = 4 - x^2 = 0$, $x = -2$, $x = 2$; i.e.
$D(-2) = D(2) = 0$, $N(-2) \neq 0$, $N(2) \neq 0$, so the lines $x = -2$ and
$x = 2$ are two vertical asymptotes.

Step 2. Analyze $f'(x)$:

$$f'(x) = \dfrac{4x(4 - x^2) + 2x(2x^2 + 5)}{(4 - x^2)^2} = \dfrac{16x - 4x^3 + 4x^3 + 10x}{(4 - x^2)^2} = \dfrac{26x}{(4 - x^2)^2}$$

Critical values: $x = 0$
Partition numbers: $x = -2$, $x = 0$, $x = 2$
Sign chart for f':

```
                ND    0    ND
f'(x)  - - - -¦- - - -¦+ + +¦+ + + +
     ──┼──o──┼──●──┼──o──┼──→ x
f(x)    -3 -2 -1  0  1  2  3
              ¦       ¦
           Decr.¦Decr.¦ Incr.¦ Incr.
```

Test Numbers	
x	$f'(x)$
-3	$-\dfrac{78}{25}$ $(-)$
-1	$-\dfrac{26}{9}$ $(-)$
1	$\dfrac{26}{9}$ $(+)$
3	$\dfrac{78}{25}$ $(+)$

Thus, f is decreasing on $(-\infty, -2)$ and on $(-2, 0)$ and is increasing on
$(0, 2)$ and on $(2, \infty)$; f has a local minimum at $x = 0$.

Step 3. Analyze $f''(x)$:

$$f''(x) = 26(4 - x^2)^{-2} + 4x(4 - 2x^2)^{-3}(26x)$$

$$= \frac{26(4 - x^2) + 4x(26x)}{(4 - x^2)^3} = \frac{104 - 26x^2 + 104x^2}{(4 - x^2)^3} = \frac{78x^2 + 104}{(4 - x^2)^3}$$

Partition numbers for f'': $x = -2$, $x = 2$
Sign chart for f'':

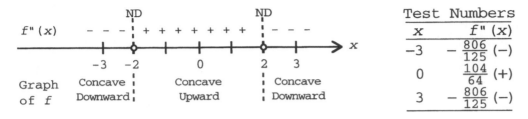

Test Numbers	
x	$f''(x)$
-3	$-\frac{806}{125}$ (−)
0	$\frac{104}{64}$ (+)
3	$-\frac{806}{125}$ (−)

Thus, the graph of f is concave downward on $(-\infty, -2)$ and on $(2, \infty)$ and concave upward on $(-2, 2)$; there are no inflection points.

Step 4. Sketch the graph of f:

x	$f(x)$
-3	$-\frac{23}{5}$
0	$\frac{5}{4}$
3	$-\frac{23}{5}$

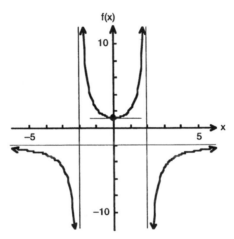

44. $f(x) = \dfrac{x^3}{4 - x}$

Step 1. Analyze $f(x)$:

(A) Domain: All real numbers except $x = 4$.

(B) Intercepts: y-intercept: $f(0) = 0$
   x-intercepts: $x^3 = 0$
   $x = 0$

(C) Asymptotes:

Horizontal asymptote: $\lim\limits_{x \to \infty} \dfrac{x^3}{4 - x} = -\infty$, so there is no horizontal asymptote.

Vertical asymptote: $D(x) = 4 - x = 0$, $x = 4$; i.e. $D(4) = 0$, $N(4) \neq 0$, so the line $x = 4$ is a vertical asymptote.

Step 2. Analyze $f'(x)$:

$$f'(x) = \frac{3x^2(4-x) + x^3}{(4-x)^2} = \frac{12x^2 - 3x^3 + x^3}{(4-x)^2} = \frac{2x^2(6-x)}{(4-x)^2}$$

Critical values: $x = 0$, $x = 6$
Partition numbers: $x = 0$, $x = 4$, $x = 6$
Sign chart for f':

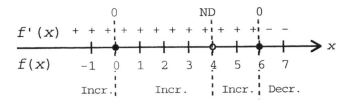

Test Numbers	
x	$f'(x)$
-1	$\frac{14}{25}$ (+)
1	$\frac{10}{9}$ (+)
5	50 (+)
7	$-\frac{98}{9}$ (−)

Thus, f is increasing on $(-\infty, 4)$ and on $(4, 6)$ and decreasing on $(6, \infty)$; f has a local maximum at $x = 6$.

Step 3. Analyze $f''(x)$:

$$f''(x) = (24x - 6x^2)(4-x)^{-2} + 2(4-x)^{-3}(12x^2 - 2x^3)$$
$$= \frac{(24x - 6x^2)(4-x) + 2(12x^2 - 2x^3)}{(4-x)^3} = \frac{2x(x^2 - 12x + 48)}{(4-x)^3}$$

Partition numbers for f'':

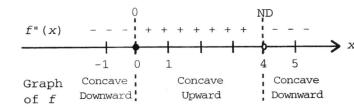

Test Numbers	
x	$f''(x)$
-1	$-\frac{122}{125}$ (−)
1	$\frac{74}{27}$ (+)
5	-26 (−)

Thus, the graph of f is concave downward on $(-\infty, 0)$ and on $(4, \infty)$ and concave upward on $(0, 4)$; there is an inflection point at $x = 0$.

Step 4. Sketch the graph of f:

x	$f(x)$
-1	$-\frac{1}{5}$
1	$\frac{1}{3}$
5	-125

46. $f(x) = \dfrac{1}{3 - 2x - x^2} = \dfrac{1}{(3 + x)(1 - x)}$

<u>Step 1. Analyze $f(x)$</u>:

(A) Domain: All real numbers except $x = -3$, $x = 1$.

(B) Intercepts: y-intercept: $f(0) = \dfrac{1}{3}$

                 x-intercept: None

(C) Asymptotes:

  <u>Horizontal asymptote</u>: $\displaystyle\lim_{x \to \infty} \dfrac{1}{3 - 2x - x^2} = 0$, and x axis is a

  horizontal asymptote.

  <u>Vertical asymptote</u>: $D(x) = (3 + x)(1 - x) = 0$, $x = -3$, $x = 1$,
  i.e. $D(-3) = D(1) = 0$, $N(-3) \neq 0$, $N(1) \neq 0$, so the lines $x = -3$
  and $x = 1$ are two vertical asymptotes.

<u>Step 2. Analyze $f'(x)$</u>:

$f'(x) = \dfrac{2 + 2x}{(3 - 2x - x^2)^2} = \dfrac{2(x + 1)}{(3 - 2x - x^2)^2}$

Critical values: $x = -1$

Partition numbers: $x = -3$, $x = -1$, $x = 1$

Sign chart for f':

Test Numbers	
x	$f'(x)$
-4	$-\frac{6}{25}$ (−)
-2	$-\frac{2}{9}$ (−)
0	$\frac{2}{9}$ (+)
2	$\frac{6}{25}$ (+)

Thus, f is decreasing on $(-\infty, -3)$ and on $(-3, -1)$ and increasing on $(-1, 1)$ and on $(1, \infty)$; f has a local minimum at $x = -1$.

<u>Step 3. Analyze $f''(x)$</u>:

$f''(x) = \dfrac{2(3 - 2x - x^2)^2 - 2(3 - 2x - x^2)(-2 - 2x)[2(x + 1)]}{(3 - 2x - x^2)^4}$

$= \dfrac{2(3 - 2x - x^2) + 8(x + 1)^2}{(3 - 2x - x^2)^3} = \dfrac{6 - 4x - 2x^2 + 8x^2 + 16x + 8}{(3 - 2x - x^2)^3}$

$= \dfrac{2(3x^2 + 6x + 7)}{(3 - 2x - x^2)^3}$

Partition numbers for f'': $x = -3$, $x = 1$

Sign chart for f'':

Test Numbers	
x	$f''(x)$
-4	$-\frac{62}{125}$ (−)
0	$\frac{14}{27}$ (+)
2	$-\frac{62}{125}$ (−)

Thus, the graph of f is concave upward on $(-3, 1)$; concave downward on $(-\infty, -3)$ and on $(1, \infty)$; there are no inflection points.

Step 4. Sketch the graph of f:

x	$f(x)$
-4	$-\frac{1}{5}$
0	$\frac{1}{3}$
-2	$\frac{1}{3}$

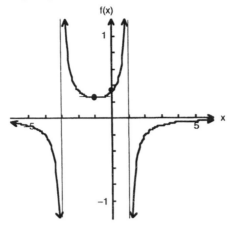

48. $f(x) = \dfrac{x}{x^2 - 36} = \dfrac{x}{(x + 6)(x - 6)}$

Step 1. Analyze $f(x)$:

(A) Domain: All real numbers except $x = -6$, $x = 6$.

(B) Intercepts: y-intercept: $f(0) = 0$

$\qquad\qquad\qquad\quad$ x-intercepts: $x = 0$

(C) Asymptotes:

$\quad$ <u>Horizontal asymptote</u>: $\lim\limits_{x \to \infty} \dfrac{x}{x^2 - 36} = 0$, and x axis is a

$\quad$ horizontal asymptote.

$\quad$ <u>Vertical asymptote</u>: $D(x) = (x + 6)(x - 6)$, $x = -6$, $x = 6$,
$\quad$ i.e. $D(-6) = D(6) = 0$, $N(-6) \neq 0$, $N(6) \neq 0$, so the lines $x = -6$
$\quad$ and $x = 6$ are two vertical asymptotes.

Step 2. Analyze $f'(x)$:

$f'(x) = \dfrac{x^2 - 36 - (2x)x}{(x^2 - 36)^2} = -\dfrac{(x^2 + 36)}{(x^2 - 36)^2}$

Critical values: None
Partition numbers: $x = -6$, $x = 6$
Sign chart for f': $f'(x) < 0$ for x in $D(f)$.

$\qquad\qquad$ ND $\qquad\qquad$ ND
$f'(x)$ - - -:- - - - - - -:- - -
$\qquad$ ———+—○—+——+—+—○—+——→ x
$f(x)$ $\qquad$ -6 $\qquad\qquad$ 6
$\quad$ Decreasing$\vdots$ Decreasing $\vdots$ Decreasing

Test Numbers	
x	$f'(x)$
-6	$(-)$
6	$(-)$

Thus, f is decreasing on $(-\infty, -6)$, on $(-6, 6)$ and on $(6, \infty)$; there are no local extrema.

Step 3. Analyze $f''(x)$:

$f''(x) = -2x(x^2 - 36)^{-2} - (x^2 + 36)(-2)(2x)(x^2 - 36)^{-3}$

$\qquad = \dfrac{-2x(x^2 - 36) - (x^2 + 36)(-2)(2x)}{(x^2 - 36)^3} = \dfrac{2x(x^2 + 103)}{(x^2 - 36)^3}$

Partition numbers for f'': $x = -6$, $x = 0$, $x = 6$

Sign chart for f'':

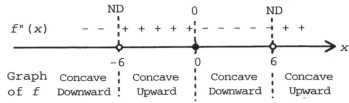

Thus, the graph of f is concave downward on $(-\infty, -6)$ and on $(0, 6)$ and is concave upward on $(-6, 0)$ and on $(6, \infty)$; there is an inflection point at $x = 0$.

Step 4. Sketch the graph of f:

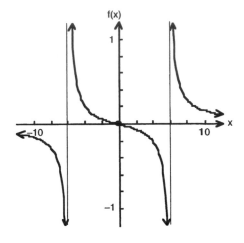

50. $f(x) = \dfrac{x^3}{(x + 2)^2}$

Step 1. Analyze $f(x)$:
(A) Domain: All real numbers except $x = -2$.
(B) Intercepts: y-intercept: $f(0) = 0$
x-intercepts: $x^3 = 0$
$x = 0$

(C) Asymptotes:

Horizontal asymptote: $\lim\limits_{x \to \infty} \dfrac{x^3}{(x + 2)^2} = \infty$, so there are no horizontal asymptotes.

Vertical asymptote: $D(x) = (x + 2)^2 = 0$, $x = -2$, i.e. $D(-2) = 0$, $N(-2) \neq 0$, so the line $x = -2$ is a vertical asymptote.

Step 2. Analyze $f'(x)$:

$$f'(x) = \frac{3x^2(x + 2)^2 - 2(x + 2)x^3}{(x + 2)^4} = \frac{3x^3 + 6x^2 - 2x^3}{(x + 2)^3} = \frac{x^2(x + 6)}{(x + 2)^3}$$

Critical values: $x = -6$, $x = 0$
Partition numbers: $x = -6$, $x = -2$, $x = 0$
Sign chart for f':

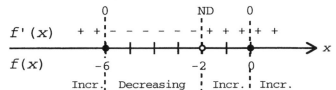

Thus, f is increasing on $(-\infty, -6)$ and on $(-2, \infty)$ and is decreasing on $(-6, -2)$; f has a local maximum at $x = -6$.

Step 3. Analyze $f''(x)$:

$f'(x) = x^2(x + 6)(x + 2)^{-3}$

$f''(x) = 2x(x + 6)(x + 2)^{-3} + x^2(x + 2)^{-3} - 3(x + 2)^{-4}x^2(x + 6)$

$$= \frac{2x(x + 6)(x + 2) + x^2(x + 2) - 3x^2(x + 6)}{(x + 2)^4} = \frac{24x}{(x + 2)^4}$$

Partition numbers for f'': $x = -2$, $x = 0$

Sign chart for f'':

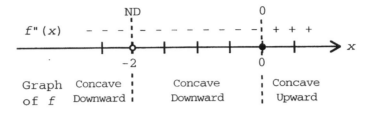

Thus, the graph of f is concave downward on $(-\infty, -2)$ and on $(-2, 0)$ and concave upward on $(0, \infty)$; there is an inflection point at $x = 0$.

Step 4. Sketch the graph of f:

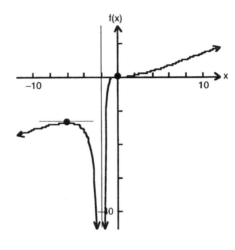

52. $f(x) = \dfrac{x^3}{x^2 - 12} = \dfrac{x^3}{\left(x + 2\sqrt{3}\right)\left(x - 2\sqrt{3}\right)}$

Step 1. Analyze $f(x)$:

(A) Domain: All real numbers except $x = -2\sqrt{3}$, $x = 2\sqrt{3}$.

(B) Intercepts: y-intercept: $f(0) = 0$
                   x-intercept: $x^3 = 0$
                            $x = 0$

(C) Asymptotes:

Horizontal asymptote: $\displaystyle\lim_{x\to\infty} \frac{x^3}{x^2 - 12} = \infty$, so there are no horizontal asymptotes.

Vertical asymptote: $D(x) = x^2 - 12 = 0$, $x = -2\sqrt{3}$, $x = 2\sqrt{3}$, i.e. $D(-2\sqrt{3}) = D(2\sqrt{3}) = 0$, $N(-2\sqrt{3}) \neq 0$, $N(2\sqrt{3}) \neq 0$, so the lines $x = -2\sqrt{3}$ and $x = 2\sqrt{3}$ are two vertical asymptotes.

Step 2. Analyze $f'(x)$:

$$f'(x) = \frac{3x^2(x^2 - 12) - 2x(x^3)}{(x^2 - 12)^2} = \frac{3x^4 - 36x^2 - 2x^4}{(x^2 - 12)^2} = \frac{x^2(x + 6)(x - 6)}{(x^2 - 12)^2}$$

Critical values: $x = -6$, $x = 0$, $x = 6$
Partition numbers: $x = -6$, $x = -2\sqrt{3}$, $x = 0$, $x = 2\sqrt{3}$, $x = 6$

Sign chart for f':

Thus, f is increasing on $(-\infty, -6)$ and on $(6, \infty)$ and is decreasing on $(-6, -2\sqrt{3})$, on $(-2\sqrt{3}, 2\sqrt{3})$ and on $(2\sqrt{3}, 6)$; f has a local maximum at $x = -6$ and a local minimum at $x = 6$.

<u>Step 3. Analyze $f''(x)$</u>:

$$f'(x) = (x^4 - 36x^2)(x^2 - 12)^{-2}$$

$$f''(x) = (4x^3 - 72x)(x^2 - 12)^{-2} - 4x(x^2 - 12)^{-3}(x^4 - 36x^2)$$

$$= \frac{(4x^3 - 72x)(x^2 - 12) - 4x(x^4 - 36x^2)}{(x^2 - 12)^3} = \frac{24x(x^2 + 36)}{(x^2 - 12)^3}$$

Partition numbers for f'': $x = -2\sqrt{3}$, $x = 0$, $x = 2\sqrt{3}$

Sign chart for f'':

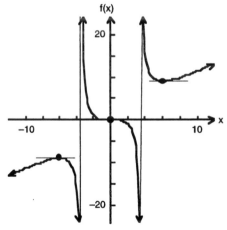

Thus, the graph of f is concave downward on $(-\infty, -2\sqrt{3})$, and on $(0, 2\sqrt{3})$ and is concave upward on $(-2\sqrt{3}, 0)$ and on $(2\sqrt{3}, \infty)$; there is an inflection point at $x = 0$.

<u>Step 4. Sketch the graph of f</u>:

54. $f(x) = x - \dfrac{9}{x}$

For $|x|$ very large, $f(x) = x - \dfrac{9}{x} \approx x$. Thus, the line $y = x$ is an oblique asymptote.

<u>Step 1. Analyze $f(x)$</u>:

(A) Domain: All real numbers except 0.

(B) Intercepts: y-intercept: There is no y-intercept since f is not defined at $x = 0$.

x-intercepts: $x - \dfrac{9}{x} = 0$

$$x^2 - 9 = 0$$
$$(x - 3)(x + 3) = 0$$
$$x = -3, \ 3$$

(C) Asymptotes:
   <u>Oblique asymptote</u>: $y = x$
   <u>Vertical asymptote</u>: $D(x) = x = 0$, $N(0) \neq 0$, so the line $x = 0$ is a
   vertical asymptote.

<u>Step 2. Analyze $f'(x)$</u>:

$$f'(x) = 1 + \frac{9}{x^2} = \frac{x^2 + 9}{x^2}$$

Critical values: None, since $f'(x) > 1$ for all x
Partition numbers: $x = 0$

Sign chart for f':

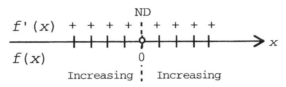

Thus, f is increasing on $(-\infty, 0)$ and on $(0, \infty)$; f has no extrema.

<u>Step 3. Analyze $f''(x)$</u>:

$$f''(x) = -\frac{18}{x^3}$$

Partition numbers for f'': $x = 0$

Sign chart for f'':

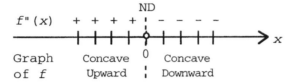

Thus, the graph of f is concave upward on $(-\infty, 0)$ and is concave
downward on $(0, \infty)$; there are no inflection points.

<u>Step 4. Sketch the graph of f</u>:

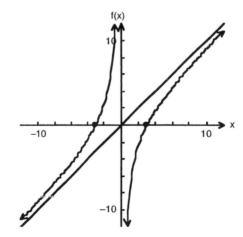

56. $f(x) = x + \dfrac{32}{x^2}$

For $|x|$ very large, $f(x) = x + \dfrac{32}{x^2} \approx x$. Thus, the line $y = x$ is an
oblique asymptote.

<u>Step 1. Analyze $f(x)$</u>:
(A) Domain: All real numbers except 0.

(B) Intercepts: y-intercept: No y-intercept since f is not defined at 0.

x-intercepts: $x + \dfrac{32}{x^2} = 0$

$$x^3 + 32 = 0$$
$$x = -\sqrt[3]{32}$$

(C) Asymptotes:

<u>Oblique asymptote</u>: $y = x$

<u>Vertical asymptote</u>: $D(x) = x^2 = 0$, $x = 0$, $N(0) \neq 0$, so the line $x = 0$ is a vertical asymptote.

<u>Step 2. Analyze $f'(x)$</u>:

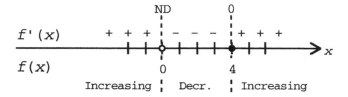

$f'(x) = 1 - \dfrac{64}{x^3} = \dfrac{x^3 - 64}{x^3} = \dfrac{(x - 4)(x^2 - 4x + 16)}{x^3}$

Critical values: $x = 4$

Partition numbers: $x = 4$, $x = 0$

Sign chart for f':

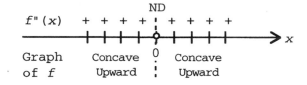

Thus, f is increasing on $(-\infty, 0)$ and on $(4, \infty)$, and is decreasing on $(0, 4)$; f has a local minimum at $x = 4$.

<u>Step 3. Analyze $f''(x)$</u>:

$f''(x) = \dfrac{192}{x^4}$

Partition numbers for f'': $x = 0$

Sign chart for f'':

Thus, the graph of f is concave upward on $(-\infty, 0)$ and on $(0, \infty)$; there are no inflection points.

<u>Step 4. Sketch the graph of f</u>:

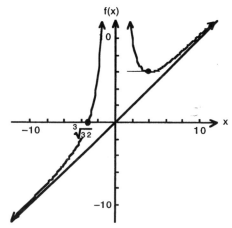

58. $f(x) = x + \dfrac{27}{x^3}$

For $|x|$ very large, $f(x) = x + \dfrac{27}{x^3} \approx x$. Thus, the line $y = x$ is an oblique asymptote.

Step 1. Analyze $f(x)$:

(A) Domain: All real numbers except 0.

(B) Intercepts: y-intercept: No y-intercept since f is not defined at 0.

x-intercept: $x + \dfrac{27}{x^3} = \dfrac{x^4 + 27}{x^3}$, so none

(C) Asymptotes:
Oblique asymptote: $y = x$

Vertical asymptote: $D(x) = x^3 = 0$, $x = 0$, $N(0) \neq 0$, so the line $x = 0$ is a vertical asymptote.

Step 2. Analyze $f'(x)$:

$f'(x) = 1 - \dfrac{81}{x^4} = \dfrac{x^4 - 81}{x^4} = \dfrac{(x - 3)(x + 3)(x^2 + 9)}{x^4}$

Critical values: $x = -3$, $x = 3$
Partition numbers: $x = -3$, $x = 0$, $x = 3$

Sign chart for f':

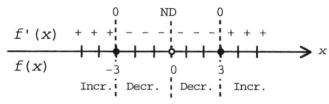

Thus, f is increasing on $(-\infty, -3)$ and on $(3, \infty)$ and is decreasing on $(-3, 0)$ and on $(0, 3)$; f has a local maximum at $x = -3$ and a local minimum at $x = 3$.

Step 3. Analyze $f''(x)$:

$f''(x) = \dfrac{324}{x^5}$

Partition numbers for f'': $x = 0$

Sign chart for f'':

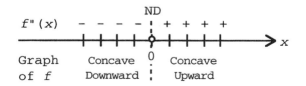

Thus, the graph of f is concave downward on $(-\infty, 0)$ and concave upward on $(0, \infty)$; there are no inflection points.

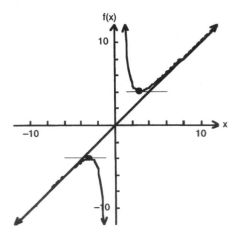

60. $f(x) = x - \dfrac{16}{x^3}$

For $|x|$ very large, $f(x) = x - \dfrac{16}{x^3} \approx x$. Thus, the line $y = x$ is an oblique asymptote.

Step 1. Analyze $f(x)$:

(A) Domain: All real numbers except 0.

(B) Intercepts: y-intercept: No y-intercept since f is not defined at 0.

$$x\text{-intercept:} \quad \frac{x^4 - 16}{x^3} = 0, \quad x = -2, \quad x = 2$$

(C) Asymptotes:

  Oblique asymptote: $y = x$

  Vertical asymptote: $D(x) = x^3 = 0$, $x = 0$; $N(0) \neq 0$, so the line $x = 0$ is a vertical asymptote.

Step 2. Analyze $f'(x)$:

$$f'(x) = 1 + \frac{48}{x^4} = \frac{x^4 + 48}{x^4}$$

Critical values: none

Partition number: $x = 0$

Sign chart for f':

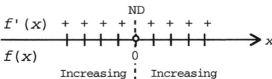

Thus, f is increasing on $(-\infty, 0)$ and on $(0, \infty)$; f has no local extrema.

Step 3. Analyze $f''(x)$:

$$f''(x) = -\frac{192}{x^5}$$

Partition numbers for f'': $x = 0$

Sign chart for f'':

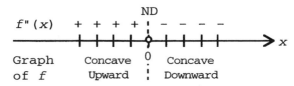

Thus, the graph of f is concave upward on $(-\infty, 0)$ and is concave downward on $(0, \infty)$; there are no inflection points.

Step 4. Sketch the graph of f:

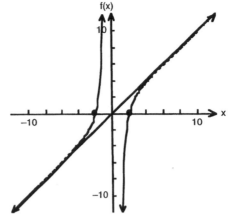

62. $f(x) = \dfrac{x^2 + x - 6}{x^2 - x - 12} = \dfrac{(x + 3)(x - 2)}{(x - 4)(x + 3)}$

Step 1. Analyze $f(x)$:

(A) Domain: All real numbers except $x = -3$, $x = 4$.

(B) Intercepts: y-intercept: $f(0) = \dfrac{-6}{-12} = \dfrac{1}{2}$

x-intercept: $x = 2$

(C) Asymptotes:

Horizontal asymptote: $\lim\limits_{x \to \infty} \dfrac{x^2 + x - 6}{x^2 - x - 12} = 1$, so the line $y = 1$ is a horizontal asymptote.

Vertical asymptote: $D(x) = (x - 4)(x + 3) = 0$, $x = -3$, $x = 4$, $D(-3) = D(4) = 0$, $N(-3) = 0$, $N(4) \neq 0$. So the line $x = 4$ is a vertical asymptote and we have to investigate the behavior of the function at $x = -3$.

$\lim\limits_{x \to -3} f(x) = \lim\limits_{x \to -3} \dfrac{(x + 3)(x - 2)}{(x - 4)(x + 3)} = \lim\limits_{x \to -3} \dfrac{x - 2}{x - 4} = \dfrac{5}{7}$

Since the limit exists as x approaches -3, f does not have a vertical asymptote at $x = -3$.

Step 2. Analyze $f'(x)$:

$f'(x) = \dfrac{(2x + 1)(x^2 - x - 12) - (2x - 1)(x^2 + x - 6)}{(x^2 - x - 12)^2} = \dfrac{-2(x + 3)^2}{(x + 3)^2(x - 4)^2}$

Thus, f is decreasing on $(-\infty, 4)$ and $(4, \infty)$.

Step 3. Analyze $f''(x)$:

$f''(x) =$

$\dfrac{-4(x + 3)[(x + 3)^2(x - 4)^2] - [2(x + 3)(x - 4)^2 + 2(x + 3)^2(x - 4)](-2(x + 3)^2)}{(x + 3)^4(x - 4)^4}$

$= \dfrac{-4(x + 3)^3(x - 4)^2 + 4(x + 3)^3(x - 4)^2 + 4(x + 3)^4(x - 4)}{(x + 3)^4(x - 4)^4}$

$= \dfrac{4(x + 3)^4(x - 4)}{(x + 3)^4(x - 4)^4}$

Partition numbers for f'': $x = -4$

Sign chart for f'':

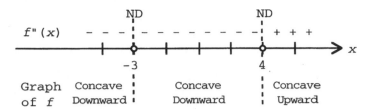

Thus, the graph of f is concave downward on $(-\infty, 4)$ and concave upward on $(4, \infty)$; there are no inflection points.

Step 4. Sketch the graph of f:

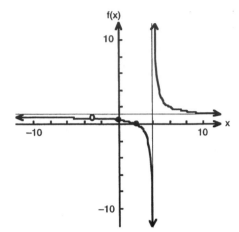

NOTE: We may express f as $f(x) = \dfrac{x - 2}{x - 4}$ for $x \neq -3$ and $x \neq 4$. Then $f'(x) = -\dfrac{2}{(x - 4)^2}$ for $x \neq -3$, $x \neq 4$ and $f''(x) = \dfrac{4}{(x - 4)^3}$ for $x \neq -3$, $x \neq 4$.

64. $f(x) = \dfrac{2x^2 + 11x + 14}{x^2 - 4} = \dfrac{(2x + 7)(x + 2)}{(x - 2)(x + 2)}$

Step 1. Analyze $f(x)$:

(A) Domain: All real numbers except $x = -2$, $x = 2$.

(B) Intercepts: y-intercept: $f(0) = -\dfrac{7}{2}$

x-intercept: $x = -\dfrac{7}{2}$

(C) Asymptotes:

Horizontal asymptote: $\displaystyle \lim_{x \to \infty} \dfrac{2x^2 + 11x + 14}{x^2 - 4} = 2$, so the line $y = 2$ is a horizontal asymptote.

Vertical asymptote: $D(x) = (x - 2)(x + 2) = 0$, $x = 2$, $x = -2$, $D(2) = D(-2) = 0$, $N(2) \neq 0$, $N(-2) = 0$. So, the line $x = 2$ is a vertical asymptote and we have to investigate the behavior of the function at $x = -2$.

$\displaystyle \lim_{x \to -2} f(x) = \lim_{x \to -2} \dfrac{(2x + 7)(x + 2)}{(x - 2)(x + 2)} = \lim_{x \to -2} \dfrac{2x + 7}{x - 2} = -\dfrac{3}{4}$

Since the limit exists as x approaches -2, f does not have a vertical asymptote at $x = -2$.

Step 2. Analyze $f'(x)$:

We can express $f(x)$ for $x \neq -2$ and $x \neq 2$ as $f(x) = \dfrac{2x + 7}{x - 2}$. Thus,

$$f'(x) = \frac{2(x - 2) - (2x + 7)}{(x - 2)^2} = \frac{2x - 4 - 2x - 7}{(x - 2)^2} = \frac{-11}{(x - 2)^2} < 0$$

for all real numbers except $x = -2$ and $x = 2$. Thus, f is decreasing on $(-\infty, 2)$ and on $(2, \infty)$.

Step 3. Analyze $f''(x)$:

$f''(x) = \dfrac{22}{(x - 2)^3}$ for $x \neq -2$ and $x \neq 2$. Thus, $f''(x) < 0$ on $(-\infty, 2)$ and $f''(x) > 0$ on $(2, \infty)$. The function f is concave downward on $(-\infty, 2)$ and concave upward on $(2, \infty)$.

Step 4. Sketch the graph of f:

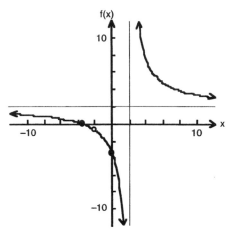

66. $f(x) = \dfrac{x^3 - 5x^2 - 6x}{x^2 + 3x + 2} = \dfrac{x(x^2 - 5x - 6)}{(x + 1)(x + 2)} = \dfrac{x(x - 6)(x + 1)}{(x + 1)(x + 2)}$

Step 1. Analyze $f(x)$:

(A) Domain: All real numbers except $x = -2$, $x = -1$.

(B) Intercepts: y-intercept: $f(0) = 0$
    x-intercepts: $x = 0$, $x = 6$

(C) Asymptotes:
    Horizontal asymptotes: None

    Vertical asymptotes: $D(x) = (x + 1)(x + 2) = 0$, $x = -1$, $x = -2$, $D(-1) = 0$, $D(-2) = 0$, $N(-1) = 0$, $N(-2) \neq 0$. So the line $x = -2$ is a vertical asymptote. Since

    $$\lim_{x \to -1} f(x) = \lim_{x \to -1} \frac{x(x - 6)}{x + 2} = 7, \quad f \text{ does not have a vertical asymptote}$$
    at $x = -1$.

<u>Step 2. Analyze $f'(x)$:</u>

We may express $f(x)$ for $x \neq -2$ and $x \neq -1$ as $f(x) = \dfrac{x(x-6)}{x+2}$. Thus,

$$f'(x) = \frac{(2x-6)(x+2) - x(x-6)}{(x+2)^2} = \frac{2x^2 - 2x - 12 - x^2 + 6x}{(x+2)^2} = \frac{(x+6)(x-2)}{(x+2)^2}$$

Sign chart for $f'(x)$:

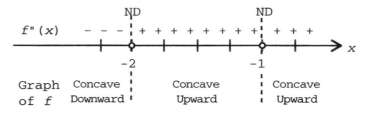

Thus, f is increasing on $(-\infty, -6)$ and $(2, \infty)$ and is decreasing on $(-6, -2)$ and $(-2, 2)$. The function f has a local maximum at $x = -6$ and a local minimum at $x = 2$.

<u>Step 3. Analyze $f''(x)$:</u>

$$f''(x) = \frac{(2x+4)(x+2)^2 - 2(x+2)(x+6)(x-2)}{(x+2)^4}$$

$$= \frac{(2x+4)(x+2) - 2(x+6)(x-2)}{(x+2)^3} = \frac{2x^2 + 8x + 8 - 2x^2 - 8x + 24}{(x+2)^3}$$

$$= \frac{32}{(x+2)^3} \quad \text{for } x \neq -2, \ x \neq -1$$

Partition number for f'': $x = -2$

Sign chart for f'':

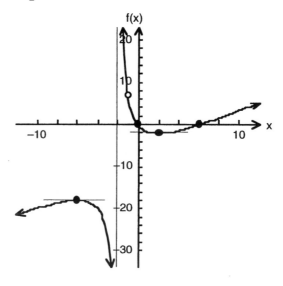

Thus, the graph of f is concave downward on $(-\infty, -2)$ and concave upward on $(-2, \infty)$. There are no inflection points.

<u>Step 4. Sketch the graph of f:</u>

68. $f(x) = \dfrac{x^2 + x - 2}{x^2 + 4x + 4} = \dfrac{(x + 2)(x - 1)}{(x + 2)^2}$

Step 1. Analyze $f(x)$:

(A) Domain: All real numbers except $x = -2$.

(B) Intercepts: y-intercept $f(0) = -\dfrac{1}{2}$

x-intercepts: $x = 1$

(C) Asymptotes:

<u>Horizontal asymptote</u>: $\lim\limits_{x \to \infty} f(x) = \lim\limits_{x \to \infty} \dfrac{x^2 + x - 2}{x^2 + 4x + 4} = 1$, thus, the line $y = 1$ is a horizontal asymptote.

<u>Vertical asymptotes</u>: $D(x) = (x + 2)^2 = 0$, $x = -2$, $D(-2) = 0$, $N(-2) = 0$. Since $\lim\limits_{x \to -2} f(x) = \lim\limits_{x \to -2} \dfrac{(x + 2)(x - 1)}{(x + 2)^2} = \lim\limits_{x \to -2} \dfrac{x - 1}{x + 2} = \pm\infty$

Thus, the line $x = -2$ is a vertical asymptote.

Step 2. Analyze $f'(x)$:

We may express $f(x)$ for $x \neq -2$ as

$f(x) = \dfrac{x - 1}{x + 2}$

$f'(x) = \dfrac{x + 2 - (x - 1)}{(x + 2)^2} = \dfrac{4}{(x + 2)^2} > 0$ for all real numbers except $x = -2$. Thus, f is increasing on $(-\infty, -2)$ and $(-2, \infty)$.

Step 3. Analyze $f''(x)$:

$f''(x) = \dfrac{-8}{(x + 2)^3}$

Partition point for f'': $x = -2$

Sign chart for f'':

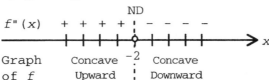

		ND	
$f''(x)$	+ + + +		– – – –

Graph	Concave	-2	Concave
of f	Upward		Downward

Step 4. Sketch the graph of f:

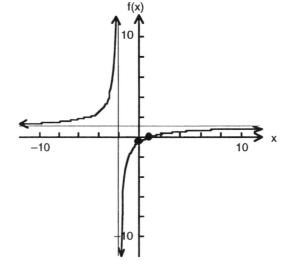

70. (A) $P(x) = R(x) - C(x) = 1,296x - 0.12x^3 - (830 + 396x)$
$$= 900x - 0.12x^3 - 830, \quad 0 \le x \le 80$$

(B) <u>Step 1.</u> <u>Analyze $P(x)$:</u>
    (A) Domain: [0, 80]
    (B) Intercepts: There are no intercepts on [0, 80].
    (C) Asymptotes: $P(x)$ is a polynomial and hence no asymptotes.

<u>Step 2.</u> <u>Analyze $P'(x)$:</u>

$P'(x) = -0.36x^2 + 900$
Critical values: [on [0, 80]]: $x = 50$
Partition number: $x = 50$
Sign chart for P':

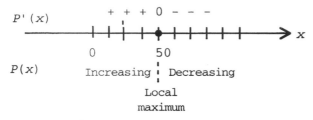

Test Numbers	
x	$P'(x)$
1	899.64 (+)
51	−36.36 (−)

Thus, $P(x)$ is increasing on (0, 50) and decreasing on (50, 80), P has a local maximum at $x = 50$.

<u>Step 3.</u> <u>Analyze $P''(x)$:</u>
$P''(x) = -0.72x < 0$ for $0 < x < 80$
Thus, the graph of P is concave downward on (0, 80).

<u>Step 4.</u> <u>Sketch the graph of P:</u>

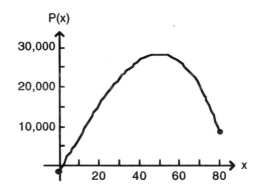

72. $N(t) = \dfrac{100t}{t + 9}, \quad t \ge 0$

(A) $N'(t) = \dfrac{100(t + 9) - 100t}{(t + 9)^2} = \dfrac{900}{(t + 9)^2}$

    $N'(t) > 0$ for $t \ge 0$. Thus, N is increasing on (0, ∞).

(B) From (A), $N'(t) = 900(t + 9)^{-2}$. Thus,
    $N''(t) = -1,800(t + 9)^{-3} = \dfrac{1,800}{(t + 9)^3}$.

    $N''(t) < 0$ for $t \ge 0$, and the graph of N is concave downward on (0, ∞).

(C) $\lim\limits_{t \to \infty} N(t) = 100$, thus $y = 100$ is a horizontal asymptote. There are no vertical asymptotes on (0, ∞).

(D) y-intercept: $N(0) = 0$
    x-intercept: $N(t) = 0$, $t = 0$
    Thus, (0, 0) is both an x and a y-intercept of the graph.

(E) The graph is:

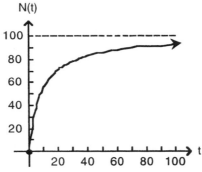

74. $L(x) = 2x + \dfrac{20,000}{x}, \quad x > 0$

(A) Step 1. Analyze $L(x)$:

(A_1) Domain: $x > 0$ or $(0, \infty)$

(B_1) Intercepts: No y-intercept

No x-intercepts

(C_1) Asymptotes: For very large x, $L(x) \approx 2x$. Thus, $y = 2x$ is an oblique asymptote. As $x \to 0$, $L(x) \to \infty$; thus, $x = 0$ is a vertical asymptote.

Step 2. Analyze $L'(x)$:

$$L'(X) = 2 - \frac{20,000}{x^2} = \frac{2x^2 - 20,000}{x^2}$$

Critical value: $x = 100$

Sign chart for $L'(x)$:

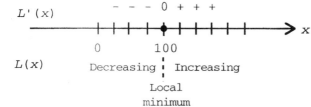

Test Numbers	
x	$L'(x)$
99	−398 (−)
101	402 (+)

Thus, L is decreasing on $(0, 100)$ and increasing on $(100, \infty)$; $x = 100$ is a local minimum.

Step 3. Analyze $L''(x)$:

$$L''(x) = \frac{40,000}{x^3}, \quad x > 0$$

$L''(x) > 0$ on $(0, \infty)$. Thus, the graph of L is concave upward on $(0, \infty)$.

Step 4. Sketch the graph of L:

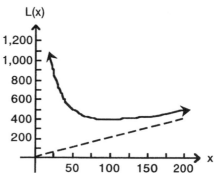

(B) 100' by 200', with the longest side parallel to the building.

76. $C(x) = 500 + 2x + 0.2x^2$, $0 < x < \infty$.

    (A) The average cost function is: $\overline{C}(x) = \dfrac{500}{x} + 2 + 0.2x$.

        Now, $\overline{C}'(x) = -\dfrac{500}{x^2} + 0.2 = \dfrac{-500 + 0.2x^2}{x^2}$

$$= \dfrac{0.2(x^2 - 2,500)}{x^2}$$

$$= \dfrac{0.2(x - 50)(x + 50)}{x^2}$$

        Critical value: $x = 50$ [in $(0, \infty)$]
        Sign chart for $\overline{C}'$:

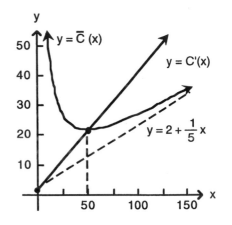

Test Numbers	
x	$\overline{C}'(x)$
49	$(-)$
51	$(+)$

$\overline{C}'(x)$ $- - - \; 0 \; + + +$

$\overline{C}(x)$ Decreasing | Increasing

           Local
          minimum

Thus, $\overline{C}$ is decreasing on $(0, 50)$ and increasing on $(50, \infty)$; $\overline{C}$ has a minimum at $x = 50$.

Since $\overline{C}''(x) = \dfrac{1,000}{x^3} > 0$ for $0 < x < \infty$, the graph of $\overline{C}$ is concave upward on $(0, \infty)$. The line $x = 0$ is a vertical asymptote and the line $y = 2 + 0.2x$ is an oblique asymptote for the graph of $\overline{C}$.

    (B) The minimum average cost is:

$$\overline{C}(50) = \dfrac{500}{50} + 2 + (0.2) = 22$$

78. (A)

```
QuadReg
y=ax²+bx+c
a=.0173928571
b=1.1725
c=489.5
```

    (B) The average cost function $\overline{y}(x) = \dfrac{y(x)}{x}$ where $y(x)$ is the regression equation found in part (A). The minimum average cost is \$7.01 when 168 pizzas are produced daily.

80. $S(w) = \dfrac{26 + 0.06w}{w}$, $w \geq 5$

Step 1.   Analyze $S(w)$:
(A) Domain: $w \geq 5$, i.e., $[5, \infty)$
(B) Intercepts: None on $[5, \infty)$
(C) Asymptotes: Horizontal asymptote: $y = 0.06$
                  Vertical asymptote: $x = 0$ (y axis)

Step 2.   Analyze $S'(w)$:

$$S(w) = \dfrac{26}{w} + 0.06 = 26w^{-1} + 0.06$$

$$S'(w) = -26w^{-2} = -\dfrac{26}{w^2} < 0 \text{ for } w \geq 5$$

Thus, $S(w)$ is decreasing on $[5, \infty)$.

Step 3. Analyze $S''(w)$:

$$S''(w) = 52w^{-3} = \frac{52}{w^3} > 0 \text{ for } w \geq 5$$

Thus, S is concave upward on $[5, \infty)$.

Step 4. Sketch the graph of S:

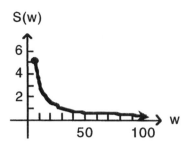

EXERCISE 4-4

2. Interval $[2, 8]$; absolute minimum: $f(7) = 5$;
absolute maximum: $f(3) = 9$

4. Interval $[2, 10]$; absolute minimum: $f(7) = 5$;
absolute maximum: $f(10) = 14$

6. Interval $[0, 9]$; absolute minimum: $f(0) = 0$;
absolute maximum: $f(3) = f(9) = 9$

8. Interval $[0, 2]$; absolute minimum: $f(0) = 0$;
absolute maximum: $f(2) = 8$

10. Interval $[5, 8]$; absolute minimum: $f(7) = 5$
absolute maximum: $f(5) = 7$

12. $f(x) = x^2 + 4x - 3$, $I = (-\infty, \infty)$
$f'(x) = 2x + 4 = 2(x + 2)$
$x = -2$ is the only critical value on I and $f(-2) = -7$.
$f''(x) = 2$
$f''(-7) = 2 > 0$. Therefore, $f(-2) = -7$ is absolute minimum. The function does not have an absolute maximum.

14. $f(x) = -x^2 + 2x + 4$, $I = (-\infty, \infty)$
$f'(x) = -2x + 2 = -2(x - 1)$
$x = 1$ is the only critical value on I and $f(1) = 5$.
$f''(x) = -2$
$f''(1) = -2 < 0$. Thus, $f(1) = 5$ is absolute maximum. The function does not have an absolute minimum.

16. $f(x) = -x^3 - 2x$, $I = (-\infty, \infty)$
$f'(x) = -3x^2 - 2 < 0$ for all x, i.e. no critical values.
Therefore, the function f is decreasing on I, and there are no extrema.

18. $f(x) = x^4 - 4x^3$, $I = (-\infty, \infty)$
$f'(x) = 4x^3 - 12x^2 = 4x^2(x - 3)$
$x = 0$ and $x = 3$ are critical values on I and $f(0) = 0$,
$f(3) = -27$
$f''(x) = 12x^2 - 24x = 12x(x - 2)$
$f''(0) = 0$, $f''(3) = 36 > 0$. Therefore, $f(3) = -27$ is absolute minimum.
The function does not have an absolute maximum.

20. $f(x) = x + \dfrac{25}{x}$, $I = (-\infty, 0) \cup (0, \infty)$

$f'(x) = 1 - \dfrac{25}{x^2} = \dfrac{x^2 - 25}{x^2} = \dfrac{(x - 5)(x + 5)}{x^2}$

Critical values: $x = -5$, $x = 5$, and $f(-5) = -10$, $f(5) = 10$
The function does not have absolute minimum or absolute maximum on I.

22. $f(x) = \dfrac{1}{x^2 + 1}$, $I = (-\infty, \infty)$

$f'(x) = -\dfrac{2x}{(x^2 + 1)^2}$

$x = 0$ is the only critical value on I and $f(0) = 1$.

$f''(x) = \dfrac{-2(x^2 + 1)^2 + 8x^2(x^2 + 1)}{(x^2 + 1)^4} = \dfrac{-2(x^2 + 1)^2 + 8x^2}{(x^2 + 1)^3} = \dfrac{6x^2 - 2}{(x^2 + 1)^3}$

$f''(0) = -2 < 0$. Therefore, $f(0) = 1$ is absolute maximum. The function does not have an absolute minimum.

24. $f(x) = \dfrac{-8x}{x^2 + 4}$, $I = (-\infty, \infty)$

$f'(x) = \dfrac{-8(x^2 + 4) + 16x^2}{(x^2 + 4)^2} = \dfrac{8(x^2 - 4)}{(x^2 + 4)^2} = \dfrac{8(x - 2)(x + 2)}{(x^2 + 4)^2}$

Critical values: $x = -2$, $x = 2$, and $f(-2) = 2$, $f(2) = -2$.
$\lim\limits_{x \to -\infty} f(x) = \lim\limits_{x \to \infty} f(x) = 0$, therefore, $f(-2) = 2$ is absolute maximum and
$f(2) = -2$ is absolute minimum for f.

26. $f(x) = \dfrac{9 - x^2}{x^2 + 4}$, $I = (-\infty, \infty)$

$f'(x) = \dfrac{-2x(x^2 + 4) - 2x(9 - x^2)}{(x^2 + 4)^2} = \dfrac{-2x^3 - 8x - 18x + 2x^3}{(x^2 + 4)^2} = \dfrac{-26x}{(x^2 + 4)^2}$

$x = 0$ is the only critical value on I and $f(0) = \dfrac{9}{4}$.

$f''(x) = \dfrac{26(3x^2 - 4)}{(x^2 + 4)^3}$ and $f''(0) = -\dfrac{13}{8} < 0$.

$\lim\limits_{x \to -\infty} f(x) = \lim\limits_{x \to \infty} f(x) = -1$, therefore, $f(0) = \dfrac{9}{4}$ is absolute maximum.

28. $f(x) = 6x - x^2 + 4$, $I = [0, \infty)$
$f'(x) = 6 - 2x = 2(3 - x)$
$x = 3$ is the only critical value on I and $f(3) = 13$. Also, $f(0) = 4$.
$f''(x) = -2$
$f''(3) = -2 < 0$. Therefore, $f(3) = 13$ is absolute maximum.

30. $f(x) = x^3 - 6x^2$, $I = [0, \infty)$
$f'(x) = 3x^2 - 12x = 3x(x - 4)$
Critical values: $x = 0$, $x = 4$ and $f(0) = 0$, $f(4) = -32$.
$f''(x) = 6x - 12 = 6(x - 2)$
$f''(0) = -12 < 0$, $f''(4) = 12 > 0$. Therefore, $f(4) = -32$ is absolute minimum.

32. $f(x) = (2 - x)(x + 1)^2$, $I = [0, \infty)$

$f'(x) = -(x + 1)^2 + 2(2 - x)(x + 1) = (x + 1)[2(2 - x) - (x + 1)]$
$$= (x + 1)[3(1 - x)]$$
$$= 3(x + 1)(1 - x)$$

Critical values: $x = -1$, $x = 1$ and $f(-1) = 0$, $f(1) = 4$.
Also, $f(0) = 2$ and $\lim_{x \to \infty} f(x) = -\infty$. Therefore, f does not have an absolute minimum.

34. $f(x) = 4x^3 - 8x^4$, $I = (0, \infty)$

$f'(x) = 12x^2 - 32x^3 = 4x^2(3 - 8x)$

Critical value: $x = \dfrac{3}{8}$ [Note: $x = 0$ is not a critical value, since the domain of f is $x > 0$.]

$f''(x) = 24x - 96x^2$
$$= 24x(1 - 4x)$$

$f''\left(\dfrac{3}{8}\right) = -\dfrac{9}{2} < 0$. Therefore, the absolute maximum of f is $f\left(\dfrac{3}{8}\right) = \dfrac{27}{512}$.

36. $f(x) = 4 + x + \dfrac{9}{x}$, $x > 0$

$f'(x) = 1 - \dfrac{9}{x^2} = \dfrac{x^2 - 9}{x^2} = \dfrac{(x - 3)(x + 3)}{x^2}$

critical value: $x = 3$ [Note: $x = -3$ is not a critical value, since the domain of f is $x > 0$.]

$f''(x) = \dfrac{18}{x^3} > 0$. Thus, the absolute minimum of f is $f(3) = 10$.

38. $f(x) = 20 - 4x - \dfrac{250}{x^2}$, $x > 0$

$f'(x) = -4 + \dfrac{500}{x^3} = \dfrac{-4x^3 + 500}{x^3} = \dfrac{-4(x^3 - 125)}{x^3}$

critical value: $x = 5$

$f''(x) = -\dfrac{1,500}{x^4} < 0$. Thus, the absolute maximum of f is $f(5) = -10$.

40. $f(x) = 2x - \dfrac{5}{x} + \dfrac{4}{x^3}$, $I = (0, \infty)$

$f'(x) = 2 + \dfrac{5}{x^2} - \dfrac{12}{x^4} = \dfrac{2x^4 + 5x^2 - 12}{x^4} = \dfrac{2(x^2 + 4)\left(x^2 - \dfrac{3}{2}\right)}{x^4}$

$$= \dfrac{2(x^2 + 4)\left(x - \sqrt{\dfrac{3}{2}}\right)\left(x + \sqrt{\dfrac{3}{2}}\right)}{x^4}$$

Critical value: $x = \sqrt{\dfrac{3}{2}}$ $\left(x = -\sqrt{\dfrac{3}{2}}\text{is not in the domain of } f.\right)$

$f''(x) = -\dfrac{10}{x^3} + \dfrac{48}{x^5}$

$$f''\left(\sqrt{\frac{3}{2}}\right) = -\frac{10}{\frac{3}{2}\sqrt{\frac{3}{2}}} + \frac{48}{\frac{9}{4}\sqrt{\frac{3}{2}}} = -\frac{40}{9}\sqrt{\frac{3}{2}} + \frac{128}{9}\sqrt{\frac{3}{2}} = \frac{88}{9}\sqrt{\frac{3}{2}} > 0.$$

Thus, the absolute minimum of f is $f\left(\sqrt{\frac{3}{2}}\right) = \frac{4}{9}\sqrt{\frac{3}{2}} \approx 0.544$

42. $f(x) = 2x^3 - 3x^2 - 12x + 24$
$f'(x) = 6x^2 - 6x - 12 = 6(x^2 - x - 2) = 6(x - 2)(x + 1)$
critical values: $x = -1, 2$

(A) On the interval $[-3, 4]$: $f(-3) = -21$
$\qquad\qquad\qquad\qquad\qquad f(-1) = 31$
$\qquad\qquad\qquad\qquad\qquad\quad f(2) = 4$
$\qquad\qquad\qquad\qquad\qquad\quad f(4) = 56$
Thus, the absolute maximum of f is $f(4) = 56$, and the absolute minimum of f is $f(-3) = -21$.

(B) On the interval $[-2, 3]$: $f(-2) = 20$
$\qquad\qquad\qquad\qquad\qquad f(-1) = 31$
$\qquad\qquad\qquad\qquad\qquad\quad f(2) = 4$
$\qquad\qquad\qquad\qquad\qquad\quad f(3) = 15$
Absolute maximum of f: $f(-1) = 31$
Absolute minimum of f: $\quad f(2) = 4$

(C) On the interval $[-2, 1]$: $f(-2) = 20$
$\qquad\qquad\qquad\qquad\qquad f(-1) = 31$
$\qquad\qquad\qquad\qquad\qquad\quad f(1) = 11$
Absolute maximum of f: $f(-1) = 31$
Absolute minimum of f: $\quad f(1) = 11$

44. $f(x) = x^4 - 8x^2 + 16$
$f'(x) = 4x^3 - 16x = 4x(x^2 - 4)$
$\qquad\qquad\quad\; = 4x(x - 2)(x + 2)$
critical values: $x = -2, 0, 2$

(A) On the interval $[-1, 3]$: $f(-1) = 9$
$\qquad\qquad\qquad\qquad\qquad\; f(0) = 16$
$\qquad\qquad\qquad\qquad\qquad\; f(2) = 0$
$\qquad\qquad\qquad\qquad\qquad\; f(3) = 25$

Absolute maximum of f: $f(3) = 25$
Absolute minimum of f: $f(2) = 0$

(B) On the interval $[0, 2]$: $f(0) = 16$
$\qquad\qquad\qquad\qquad\qquad f(2) = 0$

Absolute maximum of f: $f(0) = 16$
Absolute minimum of f: $f(2) = 0$

(C) On the interval $[-3, 4]$: $f(-3) = 25$
$\qquad\qquad\qquad\qquad\qquad\; f(-2) = 0$
$\qquad\qquad\qquad\qquad\qquad\;\; f(0) = 16$
$\qquad\qquad\qquad\qquad\qquad\;\; f(2) = 0$
$\qquad\qquad\qquad\qquad\qquad\;\; f(4) = 144$

Absolute maximum of f: $f(4) = 144$
Absolute minimum of f: $f(-2) = f(2) = 0$

46. $f(x) = x^4 - 18x^2 + 32$

$f'(x) = 4x^3 - 36x = 4x(x^2 - 9)$
$= 4x(x - 3)(x + 3)$

Critical values: $x = -3$, $x = 0$, $x = 3$

(A) On the interval $[-4, 4]$: $f(-4) = 0$
$f(-3) = -49$
$f(0) = 32$
$f(3) = -49$
$f(4) = 0$

Absolute maximum of f: $f(0) = 32$
Absolute minimum of f: $f(-3) = f(3) = -49$

(B) On the interval $[-1, 1]$: $f(-1) = 15$
$f(0) = 32$
$f(1) = 15$

Absolute maximum of f: $f(0) = 32$
Absolute minimum of f: $f(-1) = f(1) = 15$

(C) On the interval $[1, 3]$: $f(1) = 15$
$f(3) = -49$

Absolute maximum of f: $f(1) = 15$
Absolute minimum of f: $f(3) = -49$

48. Neither a local maximum nor a local minimum at $x = 4$; $x = 4$ is not a critical value.

50. f has a local maximum at $x = -1$.

52. Unable to determine from the information given.

54. f has a local minimum at $x = 1$.

EXERCISE 4-5
_____

2. Let x be that quantity. Then we like to find the maximum value of
$f(x) = (5 + x)(5 - x)$.
$f(x) = 25 - x^2$
$f'(x) = -2x$
critical value: $x = 0$
$f'(x) > 0$ for $x < 0$ and $f'(x) < 0$ for $x > 0$.
Thus, f is increasing for $x < 0$ and decreasing for $x > 0$. Therefore, the maximum occurs at $x = 0$, which is $f(0) = 25$.

4. Let one number $= x$. Then the other number $= 60 - x$. Since both have to be positive, we must have $x > 0$ and $60 - x > 0$ or $60 > x$,
i.e. $0 < x < 60$.
Let $f(x) = x(60 - x) = 60x - x^2$
$f'(x) = 60 - 2x = 2(30 - x)$
critical value: $x = 30$
$f''(x) = -2 < 0$
Thus, the function f has its maximum at $x = 30$. Thus each number must be 30.

6. Let x be the length and y be the width. Then $xy = 225$ and $y = \dfrac{225}{x}$,

and the perimeter is $2(x + y) = 2\left(x + \dfrac{225}{x}\right)$.

Let $f(x) = 2\left(x + \dfrac{225}{x}\right)$ and minimize f.

$f'(x) = 2 - \dfrac{450}{x^2} = \dfrac{2x^2 - 450}{x^2} = \dfrac{2(x^2 - 225)}{x^2} = \dfrac{2(x - 15)(x + 15)}{x^2}$

critical value: $x = 15$

$f''(x) = \dfrac{900}{x^3} > 0$ for $x > 0$.

Thus, the least perimeter occurs when $x = 15$, $y = \dfrac{225}{15} = 15$. Therefore, we will have a square of side 15 cm; minimum perimeter = 60 cm.

8. Let the rectangle of fixed area A have dimensions x and y.

Then $A = xy$ and $y = \dfrac{A}{x}$. The cost of the fence is

$C = 2Bx + 2By = 2Bx + \dfrac{2AB}{x}$, $x > 0$

Thus, we want to find the absolute maximum of

$C(x) = 2Bx + \dfrac{2AB}{x}$, $x > 0$

Since $\lim\limits_{x \to 0} C(x) = \infty$, this problem does not have a solution.

10. Let x and y be the dimensions of the rectangle and let C be the fixed amount which can be spent. Then

$C = 2Bx + 2By$ and $y = \dfrac{C - 2Bx}{2B}$

The area enclosed by the fence is:

$A = xy = x\left[\dfrac{C - 2Bx}{2B}\right]$

Thus, we want to find the absolute minimum value of

$A(x) = \dfrac{C}{2B}x - x^2$, $0 \le x \le \dfrac{C}{2B}$

Since A is continuous on the closed interval $\left[0, \dfrac{C}{2B}\right]$, it has an absolute minimum value

$A'(x) = \dfrac{C}{2B} - 2x$

critical value: $x = \dfrac{C}{4B}$

$A(0) = 0$, $A\left(\dfrac{C}{4B}\right) = \left(\dfrac{C}{2B}\right)\left(\dfrac{C}{4B}\right) - \left(\dfrac{C}{4B}\right)^2 = \left(\dfrac{C}{4B}\right)^2$

$A\left(\dfrac{C}{2B}\right) = \left(\dfrac{C}{2B}\right)\left(\dfrac{C}{2B}\right) - \left(\dfrac{C}{2B}\right)^2 = 0$

Thus, the absolute minimum of $A = 0$ at $x = 0$ and $x = \dfrac{C}{2B}$.

12. (A) Revenue $R(x) = x \cdot p(x) = x(400 - 0.4x)$
$$= 400x - 0.4x^2$$
$R'(x) = 400 - 0.8x = 0$ implies $x = 500$.
$R''(x) = -0.8 < 0$
Thus, $R''(500) = -0.8 < 0$ and we conclude that R has an absolute maximum at $x = 500$. The maximum revenue is
$R(500) = 400(500) - 0.4(500)^2 = \$100,000$
when 500 cameras are produced and sold for \$200 each.

(B) Profit $P(x) = R(x) - C(x) = 400x - 0.4x^2 - (2,000 + 160x)$
$$= 240x - 0.4x^2 - 2,000$$
$P'(x) = 240 - 0.8x$
Now, $240 - 0.8x = 0$ implies $x = 300$.

$P''(x) = -0.8$ and $P''(300) = -0.8 < 0$. Thus, the maximum profit occurs when 300 cameras are produced weekly. The maximum profit is
$P(300) = 240(300) - 0.4(300)^2 - 2,000 = \$34,000$. The price that the company should charge is $p(300) = 400 - 0.4(300) = \$280$ for each camera.

14. (A) Revenue $R(x) = x \cdot p(x) = x\left(200 - \dfrac{x}{50}\right) = 200x - \dfrac{x^2}{50}$, $0 \le x \le 10,000$

$R'(x) = 200 - \dfrac{x}{25}$

Now $R'(x) = 200 - \dfrac{x}{25} = 0$ implies $x = 5,000$.

$R''(x) = -\dfrac{1}{25} < 0$.

Thus, $R''(5,000) = -\dfrac{1}{25} < 0$ and we conclude that R has an absolute maximum at $x = 5,000$. The maximum revenue is

$R(5,000) = 200(5,000) - \dfrac{(5,000)^2}{50} = \$500,000$

(B) Profit $P(x) = R(x) - C(x) = 200x - \dfrac{x^2}{50} - (60,000 + 60x)$

$$= 140x - \dfrac{x^2}{50} - 60,000$$

$P'(x) = 140 - \dfrac{x}{25}$

Now $140 - \dfrac{x}{25} = 0$ implies $x = 3,500$.

$P''(x) = -\dfrac{1}{25}$ and $P''(3,500) = -\dfrac{1}{25} < 0$. Thus, the maximum profit occurs when 3,500 television sets are produced. The maximum profit is

$$P(3,500) = 140(3,500) - \dfrac{(3,500)^2}{50} - 60,000 = \$185,000$$

the price that the company should charge is

$$p(3,500) = 200 - \dfrac{3,500}{50} = \$130 \text{ for each set.}$$

(C) If the government taxes the company $5 for each set, then the profit $P(x)$ is given by

$$P(x) = 200x - \frac{x^2}{50} - (60,000 + 60x) - 5x$$

$$= 135x - \frac{x^2}{50} - 60,000.$$

$$P'(x) = 135 - \frac{x}{25}.$$

Now $135 - \dfrac{x}{25} = 0$ implies $x = 3,375$.

$P''(x) = -\dfrac{1}{25}$ and $P''(3,375) = -\dfrac{1}{25} < 0$. Thus, the maximum profit in this case occurs when 3,375 television sets are produced. The maximum profit is

$$P(3,375) = 135(3,375) - \frac{(3,375)^2}{50} - 60,000$$

$$= \$167,812.50$$

and the company should charge $p(3,375) = 200 - \dfrac{3,375}{50} = \$132.50/\text{set}$.

16. (A)

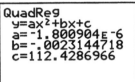

```
QuadReg
y=ax²+bx+c
a=⁻1.800904E⁻6
b=⁻.0023144718
c=112.4286966
```

(B)
```
LinReg
y=ax+b
a=21.55128853
b=96316.32137
```

(C) The revenue at the demand level x is:
$$R(x) = xp(x)$$
where $p(x)$ is the quadratic regression equation in (A).

The cost at the demand level x is $C(x)$ given by the linear regression equation in (B). The profit $P(x) = R(x) - C(x)$.

The maximum profit is $117,024 when the price per air brush is $79.

18. (A) Let x be the number of price reductions, then the price of a cup of coffee will be $p = 2.40 - 0.05x$ and the number of cups sold will be $1,600 + 50x$.

The revenue function is:
$R(x) = (1,600 + 50x)(2.40 - 0.05x)$

$\qquad = 3,840 + 40x - 2.5x^2$

$R'(x) = 40 - 5x = 0$ implies $x = 8$.

$R''(x) = -5 < 0$.

Thus, $R''(8) = -5 < 0$ and we conclude that R has an absolute maximum at $x = 8$. The maximum revenue is
$R(8) = 3,840 + 40(8) - 2.5(8^2) = \$4,000$, when 1,600 cups of coffee sold at the price of $p = 2.40 - 0.05(8) = \$2.00$ a cup.

(B) In this case
$\qquad R(x) = (1,600 + 60x)(2.40 - 0.10x)$

$\qquad\qquad = 3,840 - 16x - 6x^2$

$\qquad R'(x) = -16 - 12x = -4(4 + 3x) < 0$ for $x \geq 0$.

Thus, $R(x)$ is decreasing and its maximum occurs at $x = 0$, i.e. charge $2.40 per cup.

20. Let x = number of dollar increases in the rate per night.
Then $300 - 3x$ = total number of rooms rented and $80 + x$ = rate per night.
Total income = (total number of rooms rented)(rate - 10)

$$y(x) = (300 - 3x)(80 + x - 10), \quad 0 \le x \le 100$$
$$y(x) = (300 - 3x)(70 + x)$$
$$y'(x) = -3(70 + x) + (300 - 3x)$$
$$= -210 - 3x + 300 - 3x$$
$$= 90 - 6x$$
$$= 6(15 - x)$$

Thus, $x = 15$ is the only critical value and

$y(15) = (300 - 45)(70 + 15) = 21,675$.
$y''(x) = -6$
$y''(15) = -6 < 0$

Therefore, the absolute maximum income is $y(15) = \$21,675$ when the rate is \$95 per night.

22. Let x = number of additional weeks the grower waits to pick the pears.
Then $60 + 6x$ = the yield of a pear tree in pounds. The return will be:
$$f(x) = (60 + 6x)(0.30 - 0.02x), \quad 0 \le x \le 4$$
since every week the price is dropped 2¢ per pound.

Now we want to maximize $f(x)$ over $[0, 4]$.
$$f'(x) = 6(0.30 - 0.02x) - 0.02(60 + 6x)$$
$$= 1.8 - 0.12x - 1.2 - 0.12x$$
$$= 0.6 - 0.24x = 0, \quad x = 2.5$$
critical value: $x = 2.5$
$f''(x) = -0.24 < 0$
$f''(2.5) = -0.24 < 0$. Thus, f has an absolute maximum of $f(2.5) = \$18.75$ at $x = 2.5$ weeks.

24. (A) Let x = length of the side of the square.
Then $L + 4x = 108$ or $L = 108 - 4x$.
The volume of the base = $Lx^2 = x^2(108 - 4x)$.
Let $y(x) = x^2(108 - 4x)$, $0 \le x \le 27$.

Would like to maximize $y(x)$ on $(0, 27)$.
$$y'(x) = 2x(108 - 4x) - 4x^2$$
$$= 216x - 8x^2 - 4x^2$$
$$= 216x - 12x^2$$
$$= 12x(18 - x)$$

Critical value: $x = 18$ [<u>Note</u>: $x = 0$ is not in the domain of $y(x)$]
$y''(x) = 216 - 24x$
$y''(18) = 216 - 24(18) = -216 < 0$. Thus, $y(x)$ has an absolute maximum at $x = 18$.

The maximum value = $y(18) = 11.664$. Note that $L = 108 - 4(18) = 36$.
Therefore, volume is maximum at 11,644 in^3 for an
18" by 18" by 36" container.

(B) Let x be the radius and L the height of the cylindrical container. Then its volume = $\pi x^2 L$. Since $L + 2\pi x = 108$, then $L = 108 - 2\pi x$ and consequently $y(x) = \pi x^2 L = \pi x^2 (108 - 2\pi x)$, $0 < x < \dfrac{54}{\pi}$.

We want to maximize $y(x)$ on $\left(0, \dfrac{54}{\pi}\right)$.

$$
\begin{aligned}
y'(x) &= 2\pi x(108 - 2\pi x) - 2\pi^2 x^2 \\
&= 216\pi x - 4\pi^2 x^2 - 2\pi^2 x^2 \\
&= 216\pi x - 6\pi^2 x^2 \\
&= 6\pi x(36 - \pi x)
\end{aligned}
$$

critical value: $x = \dfrac{36}{\pi}$

$y''(x) = 216\pi - 12\pi^2 x$

$y''\left(\dfrac{36}{\pi}\right) = 216\pi - 12\pi^2\left(\dfrac{36}{\pi}\right) = 216\pi - 432\pi = -216\pi < 0$

Thus, $y(x)$ has an absolute maximum at $x = \dfrac{36}{\pi}$.

Also, $L = 108 - 2\pi x = 36$.

Therefore, volume is maximum at

$$
y\left(\frac{36}{\pi}\right) = \pi\left(\frac{36}{\pi}\right)^2\left(108 - 2\pi\left(\frac{36}{\pi}\right)\right) = 14{,}851 \text{ in}^3 \text{ for a container of radius}
$$

$\dfrac{36}{\pi}$ inches and height of 36 inches.

26. (A) Let x and y be the width and the length of the rectangle respectively. Then we have $2x + y + y - 100 = 240$ or $x + y = 170$ where $100 \le y \le 170$. The Area = $xy = (170 - y)y$.

Let $f(y) = (170 - y)y$, $100 \le y \le 170$
$f'(y) = 170 - 2y$ and $f''(y) = -2 < 0$.
$f'(y) = 0$ implies $y = 85$ which is not in the domain of f. We note that $f(100) = 7{,}000$, $f(170) = 0$. Thus, the maximum of f occurs when $y = 100$ and hence $x = 170 - y = 70$.

(B) In this case, $2x + 2y - 100 = 400$ or $x + y = 250$,
and $f(y) = (250 - y)y$, $100 \le y \le 250$
$f'(y) = 250 - 2y$
$f'(y) = 0$ implies $y = 125$
$f''(y) = -2 < 0$

Thus, f has an absolute maximum at $y = 125$. So $x = 250 - y = 125$ and hence 125 feet by 125 feet.

28. Let x be the number of times the pharmacy places order and let y be the number of demands. Then the cost will be

$$C = 40x + 10\left(\frac{y}{2}\right) = 40x + 5y$$

We also have $xy = 200$. From this equation we find $y = \frac{200}{x}$ and substitute for y in the cost function to obtain:

$$C(x) = 40x + \frac{1000}{x}$$

$$C'(x) = 40 - \frac{1000}{x^2} = \frac{40x^2 - 1000}{x^2} = \frac{40(x^2 - 25)}{x^2} = \frac{40(x - 5)(x + 5)}{x^2}$$

$C'(x) = 0$ implies $x = -5$, $x = 5$ of which $x = 5$ is the only critical value (since $x > 0$).

$$C''(x) = \frac{2000}{x^3} > 0 \text{ for } x > 0.$$

Thus, $C''(5) = \frac{2000}{125} > 0$ and hence $C(5) = 400$ is the minimum cost.

30. Let x = number of hours it takes the train to travel 360 miles. Then $360 = xv$ or $x = \frac{360}{v}$.

$$\text{Cost} = \left(300 + \frac{v^2}{4}\right)x = \left(300 + \frac{v^2}{4}\right)\left(\frac{360}{v}\right)$$

$$= \frac{108,000}{v} + 90v$$

Let $C(v) = \frac{108,000}{v} + 90v$, $v > 0$.

We want to minimize $C(v)$.

$$C'(v) = -\frac{108,000}{v^2} + 90 = \frac{-108,000 + 90v^2}{v^2}$$

$C'(v) = 0$ implies $90v^2 = 108,000$ or $v = 34.64$

$$C''(v) = \frac{108,000}{v^3} > 0 \text{ for } v > 0$$

So, $C(v)$ has an absolute minimum at $v = 34.64$ miles per hour.

32. Let R = radius of the base and h the height of the can.
Then we have $\pi R^2 h = 22$

$$h = \frac{22}{\pi R^2}$$

The material needed = $(2\pi R)h + 8R^2$, and if we let

$$f(R) = (2\pi R)h + 8R^2$$

$$= (2\pi R)\left(\frac{22}{\pi R^2}\right) + 8R^2$$

$$= \frac{44}{R} + 8R^2$$

we want to minimize $f(R)$.

$$f'(R) = -\frac{44}{R^2} + 16R$$

$$= \frac{-44 + 16R}{R^2}$$

$f'(R) = 0$ implies $R \approx 1.40$ inches

$$h = \frac{22}{\pi R^2} = \frac{22}{\pi(1.40)^2} \approx 3.57 \text{ inches.}$$

34. $C(t) = \dfrac{0.16t}{t^2 + 4t + 4} = \dfrac{0.16t}{(t + 2)^2}$

$$C'(t) = \frac{0.16(t + 2)^2 - 2(t + 2)(0.16t)}{(t + 2)^4}$$

$$= \frac{0.16(t + 2) - 0.32t}{(t + 2)^3}$$

$$= \frac{0.16 + 0.32 - 0.32t}{(t + 2)^3} = \frac{0.32 - 0.16t}{(t + 2)^3}$$

$C'(t) = 0$ implies $t = 2$

$$C''(t) = \frac{-0.16(t + 2)^3 - 3(t + 2)^2(0.32 - 0.16t)}{(t + 2)^6}$$

$$= \frac{-0.16(t + 2) - 3(0.32 - 0.16t)}{(t + 2)^4}$$

$$= \frac{-0.16t - 0.32 - 0.96 + 0.48t}{(t + 2)^4}$$

$$= \frac{0.32t - 1.28}{(t + 2)^4}$$

$$C''(2) = \frac{0.64 - 1.28}{4^4} < 0$$

Thus, $C(t)$ has an absolute maximum at $t = 2$ hours, and the maximum va
is $C(2) = \dfrac{.32}{4^2} = .02 \text{ mg/cm}^3$

36. (A) Let the energy to fly over land be 1 unit; then the energy to fly over the water is 1.4 units.

$E(x)$ = total energy = $(1.4)\sqrt{x^2 + 25} + (1)(10 - x)$

$E(x) = 1.4(x^2 + 25)^{1/2} + 10 - x, \quad 0 \le x \le 10$

$E'(x) = (1.4)\dfrac{1}{2}(x^2 + 25)^{-1/2}(2x) - 1$

$\qquad = 1.4x(x^2 + 25)^{-1/2} - 1$

$\qquad = \dfrac{1.4x - \sqrt{x^2 + 25}}{\sqrt{x^2 + 25}}$

$E'(x) = 0$ when $1.4 - \sqrt{x^2 + 25} = 0$ or

$\qquad 1.96x^2 = x^2 + 25$

$\qquad .96x^2 = 25$

$\qquad x^2 = \dfrac{25}{0.96} = 26.04$

$\qquad x = \pm 5.1$

Thus, the critical value is $x = 5.1$.

$E''(x) = 1.4(x^2 + 25)^{-1/2} + 1.4x\left(-\dfrac{1}{2}\right)(x^2 + 25)^{-3/2}(2x)$

$\qquad = \dfrac{1.4}{(x^2 + 25)^{1/2}} - \dfrac{1.4x^2}{(x^2 + 25)^{3/2}} = \dfrac{35}{(x^2 + 25)^{3/2}}$

$E''(5.1) = \dfrac{35}{[(5.1)^2 + 25]^{3/2}} > 0$

Thus, the energy will be minimum when $x = 5.1$.
Note that: $E(0) = (1.4)\sqrt{25} + 10 = 17$
$\qquad\qquad E(5.1) = (1.4)\sqrt{51.01} + (10 - 5.1) = 14.9$
$\qquad\qquad E(10) = (1.4)\sqrt{125} = 15.65$
Thus, the absolute minimum occurs when $x = 5.1$ miles.

(B) $E(x) = 1.1\sqrt{x^2 + 25} + (1)(10 - x), \quad 0 \le x \le 10$

$E'(x) = \dfrac{1.1x - \sqrt{x^2 + 25}}{\sqrt{x^2 + 25}}$

$E'(x) = 0$ when $1.1x - \sqrt{x^2 + 25} = 0$ or

$\qquad\qquad 1.21x^2 = x^2 + 25$

$\qquad\qquad x^2 = \dfrac{25}{.21} = 119.05$

$\qquad\qquad x = \pm 10.91$

critical value: $x = 10.91 > 10$, i.e., there are no critical values on the interval $[0, 10]$.

Now, $E(0) = 1.1\sqrt{25} + 10 = 15.5,$
$\qquad E(10) = 1.1\sqrt{125} \approx 12.30$

Therefore, the absolute minimum occurs when $x = 10$ miles.

38. $C(x) = \dfrac{8k}{x^2} + \dfrac{k}{(10-x)^2}, \quad 0.5 \le x \le 9.5, \quad k > 0$

$$C'(x) = -\dfrac{16k}{x^3} + \dfrac{2k}{(10-x)^3}$$

$$= \dfrac{-16k(10-x)^3 + 2kx^3}{x^3(10-x)^3}$$

$C'(x) = 0$ when $-16k(10-x)^3 + 2kx^3 = 0$ or

$$2kx^3 = 16k(10-x)^3$$
$$x^3 = 8(10-x)^3$$
$$x = 2(10-x)$$
$$3x = 20$$
$$x = \dfrac{20}{3}$$

critical value: $x = \dfrac{20}{3}$

$C''(x) = \dfrac{48k}{x^4} + \dfrac{6k}{(10-x)^4} > 0$ for all x.

Thus, $C''\left(\dfrac{20}{3}\right) > 0$ and $C(x)$ has a local minimum at $x = \dfrac{20}{3}$.

$C(0.5) = \dfrac{8k}{(0.5)^2} + \dfrac{k}{(9.5)^2} = k(32.01) = 32.01k$

$C\left(\dfrac{20}{3}\right) = \dfrac{8k}{\left(\dfrac{20}{3}\right)^2} + \dfrac{k}{\left(10 - \dfrac{20}{3}\right)^2} = k(0.27) = 0.27k$

$C(9.5) = \dfrac{8k}{(9.5)^2} + \dfrac{k}{(0.5)^2} = k(4.09) = 4.09k$

Therefore, $C(x)$ has an absolute minimum at $x = \dfrac{20}{3}$ miles.

40. $P(x) = 96x - 24x^2, \quad 0 \le x \le 3$

$P'(x) = 96 - 48x$

$P'(x) = 0$ implies $96 - 48x = 0$ or $x = 2$

critical value: $x = 2$

$P''(x) = -48 < 0$

$P''(2) = -48 < 0$. Thus, $P(x)$ has a local maximum at $x = 2$.

$P(0) = 0$

$P(2) = 96(2) - 24(2)^2 = 96$

$P(3) = 96(3) - 24(3)^2 = 72$

Therefore, $P(x)$ has its absolute maximum at $x = 2$ and $P(2) = 96$ is maximum percentage.

5 ADDITIONAL DERIVATIVE TOPICS

2. $A = \$5,000e^{0.08t}$

When $t = 1$, $A = \$5,000e^{(0.08)1} = \$5,000e^{0.08} = \$5,416.44$.

When $t = 4$, $A = \$5,000e^{(0.08)4} = \$5,000e^{0.32} = \$6,885.64$.

When $t = 10$, $A = \$5,000e^{(0.08)10} = \$5,000e^{0.8} = \$11,127.70$.

4.

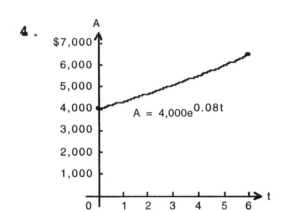

$A = 4,000e^{0.08t}$

6. $2 = e^{0.03t}$

Take the natural log of both sides of this equation

$$\ln(e^{0.03t}) = \ln 2$$
$$0.03t \ln e = \ln 2$$
$$0.03t = \ln 2 \qquad (\ln e = 1)$$
$$t = \frac{\ln 2}{0.03} \approx 23.10$$

8. $3 = e^{0.25t}$

$$\ln(e^{0.25t}) = \ln 3$$
$$0.25t = \ln 3$$
$$t = \frac{\ln 3}{0.25} \approx 4.39$$

10. $3 = e^{10r}$

$$\ln(e^{10r}) = \ln 3$$
$$10r = \ln 3$$
$$r = \frac{\ln 3}{10} \approx 0.11$$

12.

s	$(1 + s)^{1/s}$
0.01	2.70481
-0.01	2.73200
0.001	2.71692
-0.001	2.71964
0.0001	2.71815
-0.0001	2.71842
0.00001	2.71827
-0.00001	2.71830
⇓	⇓
0	e = 2.7182818...

14.

s	0.1	0.01	0.001	0.0001
$\left(1 + \dfrac{1}{s}\right)^s$	1.270982	1.047232	1.006933	1.000921

$$\lim_{s \to 0^+} \left(1 + \frac{1}{s}\right)^s = 1$$

16. The graphs of $y_1 = \left(1 + \dfrac{2}{n}\right)^n$,

$y_2 = 7.3890560999 \approx e^2$ for $1 \leq n \leq 50$

are given at the right.

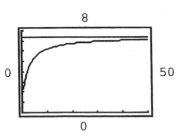

18. (A) $A = Pe^{rt} = \$10{,}000e^{0.0528(3)}$
$= \$10{,}000e^{0.1584}$
$= \$11{,}716.35$

(B) $11{,}000 = 10{,}000e^{0.0528t}$
$e^{0.0528t} = 1.1$
$0.0528t = \ln 1.1$
$t = \dfrac{\ln 1.1}{0.0528} \approx 1.81$ years

20. $A = Pe^{rt}$
$\$50{,}000 = Pe^{0.064(5)} = Pe^{0.32}$
Therefore,
$P = \dfrac{\$50{,}000}{e^{0.32}} = \$50{,}000e^{-0.32} \approx \$36{,}307.45$

22. $100{,}000 = 40{,}000e^{15r}$
$e^{15r} = 2.5$
$r = \dfrac{\ln(2.5)}{15} \approx 0.0611$ or 6.11%

24. $P = 10{,}000e^{-0.08t} = 5{,}000$
$e^{-0.08t} = 0.5$
$-0.08t = \ln(0.5)$
$t = -\dfrac{\ln(0.5)}{0.08} \approx 8.66$ years

26. $2P = Pe^{0.05t}$
$e^{0.05t} = 2$
$\ln(e^{0.05t}) = \ln 2$
$0.05t = \ln 2$
$t = \dfrac{\ln 2}{0.05} \approx 13.86$ years

28. $2P = Pe^{r(10)}$
$\ln(e^{10r}) = \ln 2$
$10r = \ln 2$
$r = \dfrac{\ln 2}{10} \approx 0.0693$ or 6.93%

30. The total investment in the two accounts is given by
$A = 5{,}000e^{0.088t} + 7{,}000(1 + 0.096)^t$

On a graphing utility, locate the intersection point of
$y_1 = 5{,}000e^{0.088x} + 7{,}000(1 + 0.096)^x$
and $y_2 = 20{,}000$.

The result is: $x = t \approx 5.7$ years.

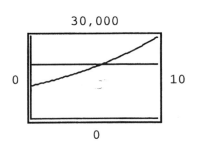

32. (A) $A = Pe^{rt}$; (B)

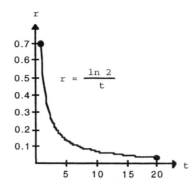

$$2P = Pe^{rt}$$
$$2 = e^{rt};$$
$$rt = \ln 2;$$
$$r = \frac{\ln 2}{t}$$

$$r = \frac{\ln 2}{t}$$

Although t could be any positive number, the restrictions on t are reasonable in the sense that the doubling times for most investments would be expected to be between 1 and 20 years.

(C) $t = 2$; $r = \dfrac{\ln 2}{2} \approx 0.347$ or 34.7%

$t = 4$; $r = \dfrac{\ln 2}{4} \approx 0.173$ or 17.3%

$t = 6$; $r = \dfrac{\ln 2}{6} \approx 0.116$ or 11.6%

$t = 8$; $r = \dfrac{\ln 2}{8} \approx 0.087$ or 8.7%

$t = 10$; $r = \dfrac{\ln 2}{10} \approx 0.069$ or 6.9%

$t = 12$; $r = \dfrac{\ln 2}{12} \approx 0.058$ or 5.8%

34.

$$Q = Q_0 e^{-0.0001238t}$$
$$\frac{1}{2}Q_0 = Q_0 e^{-0.0001238t}$$
$$e^{-0.0001238t} = \frac{1}{2}$$
$$\ln(e^{-0.0001238t}) = \ln\left(\frac{1}{2}\right) = \ln 1 - \ln 2$$
$$-0.0001238t = -\ln 2 \quad (\ln 1 = 0)$$
$$t = \frac{\ln 2}{0.0001238} \approx 5{,}599 \text{ years}$$

36.

$$Q = Q_0 e^{rt} \quad (r < 0)$$
$$\frac{1}{2}Q_0 = Q_0 e^{r(90)}$$
$$e^{90r} = \frac{1}{2}$$
$$\ln(e^{90r}) = \ln\left(\frac{1}{2}\right) = \ln 1 - \ln 2$$
$$90r = -\ln 2 \quad (\ln 1 = 0)$$
$$r = -\frac{\ln 2}{90} \approx -0.0077$$

Thus, the continuous compound rate of decay of the strontium isotope is approximately -0.0077.

38. $P = P_0 e^{rt}$

$2P_0 = P_0 e^{0.0085t}$ or $e^{0.0085t} = 2$

Thus, $\ln(e^{0.0085t}) = \ln 2$

and $0.0085t = \ln 2$

Therefore, $t = \dfrac{\ln 2}{0.0085} \approx 81.57$ years

40. $2P_0 = P_0 e^{r(200)}$

$e^{200r} = 2$

$\ln(e^{200r}) = \ln 2$

$200r = \ln 2$

$r = \dfrac{\ln 2}{200} \approx 0.0035$

or 0.35%

EXERCISE 5-2

---

2. $f(u) = u^4$, $g(x) = 1 - 4x^3$
$f[g(x)] = (1 - 4x^3)^4$

4. $f(u) = e^u$, $g(x) = 3x^3$
$f[g(x)] = e^{3x^3}$

6. Let $u = g(x) = 2x^3 + x + 3$ and $f(u) = u^5$.   Then $y = f(u) = u^5$.

8. Let $u = g(x) = x^4 + 2x^2 + 5$ and $f(u) = e^u$.   Then $y = f(u) = e^u$.

10. $g(x) = 3e^x - 5x^4$

$g'(x) = 3\dfrac{d}{dx}(e^x) - 5\dfrac{d}{dx}(x^4) = 3e^x - 5(4)x^3$

$\qquad\qquad\qquad\qquad\qquad = 3e^x - 20x^3$

12. $y = -7e^x + 9x^e$

$\dfrac{dy}{dx} = -7\dfrac{d}{dx}e^x + 9\dfrac{d}{dx}x^e$

$\qquad = -7e^x + 9ex^{e-1}$

[Note: $e \approx 2.71828$ is a constant and so we use the power rule on the second term.]

14. $y = 5e^{-x} - 6e^x$

$y' = 5\dfrac{d}{dx}(e^{-x}) - 6\dfrac{d}{dx}(e^x)$

$\quad = 5(-1)e^{-x} - 6e^x = -5e^{-x} - 6e^x$

16. $f(x) = x^4 e^x$

$f'(x) = \left(\dfrac{d}{dx}x^4\right)e^x + x^4\left(\dfrac{d}{dx}e^x\right)$ (Product rule)

$\qquad = 4x^3 e^x + x^4 e^x$

$\qquad = x^3 e^x(x + 4)$

18. $f(x) = 2e^{3x}$

$f'(x) = 2\dfrac{d}{dx}(e^{3x}) = 2(3)e^{3x} = 6e^{3x}$

20. $f(x) = 6e^{-4x}$

$f'(x) = 6\dfrac{d}{dx}(e^{-4x}) = 6(-4)e^{-4x} = -24e^{-4x}$

22. $f(x) = 300e^{0.1x}$

$f'(x) = 300\dfrac{d}{dx}(e^{0.1x}) = 300(0.1)e^{0.1x} = 30e^{0.1x}$

24. $f(x) = xe^{-4x}$

$$f'(x) = \left(\frac{d}{dx} x\right)e^{-4x} + x\frac{d}{dx}(e^{-4x})$$

$$= e^{-4x} + x(-4)e^{-4x} = e^{-4x} - 4xe^{-4x} = (1 - 4x)e^{-4x}$$

26. $f(x) = \dfrac{e^x}{x^2 + 4}$

$$f'(x) = \frac{\left(\dfrac{d}{dx} e^x\right)(x^2 + 4) - \left(\dfrac{d}{dx}(x^2 + 4)\right)e^x}{(x^2 + 4)^2} \qquad \text{(Quotient rule)}$$

$$= \frac{e^x(x^2 + 4) \quad (2x)c^x}{(x^2 + 4)^2}$$

$$= \frac{e^x(x^2 + 4 - 2x)}{(x^2 + 4)^2} = \frac{e^x(x^2 - 2x + 4)}{(x^2 + 4)^2}$$

28. $\dfrac{d}{dx} e^{x^3-3x^2+1} = e^{x^3-3x^2+1}(3x^2 - 6x) = 3x(x - 2)e^{x^3-3x^2+1}$

30. $\dfrac{d}{dx}(e^{x^2} + 3)^5 = 5(e^{x^2} + 3)^4(2xe^{x^2})$

$$= 10xe^{x^2}(e^{x^2} + 3)^4$$

32. $f(x) = \dfrac{x + 1}{e^x}$

$$f'(x) = \frac{\left(\dfrac{d}{dx}(x + 1)\right)e^x - \left(\dfrac{d}{dx} e^x\right)(x + 1)}{(e^x)^2}$$

$$= \frac{e^x - e^x(x + 1)}{e^{2x}} = \frac{e^x - xe^x - e^x}{e^{2x}}$$

$$= -\frac{xe^x}{e^{2x}} = -\frac{x}{e^x}$$

34. $\dfrac{d}{dx}(1 - x)e^{2x} = (-1)e^{2x} + (1 - x)(2e^{2x})$

$$= e^{2x}[2 - 2x - 1]$$

$$= (1 - 2x)e^{2x}$$

36. $f(x) = x^2 e^x - 2xe^x + 2e^x$

$$= (x^2 - 2x + 2)e^x$$

$$f'(x) = \left(\frac{d}{dx}(x^2 - 2x + 2)\right)e^x + (x^2 - 2x + 2)\left(\frac{d}{dx} e^x\right)$$

$$= (2x - 2)e^x + (x^2 - 2x + 2)e^x$$

$$= [(2x - 2) + (x^2 - 2x + 2)]e^x$$

$$= (2x - 2 + x^2 - 2x + 2)e^x$$

$$= (x^2)e^x = x^2 e^x$$

40. $f(x) = \dfrac{x^4}{e^x}$

$$f'(x) = \frac{\left(\dfrac{d}{dx}\, x^4\right)e^x - \left(\dfrac{d}{dx}\, e^x\right)x^4}{(e^x)^2}$$

$$= \frac{4x^3 e^x - x^4 e^x}{(e^x)^2} = \frac{4x^3 - x^4}{e^x} = \frac{x^3(4 - x)}{e^x}$$

$f'(x) = 0$ if $x = 4$ (since $x > 0$); $f'(x) > 0$ on $(0, 4)$ and $f'(x) < 0$ on $(4, \infty)$. Thus f is increasing on $(0, 4)$ and decreasing on $(4, \infty)$.

Therefore, maximum $f(x) = f(4) = \dfrac{4^4}{e^4} \approx 4.689$.

Note: $f''(x) = \dfrac{(12x^2 - 4x^3)e^x - (4x^3 - x^4)e^x}{(e^x)^2} = \dfrac{x^4 - 8x^3 + 12x^2}{e^x}$

and $f''(4) = -\dfrac{64}{e^4} < 0$. Since $x = 4$ is the only critical value in $(0, \infty)$, and $f''(4) < 0$, the function f has absolute maximum at $x = 4$.

42. $f(x) = \dfrac{e^x}{x}$

$$f'(x) = \frac{\left(\dfrac{d}{dx}\, e^x\right)x - \left(\dfrac{d}{dx}\, x\right)e^x}{x^2} = \frac{xe^x - e^x}{x^2} = \frac{(x - 1)e^x}{x^2}$$

$f'(x) = 0$ if $x = 1$.

$f''(x) = \dfrac{(e^x + (x - 1)e^x)x^2 - 2x(x - 1)e^x}{x^4}$ and $f''(1) = 1 > 0$.

Thus, $f(x)$ has an absolute minimum at $x = 1$, $f(1) = \dfrac{e}{1} = e \approx 2.718$.

44. $f(x) = 2 - 3e^{-2x}$
Step 1. Analyze $f(x)$:
(A) Domain: All real numbers, $(-\infty, \infty)$.
(B) Intercepts: y intercept: $f(0) = 2 - 3 = -1$

x intercept: $2 - 3e^{-2x} = 0$

$$3e^{-2x} = 2$$

$$e^{-2x} = \frac{2}{3}$$

$$-2x = \ln \frac{2}{3}$$

$$x = -\frac{1}{2} \ln \frac{2}{3} = \frac{1}{2} \ln \frac{3}{2} \approx 0.203$$

(C) Asymptotes:
Horizontal asymptote: $\lim\limits_{x \to \infty} (2 - 3e^{-2x}) = 2$

$\lim\limits_{x \to -\infty} (2 - 3e^{-2x}) = -\infty$,

thus $y = 2$ is the only horizontal asymptote.
Vertical asymptotes: There are no vertical asymptotes.

Step 2. Analyze $f'(x)$:

$f'(x) = 6e^{-2x} > 0$ for all x. Thus, f is increasing on $(-\infty, \infty)$; there are no local extrema.

Step 3. Analyze $f''(x)$:

$f''(x) = -12e^{-2x} < 0$ for all x. Thus, the graph of f is concave downward on $(-\infty, \infty)$.

Step 4. Sketch the graph of f:

x	$f(x)$
0	-1
-1	≈ -20.17
1	≈ 1.59

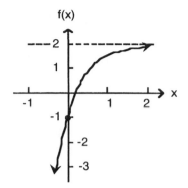

46. $f(x) = 3 + 7e^{-0.2x}$

Step 1. Analyze $f(x)$:

(A) Domain: All real numbers, $(-\infty, \infty)$.

(B) Intercepts: y-intercept: 10

   x-intercept: None, $f(x) > 3$ for all x.

(C) Asymptotes:

   Horizontal asymptote: $\lim\limits_{x \to \infty} f(x) = 3 + 7(0) = 3$, thus $y = 3$ is a horizontal asymptote.

   Vertical asymptotes: None

Step 2. Analyze $f'(x)$:

$f'(x) = -1.4e^{-0.2x} < 0$ for all x and hence $f(x)$ is decreasing on $(-\infty, \infty)$.

Step 3. Analyze $f''(x)$:

$f''(x) = 0.28e^{-0.2x} > 0$ for all x and hence $f(x)$ is concave upward on $(-\infty, \infty)$.

Step 4. Sketch the graph of f:

x	$f(x)$
-1	11.55
0	10
1	8.73

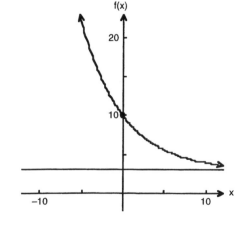

48. $f(x) = 10xe^{-0.1x}$

Step 1. Analyze $f(x)$:

(A) Domain: All real numbers, $(-\infty, \infty)$

(B) Intercepts: y-intercept: 0
    x-intercept: 0

(C) Asymptotes:

  Horizontal asymptote: $\displaystyle\lim_{x \to \infty} f(x) = 0$, thus $y = 0$ (x axis) is a horizontal asymptote.

  Vertical asymptotes: None

Step 2. Analyze $f'(x)$:

$f'(x) = 10e^{-0.1x} - xe^{-0.1x} = (10 - x)e^{-0.1x}$
$f'(x) = 0$ if $x = 10$
Thus, the only critical value of f is $x = 10$.
$x = 10$ is also a partition number for f'.
Sign chart for f':

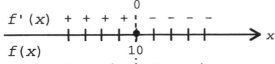

Test Numbers	
x	$f'(x)$
0	10 (+)
11	$-e^{-1.1}$ (−)

Thus, f has a local maximum at $x = 10$;

$f(10) = 10(10)e^{-0.1(10)} = 100e^{-1} \approx 36.79$ is absolute maximum value of f.

Step 3. Analyze $f''(x)$:

$f''(x) = 10(-0.1)e^{-0.1x} - e^{-0.1x} - x(-0.1)e^{-0.1x}$
$\quad\quad = -e^{-0.1x} - e^{-0.1x} + 0.1xe^{-0.1x}$
$\quad\quad = (0.1x - 2)e^{-0.1x}$

Partition number for f'': $x = 20$
Sign chart for f'':

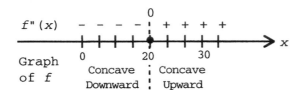

Test Numbers	
x	$f''(x)$
0	−2 (−)
30	e^{-3} (+)

Thus, the graph of f is concave downward on $(-\infty, 20)$ and concave upward on $(20, \infty)$; the graph of f has an inflection point at $x = 20$.

Step 4. Sketch the graph of f:

x	$f(x)$
−10	$-100e^{1}$
0	0
10	$100e^{1}$

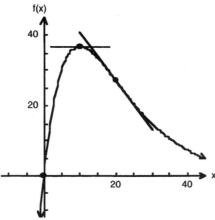

50. $f(x) = (x - 2)e^x$

<u>Step 1. Analyze $f(x)$</u>:

(A) Domain: All real numbers, $(-\infty, \infty)$.

(B) Intercepts: y intercept: $f(0) = (0 - 2)e^0 = -2$

x intercept: $(x - 2)e^x = 0$

$x - 2 = 0$

$x = 2$

(C) Asymptotes:

<u>Horizontal asymptote</u>: $\lim\limits_{x \to \infty} (x - 2)e^x = 0$

$\lim\limits_{x \to \infty} (x - 2)e^x = \infty$;

Thus, $y = 0$ is a horizontal asymptote.

<u>Vertical asymptotes</u>: There are no vertical asymptotes.

<u>Step 2. Analyze $f'(x)$</u>:

$f'(x) = e^x + (x - 2)e^x = (x - 1)e^x$

Critical values: $f'(x) = (x - 1)e^x = 0$

$x - 1 = 0$

$x = 1$

Thus, the only critical value of f is $x = 1$.
$x = 1$ is also a partition number for f'.
Sign chart for f':

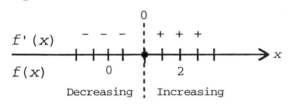

Test Numbers	
x	$f'(x)$
0	-1 $(-)$
2	e^2 $(+)$

Thus, f has a minimum value at $x = 1$; $f(1) = (1 - 2)e^1 = -e$ is the absolute minimum of f.

<u>Step 3. Analyze $f''(x)$</u>:

$f''(x) = e^x + (x - 1)e^x = xe^x$
Partition number for f'': $x = 0$
Sign chart for f'':

Test Numbers	
x	$f''(x)$
-1	$-e^{-1}$ $(-)$
1	e $(+)$

Thus, the graph of f is concave downward on $(-\infty, 0)$ and concave upward on $(0, \infty)$; the graph has an inflection point at $x = 0$.

Step 4. Sketch the graph of f:

x	$f(x)$
-1	$-3e^{-1}$
0	-2
2	0
3	e^3

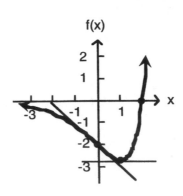

52. $f(x) = e^{-2x^2}$

Step 1. Analyze $f(x)$:
(A) Domain: All real numbers, $(-\infty, \infty)$.
(B) Intercepts: y-intercept: 1
    x-intercepts: None, $f(x) > 0$ for all x

(C) Asymptotes:
   <u>Horizontal asymptote</u>: $\lim\limits_{x\to-\infty} f(x) = \lim\limits_{x\to+\infty} f(x) = 0$, thus $y = 0$
   is a horizontal asymptote.
   <u>Vertical asymptotes</u>: None

Step 2. Analyze $f'(x)$:
$f'(x) = -4xe^{-2x^2}$
Critical values: $f'(x) = -4xe^{-2x^2} = 0$
                    $x = 0$
Thus, the only critical value of f is $x = 0$. $x = 0$ is a partition number of f'.
Sign chart for $f'(x) = -4xe^{-2x^2}$

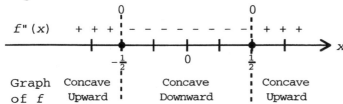

Test Numbers

x	$f'(x)$
-1	$4e^{-2}$ (+)
1	$-4e^{-2}$ (−)

Thus, f has a maximum value at $x = 0$; $f(0) = 1$ is the absolute maximum of f.

Step 3. Analyze $f''(x)$:
$f''(x) = -4e^{-2x^2} - 4x(-4x)e^{-2x^2} = (16x^2 - 4)e^{-2x^2}$
Partition numbers for f'': $x = -\dfrac{1}{2}$, $x = \dfrac{1}{2}$

Sign chart for f'':

Test Numbers

x	$f''(x)$
-1	$12e^{-2}$ (+)
0	-4 (−)
1	$12e^{-2}$ (+)

Thus, the graph of f is concave upward on $(-\infty, -0.5)$ and on $(0.5, \infty)$ and concave downward on $(-0.5, 0.5)$; the graph of f has inflection points at $x = -0.5$ and $x = 0.5$.

x	$f(x)$
-1	e^{-2}
0	1
1	e^{-2}

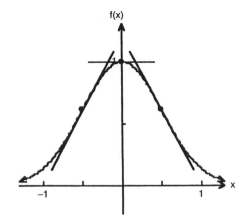

54. $f(x) = e^x + x^2, \qquad -\infty < x < \infty$

$f'(x) = e^x + 2x$
Critical values:

Solve $f'(x) = e^x + 2x = 0$
To two decimal places, $x = -0.35$
Increasing/Decreasing: $f(x)$ is increasing on $(-0.35, \infty)$;
$f(x)$ is decreasing on $(-\infty, -0.35)$.
Local extrema: $f(x)$ has a local minimum at $x = -0.35$.

56. On a graphing utility, graph $y_1 = e^x$ and $y_2 = x^5$. Rounded off to two decimal places, the points of intersection are: $(1.30, 3.65)$, $(12.71, 332,105.11)$.

58. Demand: $p = 12e^{-x} = \dfrac{12}{e^x}$, $0 \leq x \leq 2$

Revenue: $R(x) = xp = \dfrac{12x}{e^x}$

(B) $R'(x) = \dfrac{12e^x - 12xe^x}{(e^x)^2} = \dfrac{12e^x(1 - x)}{(e^x)^2} = \dfrac{12(1 - x)}{e^x}$, $0 \leq x \leq 2$

critical value(s): $\dfrac{12(1 - x)}{e^x} = 0$

$$12(1 - x) = 0$$
$$x = 1$$

$R''(x) = \dfrac{-12e^x - 12(1 - x)e^x}{(e^x)^2} = \dfrac{-12e^x(1 + 1 - x)}{(e^x)^2} = \dfrac{-12(2 - x)}{e^x}$

$R''(1) = \dfrac{-12(2 - 1)}{e^1} = -\dfrac{12}{e} < 0$

Now, $R(0) = 0$

$R(1) = \dfrac{12}{e} \approx 4.41$ Absolute maximum

$R(2) = \dfrac{24}{e^2} \approx 3.25$

Thus, the maximum weekly revenue occurs at price $p = \dfrac{12}{e} \approx \$4.41$.

The maximum weekly revenue is $R(1) = 4.41$ thousand dollars, or $\$4,410$.

(C) The sign chart for R' is:

$$R'(x) \quad + + + \mid - - -$$

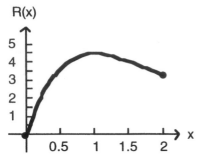

Test Numbers	
x	$R'(x)$
0	12 (+)
2	$-\frac{12}{e^2}$ (−)

Thus, R is increasing on $(0, 1)$ and decreasing on $(1, 2)$; the maximum value of R occurs at $x = 1$, as noted in (A).

$R''(x) = 12(x - 2)e^{-x} < 0$ on $(0, 2)$.

Thus, the graph of R is concave downward on $(0, 2)$. The graph is shown at the right.

x	$R(x)$
0	0
1	4.41
2	3.25

60. Price: $p = 10e^{-0.04x}$, $x \geq 0$

Revenue: $R(x) = xp = 10xe^{-0.04x}$

$$R'(x) = 10e^{-0.04x} + 10xe^{-0.04x}(-0.04)$$
$$= 10e^{-0.04x}(1 - 0.04x)$$

Critical value(s): $R'(x) = 10e^{-0.04x}(1 - 0.04x) = 0$

$$1 - 0.04x = 0$$
$$0.04x = 1$$
$$x = \frac{1}{0.04} = 25$$

$$R''(x) = 10e^{-0.04x}(-0.04)(1 - 0.04x) + 10e^{-0.04x}(-0.04)$$

$$= 10e^{-0.04x}[-0.04 + 0.0016x - 0.04]$$

$$= 10e^{-0.04x}[0.0016x - 0.08]$$

$$R''(25) = 10e^{-0.04(25)}[(0.0016)(25) - 0.08] = -0.4e^{-1} < 0$$

Since $x = 25$ is the only critical value and $R''(25) < 0$, the production level that maximizes the revenue is 25 units. The maximum revenue is $R(25) = 10(25)e^{-0.04(25)} \approx 92$ or \$92, and the price is $p(25) = 10e^{-0.04(25)} \approx 3.68$ or \$3.68 each.

62. The cost function $C(x)$ is given by
$$C(x) = 30 + 0.7x$$
and the revenue function $R(x)$ is
$$R(x) = xp = 10xe^{-0.04x}$$
The profit function $P(x)$ is
$$P(x) = R(x) - C(x)$$
$$= 10xe^{-0.04x} - 30 - 0.7x$$
and $P'(x) = 10e^{-0.04x} - 0.4xe^{-0.04x} - 0.7$.
We graph $y_1 = P(x)$ and $y_2 = P'(x)$ in the

viewing rectangle $0 \leq x \leq 30$, $-50 \leq y \leq 50$

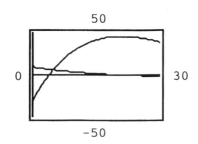

Critical value: Solve $P'(x) = (10 - 0.4x)e^{-0.04x} - 0.7 = 0$
To the nearest integer, $x = 21$ units.
$P(x)$ is increasing on $(0, 21)$ and decreasing on $(21, \infty)$; $P(x)$ has a maximum at $x = 21$. Thus, the maximum profit $P(21) = \$45.96$ is realized at a production level of 21 units at a price of $\$4.32$ per unit.

64. $R(t) = 20,000e^{-0.15t}$

$R'(t) = 20,000e^{-0.15t}(-0.15) = -3,000e^{-0.15t}$

The rate of depreciation after one year is:
$R'(1) = -3,000e^{-0.15(1)} = -3,000e^{-0.15} \approx -\$2,582$ per year.

The rate of depreciation after two years is:
$R'(2) = -3,000e^{-0.15(2)} \approx -\$2,222$ per year.

The rate of depreciation after three years is:
$R'(3) = -3,000e^{-0.15(3)} \approx -\$1,913$ per year.

66. Revenue: $R(t) = (3)(60,000)(1 - e^{-0.04t})$, $t \geq 0$
$$= 180,000(1 - e^{-0.04t})$$
Cost: $C(t) = 4,000 + 3,000t$, $t \geq 0$
Profit: $P(t) = R(t) - C(t) = 180,000(1 - e^{-0.04t}) - 4,000 - 3,000t$

(A) $P'(t) = 180,000(-e^{-0.04t})(-0.04) - 3000 = 7,200e^{-0.04t} - 3,000$

Critical value(s): $P'(t) = 7,200e^{-0.04t} - 3,000 = 0$
$$e^{-0.04t} = \frac{5}{12}$$
$$-0.04t = \ln\left(\frac{5}{12}\right)$$
$$t = -\frac{\ln\left(\frac{5}{12}\right)}{0.04} \approx 22 \text{ days}$$

$P''(t) = 7,200e^{-0.04t}(-0.04) = -288e^{-0.04t}$
$P''(22) = -288e^{-0.04(22)} < 0$
Since $t = 22$ is the only critical value and $P''(22) < 0$, 22 days of TV promotion should be used to maximize profits. The maximum profit is:

$\quad P(22) = 180,000(1 - e^{-0.04(22)}) - 4,000 - 3,000(22) \approx \$35,399$.
The proportion of people buying the disk after t days is:
$\quad p(t) = 1 - e^{-0.04t}$
Thus, $p(22) = 1 - e^{-0.04(22)} \approx 0.59$ or approximately 59%.

(B) From (A), the sign chart for P' is:

Test Numbers	
t	$P'(t)$
0	4,200 (+)
50	2,025.59 (−)

Thus, P is increasing on $(0, 22)$ and decreasing on $(22, \infty)$; P has a maximum at $t = 22$. Since $P''(t) = -288e^{-0.04t} < 0$ on $(0, \infty)$, the graph of P is concave downward on $(0, \infty)$; $P(0) = -4{,}000$ and $P(50) \approx 0$. The graph of P is shown at the right.

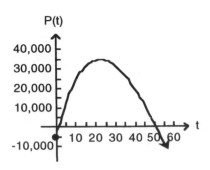

68. $C(t) = 250(1 - e^{-t})$, $t \geq 0$

(A) $C'(t) = 250e^{-t}$

$C'(1) = 250e^{-1} \approx 92$

$C'(2) = 250e^{-2} \approx 4.6$

Thus, at the end of 1 minute concentration is increasing at the rate of 92 micrograms/milliliter per minute; At the end of 4 minutes the concentration is increasing at the rate of 4.6 micrograms/milliliter per minute.

(B) $C'(t) = 250e^{-t} > 0$ on $(0, 5)$
Thus, C is increasing on $(0, 5)$; there are no local extrema.
$C''(t) = -250e^{-t} < 0$ on $(0, \infty)$.
Thus, the graph is concave downward on $(0, 5)$.

t	$C(t)$
0	0
1	158.03
4	245.42
5	248.32

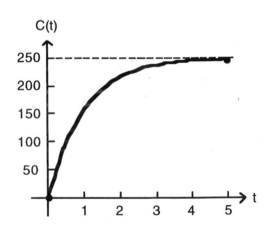

70. $N(t) = 434e^{-0.0866t}$

$N'(t) = 434e^{-0.0866t}(-0.0866)$

$\qquad = -37.5844e^{-0.0866t}$

$N''(2) = -37.5844e^{-0.0866(2)} \approx -32$ legislators per year.

$N'(10) = -37.5844^{-0.0866(10)} \approx -16$ legislators per year.

EXERCISE 5-3

2. $\dfrac{d}{dw} \ln(w + 100) = \dfrac{1}{w + 100}$ (1) (General derivative rule)

$\qquad\qquad\qquad = \dfrac{1}{w + 100}$

4. $\dfrac{d}{dy} \ln(4 - 5y) = \dfrac{1}{4 - 5y} (-5)$ (General derivative rule)

$$= -\dfrac{5}{4 - 5y}$$

6. $y = (\ln x)^3$

$y' = 3(\ln x)^2 \dfrac{d}{dx} \ln x$ (Power rule for functions)

$$= 3(\ln x)^2 \left(\dfrac{1}{x}\right) = \dfrac{3(\ln x)^2}{x}$$

8. $\ln x^6 = 6 \ln x$

$\dfrac{d}{dx} \ln x^6 = 6 \dfrac{d}{dx} \ln x = \dfrac{6}{x}$

10. $f(x) = x^3 \ln x$

$f'(x) = \left(\dfrac{d}{dx} x^3\right) \ln x + x^3 \left(\dfrac{d}{dx} \ln x\right)$ (Product rule)

$$= 3x^2 \ln x + x^3 \left(\dfrac{1}{x}\right) = 3x^2 \ln x + x^2$$

$$= x^2 (1 + 3 \ln x)$$

12. $\dfrac{d}{dx} \ln(x + 1)^{-3} = \dfrac{d}{dx} (-3) \ln(x + 1) = -3 \dfrac{d}{dx} \ln(x + 1) = -3 \dfrac{1}{x + 1} (1)$

$$= -\dfrac{3}{x + 1}$$

14. $f(x) = \dfrac{\ln x}{x^3}$

$f'(x) = \dfrac{\left(\dfrac{d}{dx} \ln x\right) x^3 - \left(\dfrac{d}{dx} x^3\right) \ln x}{(x^3)^2}$ (Quotient rule)

$$= \dfrac{\left(\dfrac{1}{x}\right) x^3 - (3x^2) \ln x}{x^6} = \dfrac{x^2 - 3x^2 \ln x}{x^6} = \dfrac{1 - 3 \ln x}{x^4}$$

16. $f(x) = (x - 1)^2 \ln x$

$f'(x) = \left[\dfrac{d}{dx} (x - 1)^2\right] \ln x + (x - 1)^2 \left(\dfrac{d}{dx} \ln x\right)$

$$= 2(x - 1) \ln x + (x - 1)^2 \left(\dfrac{1}{x}\right)$$

$$= (x - 1) \left(2 \ln x + \dfrac{(x - 1)}{x}\right)$$

18. $f(x) = \ln(x^4 + 5)$

$f'(x) = \dfrac{d}{dx} [\ln(x^4 + 5)] = \dfrac{\dfrac{d}{dx} (x^4 + 5)}{x^4 + 5} = \dfrac{4x^3}{x^4 + 5}$

20. $\dfrac{d}{dx}\ln(x^4 + 5)^{3/2} = \dfrac{1}{(x^4 + 5)^{3/2}}\left(\dfrac{3}{2}(x^4 + 5)^{1/2}(4x^3)\right)$

$$= \dfrac{6x^3(x^4 + 5)^{1/2}}{(x^4 + 5)^{3/2}} = \dfrac{6x^3}{x^4 + 5}$$

22. $f(x) = [\ln(x^4 + 5)]^{3/2}$

$\quad f'(x) = \dfrac{d}{dx}([\ln(x^4 + 5)]^{3/2}) = \dfrac{3}{2}[\ln(x^4 + 5)]^{1/2}\dfrac{d}{dx}(\ln(x^4 + 5))$

$$= \dfrac{3}{2}[\ln(x^4 + 5)]^{1/2}\dfrac{\dfrac{d}{dx}(x^4 + 5)}{x^4 + 5}$$

$$= \dfrac{3}{2}[\ln(x^4 + 5)]^{1/2}\dfrac{4x^3}{x^4 + 5} = \dfrac{6x^3[\ln(x^4 + 5)]^{1/2}}{x^4 + 5}$$

24. $f(x) = x(\ln x)^2$

$\quad f'(x) = \left(\dfrac{d}{dx}x\right)(\ln x)^2 + x\left(\dfrac{d}{dx}(\ln x)^2\right)$

$$= (\ln x)^2 + 2x(\ln x)\left(\dfrac{1}{x}\right)$$

$$= (\ln x)^2 + 2 \ln x$$
$$= (\ln x)(\ln x + 2)$$

26. $f(x) = (5 - \ln x)^4$

$\quad f'(x) = 4(5 - \ln x)^3\left(-\dfrac{1}{x}\right) = \dfrac{-4(5 - \ln x)^3}{x}$

28. $f(x) = x \ln x - x$

$\quad f'(x) = \left(\dfrac{d}{dx}x\right)\ln x + x\left(\dfrac{d}{dx}\ln x\right) - \dfrac{d}{dx}x$

$$= \ln x + x\left(\dfrac{1}{x}\right) - 1$$

$$= \ln x + 1 - 1 = \ln x$$

30. $\dfrac{d}{dx}\dfrac{\ln x}{e^x + 1} = \dfrac{\dfrac{1}{x}(e^x + 1) - e^x \ln x}{(e^x + 1)^2}$

$$= \dfrac{e^x + 1 - xe^x \ln x}{x(e^x + 1)^2}$$

32. $\dfrac{d}{dx}\dfrac{1}{\ln(1 - x^3)} = \dfrac{d}{dx}[\ln(1 - x^3)]^{-1}$

$$= (-1)[\ln(1 - x^3)]^{-2}\dfrac{1}{1 - x^3}(-3x^2)$$

$$= \dfrac{3x^2}{(1 - x^3)[\ln(1 - x^3)]^2}$$

34. $\dfrac{d}{dt}\sqrt[5]{\ln(1 - t^5)} = \dfrac{d}{dt}[\ln(1 - t^5)]^{1/5}$

$\qquad\qquad = \dfrac{1}{5}[\ln(1 - t^5)]^{-4/5}\dfrac{1}{1 - t^5}(-5t^4)$

$\qquad\qquad = \dfrac{-t^4}{(1 - t^5)[\ln(1 - t^5)]^{4/5}}$

36. $f(x) = \ln x$

$\quad f'(x) = \dfrac{d}{dx}\ln x = \dfrac{1}{x}$

The tangent line at $x = 1$ has an equation of the form
$y - y_1 = m(x - x_1)$
where $x_1 = 1$, $y_1 = f(1) = \ln 1 = 0$, and $m = f'(1) = 1$. Thus, we have:
$y - 0 = (1)(x - 1)$ or $y = x - 1$.

38. $f(x) = \ln(2 - \sqrt{x})$

$\quad f'(x) = \dfrac{d}{dx}(\ln(2 - \sqrt{x})) = \dfrac{\dfrac{d}{dx}(2 - \sqrt{x})}{2 - \sqrt{x}} = \dfrac{-\dfrac{1}{2\sqrt{x}}}{2 - \sqrt{x}} = \dfrac{1}{2x - 4\sqrt{x}}$

Slope of the tangent line at $x = 1$ is $f'(1) = \dfrac{1}{2 - 4} = -\dfrac{1}{2}$.

The point on the graph of f with $x = 1$ is $(1, 0)$ and the equation of the tangent line at this point is: $y - 0 = -0.5(x - 1)$ or $y = -0.5x + 0.5$

42. $f(x) = \ln(2x + 4)$

Step 1. Analyze $f(x)$:

(A) Domain: $2x + 4 > 0$ or $x > -2$, $(-2, \infty)$

(B) Intercepts: y intercept: $f(0) = \ln 4 \approx 1.386$

$\qquad\qquad\qquad\quad x$ intercepts: $\ln(2x + 4) = 0$
$\qquad\qquad\qquad\qquad\qquad\qquad 2x + 4 = 1$
$\qquad\qquad\qquad\qquad\qquad\qquad\quad 2x = -3$
$\qquad\qquad\qquad\qquad\qquad\qquad\quad\ x = -1.5$

(C) Asymptotes:
    <u>Horizontal asymptote</u>: $\lim\limits_{x \to \infty} \ln(2x + 4)$ does not exist.
                              Thus, there are no horizontal asymptotes.

    <u>Vertical asymptote</u>: $\lim\limits_{x \to -2^+} \ln(2x + 4) = -\infty$, so $x = -2$ is a
                              vertical asymptote.

Step 2. Analyze $f'(x)$:
$\quad f'(x) = \dfrac{1}{2x + 4}(2) = \dfrac{1}{x + 2} > 0$ for $x > -2$
Therefore, f is increasing on $(-2, \infty)$.

Step 3. Analyze $f''(x)$:
$\quad f''(x) = -\dfrac{1}{(x + 2)^2} < 0$ and hence the graph of f is concave downward on
$(-2, \infty)$; there are no inflection points.

Step 4. Sketch the graph of f:

x	$f(x)$
0	≈ 1.386
-1.5	0
1	≈ 1.792

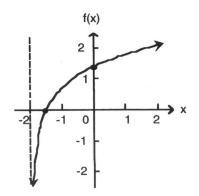

44. $f(x) = \ln(x^2 + 4)$

Step 1. Analyze $f(x)$:

(A) Domain: All real numbers, $(-\infty, \infty)$.

(B) Intercepts: y intercept: $f(0) = \ln 4 \approx 1.386$

x intercepts: None, since $x^2 + 4$ cannot be equal to 1.

(C) Asymptotes:

<u>Horizontal asymptote</u>: None; $\lim\limits_{x \to \pm\infty} \ln(x^2 + 4)$ does not exist.

Step 2. Analyze $f'(x)$:

$$f'(x) = \frac{1}{x^2 + 4}(2x) = \frac{2x}{x^2 + 4}$$

Critical value: $f'(x) = \dfrac{2x}{x^2 + 4} = 0$

$$x = 0$$

Partition numbers: $x = 0$

Sign chart for f':

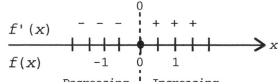

Test Numbers	
x	$f'(x)$
-1	$-\frac{2}{5}$ $(-)$
1	$\frac{2}{5}$ $(+)$

Thus, f is decreasing on $(-\infty, 0)$ and increasing on $(0, \infty)$; f has a local minimum at $x = 0$.

Step 3. Analyze $f''(x)$:

$$f''(x) = \frac{2(x^2 + 4) - 2x(2x)}{(x^2 + 4)^2} = \frac{2x^2 + 8 - 4x^2}{(x^2 + 4)^2} = \frac{2(4 - x^2)}{(x^2 + 4)^2}$$

Partition numbers for f'': $4 - x^2 = (2 - x)(2 + x) = 0$

$$x = -2 \text{ and } x = 2$$

Sign chart for f'':

f''(x)   − − − 0 + + + + + + + 0 − − −

-3 -2   0   2 3

| Graph | Concave | Concave | Concave |
| of f | Downward | Upward | Downward |

Test Numbers	
x	$f''(x)$
-3	$-\frac{10}{169}$ $(-)$
0	$\frac{1}{2}$ $(+)$
3	$-\frac{10}{169}$ $(-)$

Thus, the graph of f is concave downward on $(-\infty, -2)$ and on $(2, \infty)$; the graph of f is concave upward on $(-2, 2)$; the graph has inflection points at $x = -2$ and at $x = 2$.

Step 4. Sketch the graph of f:

x	$f(x)$
0	≈ 1.386
-2	≈ 2.079
2	≈ 2.079

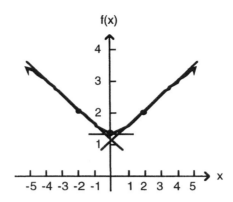

46. $f(x) = \dfrac{\ln x}{x}$.

Step 1. Analyze $f(x)$:

(A) Domain: All positive real numbers, $(0, \infty)$.

(B) Intercepts: y intercept: Does not exist;
        0 is not in the domain of f.

$\qquad\qquad$ x intercept: $f(x) = \dfrac{\ln x}{x} = 0$

$$\ln x = 0$$
$$x = 1$$

(C) Asymptotes:

$\underline{\text{Horizontal asymptote}}$: $\displaystyle\lim_{x\to\infty} \dfrac{\ln x}{x} = 0$;

$\qquad\qquad$ thus, $y = 0$ is a horizontal asymptote.

$\underline{\text{Vertical asymptote}}$: $\displaystyle\lim_{x\to 0^+} \dfrac{\ln x}{x} = -\infty$;

$\qquad\qquad$ thus, $x = 0$ is a vertical asymptote.

Step 2. Analyze $f'(x)$:

$$f'(x) = \dfrac{\dfrac{1}{x}(x) - (1)\ln x}{x^2} = \dfrac{1 - \ln x}{x^2}$$

Critical values: $f'(x) = \dfrac{1 - \ln x}{x^2} = 0$

$$1 - \ln x = 0$$
$$\ln x = 1$$
$$x = e$$

Thus, $x = e$ is the only critical value of f.
$x = e$ is also a partition number for f'.
Sign chart for f':

$$f'(x) \quad\quad + + + + + \; | - - - $$

```
f'(x)      + + + + + ¦ - - -
   ─┼┼┼┼┼┼┼●┼┼──→ x
f(x)    1     2   e 3
       Increasing ¦ Decreasing
```

Test Numbers	
x	$f'(x)$
1	$1 \ (+)$
3	$\dfrac{1-\ln 3}{9} \ (-)$

Thus, f has a maximum value at $x = e$;
$f(e) = \dfrac{\ln e}{e} = \dfrac{1}{e} = e^{-1}$ is the absolute maximum of f.

Step 3. Analyze $f''(x)$:

$$f''(x) = \frac{-\frac{1}{x}(x^2) - 2x(1 - \ln x)}{x^4} = \frac{-x - 2x + 2x \ln x}{x^4} = \frac{2 \ln x - 3}{x^3}$$

$$f''(x) = 0, \quad 2 \ln x - 3 = 0, \quad \ln x = \frac{3}{2}, \quad x = e^{3/2}$$

Thus, $x = e^{3/2}$ is a partition number for f''.

Sign chart for f'':

$f''(x)$ $- - - - -$ 0 $+ + + + +$

Test Numbers	
x	$f''(x)$
1	-3 (−)
e^2	$\frac{1}{e^6}$ (+)

1    $e^{3/2}$ e^2

Graph   Concave   Concave
of f Downward   Upward

Thus, the graph of f is concave downward on $(0, e^{3/2})$ and concave upward on $(e^{3/2}, \infty)$; the graph has an inflection point at $x = e^{3/2}$.

Step 4. Sketch the graph of f:

x	$f(x)$
$\frac{1}{2}$	$-2 \ln 2$
1	0
e	e^{-1}
e^2	$2e^{-2}$

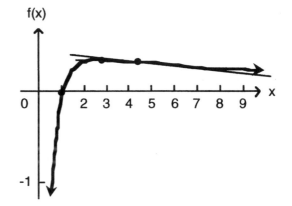

48. $f(x) = \dfrac{x}{\ln x}$

Step 1. Analyze $f(x)$:
(A) Domain: All positive real numbers, except $x = 1$.

(B) Intercepts: y-intercept: None
                 x-intercept: None

(C) Asymptotes:
    <u>Horizontal asymptotes</u>: None

    <u>Vertical asymptotes</u>: $x = 1$ (zero of the denominator)

Step 2. Analyze $f'(x)$:

$$f'(x) = \frac{\left(\frac{d}{dx}x\right)\ln x - x\frac{d}{dx}(\ln x)}{(\ln x)^2} = \frac{\ln x - 1}{(\ln x)^2}$$

Critical value: $f'(x) = 0$, $\ln x = 1$, $x = e$.
Partition numbers for f': $x = 1$, $x = e$.

Sign chart for f':

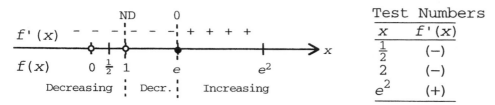

Test Numbers	
x	$f'(x)$
$\frac{1}{2}$	$(-)$
2	$(-)$
e^2	$(+)$

Thus, f is decreasing on $(0, 1)$ and on $(1, e)$ and increasing on (e, ∞); f has a local minimum at $x = e$.

Step 3. Analyze $f''(x)$:

$$f''(x) = \frac{\left(\frac{d}{dx}(\ln x - 1)\right)(\ln x)^2 - (\ln x - 1)\left(\frac{d}{dx}(\ln x)^2\right)}{(\ln x)^4}$$

$$= \frac{\frac{1}{x}(\ln x) - (\ln x - 1)\left(\frac{2}{x}\right)}{(\ln x)^3} = \frac{2 \ln x}{x(\ln x)^3}$$

$f''(x) = 0$ if $x = e^2$ and hence 1 and e^2 are partition numbers for f'' on $(0, \infty)$.

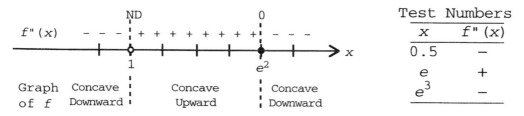

Test Numbers	
x	$f''(x)$
0.5	$-$
e	$+$
e^3	$-$

Thus, the graph of f is concave downward on $(0, 1)$ and on (e^2, ∞) and concave upward on $(1, e^2)$; the graph of f has an inflection point at $x = e^2$.

Step 4. Sketch the graph of f:

x	$f(x)$
0.5	-0.72
e	2.718
e^2	3.694

50. $f(x) = 4x \ln x - 7x$

$f'(x) = 4 \ln x + 4x \dfrac{d}{dx} \ln x - 7$

$\quad = 4 \ln x + 4x \left(\dfrac{1}{x}\right) - 7 = 4 \ln x + 4 - 7 = 4 \ln x - 3, \quad x > 0$

Critical values: $f'(x) = 4 \ln x - 3 = 0$

$$\ln x = \frac{3}{4} = 0.75$$
$$x = e^{0.75}$$

Thus, $x = e^{0.75}$ is the only critical value of f on $(0, \infty)$.

Now, $f''(x) = \dfrac{d}{dx}(4 \ln x - 3) = \dfrac{4}{x}$ and

$f''(e^{0.75}) = \dfrac{4}{e^{0.75}} > 0.$

Therefore, f has a minimum value at $x = e^{0.75}$,

and $f(e^{0.75}) = 4(e^{0.75}) \ln e^{0.75} - 7(e^{0.75})$

$\qquad = 4(e^{0.75})(0.75) - 7e^{0.75}$

$\qquad = 3e^{0.75} - 7e^{0.75} = -4e^{0.75} \approx -8.468$

52. $f(x) = x^3 (\ln x - 2), \quad x > 0$

$f'(x) = \left(\dfrac{d}{dx}(x^3)\right)(\ln x - 2) + x^3 \left(\dfrac{d}{dx}(\ln x - 2)\right)$

$\quad = 3x^2(\ln x - 2) + x^3 \left(\dfrac{1}{x}\right)$

$\quad = 3x^2(\ln x - 2) + x^2$

$\quad = x^2[3 \ln x - 6 + 1] = x^2(3 \ln x - 5)$

Critical values: $f'(x) = x^2(3 \ln x - 5) = 0$

$$3 \ln x - 5 = 0$$
$$\ln x = \frac{5}{3}$$
$$x = e^{5/3}$$

Thus, $x = e^{5/3}$ is the only critical value of f on $(0, \infty)$.

Now, $f''(x) = \left(\dfrac{d}{dx} x^2\right)(3 \ln x - 5) + x^2 \left(\dfrac{d}{dx}(3 \ln x - 5)\right)$

$\quad = 2x(3 \ln x - 5) + x^2 \left(\dfrac{3}{x}\right)$

$\quad = 2x(3 \ln x - 5) + 3x$

$\quad = x(6 \ln x - 10 + 3)$

$\quad = x(6 \ln x - 7), \quad x > 0$

$f''(e^{5/3}) = e^{5/3}(6 \ln(e^{5/3}) - 7)$

$\qquad = e^{5/3}\left(6\left(\dfrac{5}{3}\right) - 7\right)$

$\qquad = e^{5/3}(10 - 7) = 3e^{5/3} > 0$

Therefore, f has a minimum value at

$x = e^{5/3}$ and $f(e^{5/3}) = (e^{5/3})^3 (\ln(e^{5/3}) - 2)$

$$= e^5\left(\frac{5}{3} - 2\right) = -\frac{e^5}{3} \approx -49.471$$

is the absolute minimum of f.

54. $f(x) = \ln(x^2 e^{-x})$

$$f'(x) = \frac{\frac{d}{dx}(x^2 e^{-x})}{x^2 e^{-x}} = \frac{2xe^{-x} - x^2 e^{-x}}{x^2 e^{-x}} = \frac{2 - x}{x} = \frac{2}{x} - 1$$

$f'(x) = 0$ if $x = 2$. This is the only critical value on $(0, \infty)$.

$f''(x) = -\dfrac{2}{x^2} < 0$ for all x in $(0, \infty)$.

Thus, the absolute maximum of f is

$f(2) = \ln(4e^{-2}) = \ln 4 - 2 \approx -0.6137$.

56. $\dfrac{d}{dx}\log(x^3 - 1) = \dfrac{1}{\ln 10} \cdot \dfrac{1}{x^3 - 1}(3x^2) = \dfrac{1}{\ln 10} \cdot \dfrac{3x^2}{x^3 - 1}$

58. $\dfrac{d}{dx}8^{1-2x^2} = 8^{1-2x^2}(-4x)(\ln 8) = -4x\,8^{1-2x^2}(\ln 8)$

60. $\dfrac{d}{dx}\log_5(5^{x^2-1}) = \dfrac{1}{\ln 5} \cdot \dfrac{1}{5^{x^2-1}}(5^{x^2-1}(2x)(\ln 5))$

$\qquad\qquad = 2x$

or

$\dfrac{d}{dx}\log_5(5^{x^2-1}) = \dfrac{d}{dx}[(x^2 - 1)\log_5 5]$

$\qquad\qquad\qquad = \dfrac{d}{dx}(x^2 - 1) = 2x$

62. $\dfrac{d}{dx}10^{\ln x} = 10^{\ln x}\left(\dfrac{1}{x}\right)(\ln 10) = \dfrac{\ln 10}{x}10^{\ln x}$

64. Let $y_1 = (\ln x)^3$ and $y_2 = \sqrt{x}$ and use the intersection command to obtain $(3.41, 1.85)$.

66. On a graphing utility, graph $y_1 = \ln x$ and $y_2 = x^{1/4}$. There is a point of intersection at $(4.18, 1.43)$ (two decimal places). Using the hint that $\ln x < x^{1/4}$ for large x, we find a second point of intersection at $(5,503.66, 8.61)$.

68. $f'(x) = (1)\ln(x + 1) + (x + 1) \cdot \dfrac{1}{x + 1} - 1 = \ln(x + 1)$

$g'(x) = \dfrac{1}{3}(x + 1)^{-2/3}$

which are not the same function. All four functions appear in the view window $0 \le x \le 5$, $0 \le y \le 3$.

70. Demand: $p = 15 - 4 \ln x$, $1 \le x \le 40$

Revenue: $R = xp = x(15 - 4 \ln x) = 15x - 4x \ln x$

Cost: $C = x(5) = 5x$

Profit = Revenue − Cost: $P = 15x - 4x \ln x - 5x$

$$\text{or} \quad P(x) = 10x - 4x \ln x$$

$$P'(x) = 10 - 4 \ln x - 4x\left(\frac{1}{x}\right) = 10 - 4 \ln x - 4$$

$$= 6 - 4 \ln x$$

Critical value(s): $P'(x) = 6 - 4 \ln x = 0$

$$\ln x = \frac{3}{2}$$

$$x = e^{3/2}$$

$P''(x) = -\dfrac{4}{x} < 0$ for $1 \le x \le 40$

Since $x = e^{3/2}$ is the only critical value and $P''(e^{3/2}) < 0$, the maximum weekly profit occurs when $x = e^{3/2} \approx 4.48$ and the price $p = 15 - 4 \ln e^{3/2} = 15 - 4\left(\dfrac{3}{2}\right) = 15 - 6 = 9$. Thus, the T-shirts should be sold at \$9.

72. Cost: $C(x) = 1{,}000 + 200x - 200 \ln x$, $x \ge 1$

Average cost: $\overline{C}(x) = \dfrac{1{,}000}{x} + 200 - \dfrac{200}{x}\ln x$

$$\overline{C}'(x) = -\dfrac{1{,}000}{x^2} + \dfrac{200}{x^2}\ln x - \dfrac{200}{x^2}$$

$$= \dfrac{-1{,}200 + 200 \ln x}{x^2}, \quad x \ge 1$$

Critical value(s): $\overline{C}'(x) = \dfrac{-1{,}200 + 200 \ln x}{x^2} = 0$

$$-1{,}200 + 200 \ln x = 0$$

$$\ln x = 6$$

$$x = e^6$$

$$\overline{C}''(x) = \dfrac{\dfrac{200}{x}(x^2) - 2x(-1{,}200 + 200 \ln x)}{x^4}$$

$$= \dfrac{200x - 2x(-1{,}200 + 200 \ln x)}{x^3}$$

$$= \dfrac{200 + 2{,}400 - 400 \ln x}{x^3} = \dfrac{2{,}600 - 400 \ln x}{x^3}$$

$$\overline{C}''(e^6) = \dfrac{2{,}600 - 400(e^6)}{(e^6)^3} = \dfrac{2{,}600 - 2{,}400}{e^{18}}$$

$$= \dfrac{200}{e^{18}} > 0$$

Since $x = e^6$ is the only critical value and $\bar{C}''(e^6) > 0$, the minimum average cost is

$$\bar{C}(e^6) = \frac{1,000}{e^6} + 200 - \frac{200}{e^6} \ln e^6$$

$$= \frac{1,000}{e^6} + 200 - \frac{1,200}{e^6} \approx \$199.50$$

74. Let x = the number of pairs of shoes sold. Then
$C(x) = 62x$
The logarithmic regression equation for the price p is:

```
LnReg
 y=a+blnx
 a=290.4034973
 b=-26.12049991
```

and revenue $R(x) = xp(x) = x(290.4034973 - 26.12049991 \ln x)$

$$= 290.4034973x - 26.12049991x \ln x$$

Profit $P(x) = 290.4034973x - 26.12049991x \ln x - 62x$

$$= 228.4034973x - 26.12049991x \ln x$$

$P'(x) = 228.4034973 - 26.12049991 \ln x - 26.12049991$

$$= 202.2829974 - 26.12049991 \ln x$$

Critical value: $202.2829974 - 26.12049991 \ln x = 0$

$$\ln x \approx \frac{202.2829974}{26.12049991} = 7.744223813$$

$$x = e^{7.744223813} \approx 2,308$$

The maximum profit occurs when $x = 2,308$ pairs of shoes are sold at the price $p = \$88.12$.

76. Let x = the number of megabyte disks per week. The weekly cost is $C(x) = 6x$.
The weekly revenue is $R(x) = xp(x)$, where
$p(x) = ab^x$ is the exponential regression model for the given data.

```
ExpReg
 y=a*b^x
 a=19.48500402
 b=.9997305866
```

The weekly profit is $P(x) = R(x) - C(x)$. Using a graphing utility we find that the maximum profit is achieved at the demand level $x = 1837$. The price that will maximize the profit is $p(1837) = \$11.88$ (to the nearest cent).

78.

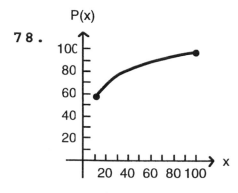

80. $T(t) = 30e^{-0.58t} + 38, \ t \geq 0$

$T'(t) = 30e^{-0.58t}(-0.58) = -17.4e^{-0.58t}$

$T'(1) = -17.4e^{-0.58(1)} \approx -9.74°\,F$ per hour.

$T'(4) = -17.4e^{-0.58(4)} \approx -1.71°\,F$ per hour.

82. $A(t) = 1,000 \cdot 2^{4t}$

$A'(t) = 1,000 \cdot 2^{4t}(4)(\ln 2) = 4,000 \cdot 2^{4t}(\ln 2)$

$A'(1) = 4,000 \cdot 2^{4(1)}(\ln 2) \approx 44,361$ bacteria per hour (rate of change at the end of the first hour);

$A'(5) = 4,000 \cdot 2^{4(5)}(\ln 2) \approx 2,907,269,992$ bacteria per hour (rate of change at the end of the fifth hour).

84. $N(t) = 10 + 6 \ln t, \ t \geq 1$

$N'(t) = \dfrac{6}{t}$

$N'(10) = \dfrac{6}{10} = 0.6$

$N'(100) = \dfrac{6}{100} = 0.06$

After 10 hours of instruction and practice, the rate of learning is 0.6 words/minute per hour of instruction and practice.

After 100 hours of instruction and practice, the rate of learning is 0.06 words/minute per hour of instruction and practice.

EXERCISE 5-4

2. $y = u^3; \ u = 3 - \ln x$

$\dfrac{dy}{du} = 3u^2, \quad \dfrac{du}{dx} = -\dfrac{1}{x}, \quad \dfrac{dy}{dx} = \dfrac{dy}{du} \cdot \dfrac{du}{dx}$

$$= 3u^2 \cdot \left(\dfrac{-1}{x}\right)$$

$$= 3(3 - \ln x)^2 \left(-\dfrac{1}{x}\right)$$

$$= -\dfrac{3(3 - \ln x)^2}{x}$$

4. $y = e^u; \ u = x^6 + 5x^2$

$\dfrac{dy}{du} = e^u, \quad \dfrac{du}{dx} = 6x^5 + 10x, \quad \dfrac{dy}{dx} = \dfrac{dy}{du} \cdot \dfrac{du}{dx}$

$$= e^u(6x^5 + 10x)$$

$$= (6x^5 + 10x)\,e^{x^6+5x^2}$$

6. $y = \ln u; \ u = 2 + 3x^4$

$\dfrac{dy}{dx} = \dfrac{1}{u}, \quad \dfrac{du}{dx} = 12x^3, \quad \dfrac{dy}{dx} = \dfrac{dy}{du} \cdot \dfrac{du}{dx}$

$$= \dfrac{1}{u} \cdot (12x^3) = \dfrac{12x^3}{2 + 3x^4}$$

8. $y = \ln w;\ w = 1 + e^4;\ u = x^2$

$\dfrac{dy}{dw} = \dfrac{1}{w},\ \dfrac{dw}{du} = e^u,\ \dfrac{du}{dx} = 2x$

$\dfrac{dy}{dx} = \dfrac{dy}{dw} \cdot \dfrac{dw}{du} \cdot \dfrac{du}{dx} = \dfrac{1}{w} \cdot e^u(2x)$

$\qquad\qquad = \dfrac{1}{1 + e^u} \cdot e^u(2x)$

$\qquad\qquad = \dfrac{2xe^{x^2}}{1 + e^{x^2}}$

10. $y = e^w;\ w = -u^2;\ u = \ln x$

$\dfrac{dy}{dw} = e^w,\ \dfrac{dw}{du} = -2u,\ \dfrac{du}{dx} = \dfrac{1}{x}$

$\dfrac{dy}{dx} = \dfrac{dy}{dw} \cdot \dfrac{dw}{du} \cdot \dfrac{du}{dx} = e^w(-2u)\left(\dfrac{1}{x}\right)$

$\qquad\qquad = e^{-u^2}(-2u)\left(\dfrac{1}{x}\right)$

$\qquad\qquad = e^{-(\ln x)^2}(-2 \ln x)\left(\dfrac{1}{x}\right)$

$\qquad\qquad = -\dfrac{2 \ln x}{xe^{(\ln x)^2}}$

12. $y = e^w;\ w = \sqrt{u};\ u = \ln x$

$\dfrac{dy}{dw} = e^w,\ \dfrac{dw}{du} = \dfrac{1}{2\sqrt{u}},\ \dfrac{du}{dx} = \dfrac{1}{x}$

$\dfrac{dy}{dx} = \dfrac{dy}{dw} \cdot \dfrac{dw}{du} \cdot \dfrac{du}{dx} = e^w \cdot \dfrac{1}{2\sqrt{u}} \cdot \dfrac{1}{x}$

$\qquad\qquad = \dfrac{e^{\sqrt{u}}}{2\sqrt{u}} \cdot \dfrac{1}{x} = \dfrac{e^{\sqrt{\ln x}}}{2x\sqrt{\ln x}}$

14. $f(x) = 5x + 200$

$f'(x) = 5$

$\dfrac{f'(x)}{f(x)} = \dfrac{5}{5x + 200} = \dfrac{1}{x + 40}$

16. $f(x) = 50x - 0.01x^2$

$f'(x) = 50 - 0.02x$

$\dfrac{f'(x)}{f(x)} = \dfrac{50 - 0.02x}{50x - 0.01x^2}$

18. $f(x) = 5 - 3e^{-x}$

$f'(x) = 3e^{-x}$

$\dfrac{f'(x)}{f(x)} = \dfrac{3e^{-x}}{5 - 3e^{-x}} = \dfrac{3}{5e^x - 3}$

20. $f(x) = 15x + 2x \ln x$

$f'(x) = 15 + 2 \ln x + 2x\left(\dfrac{1}{x}\right) = 17 + 2 \ln x$

$\dfrac{f'(x)}{f(x)} = \dfrac{17 + 2 \ln x}{15x + 2x \ln x}$

22. $x = f(p) = 1,875 - p^2$

$E(p) = \dfrac{-pf'(p)}{f(p)} = \dfrac{-p(-2p)}{1,875 - p^2} = \dfrac{2p^2}{1,875 - p^2}$

(A) $E(15) = \dfrac{2(15)^2}{1,875 - (15)^2} = 0.\overline{27} < 1;$ INELASTIC

(B) $E(25) = \dfrac{2(25)^2}{1,875 - (25)^2} = 1;$ UNIT ELASTICITY

(C) $E(40) = \dfrac{2(40)^2}{1,875 - (40)^2} = 11.64 > 1;$ ELASTIC

24. $x = f(p) = 875 - p - 0.05p^2$

$E(p) = \dfrac{-p(-1 - 0.10p)}{875 - p - 0.05p^2} = \dfrac{p + 0.10p^2}{875 - p - 0.05p^2}$

(A) $E(50) = \dfrac{50 + 0.10(50)^2}{875 - 50 - 0.05(50)^2} = 0.43 < 1;$ INELASTIC

(B) $E(70) = \dfrac{70 + 0.10(70)^2}{875 - 70 - 0.05(70)^2} = 1;$ UNIT ELASTICITY

(C) $E(100) = \dfrac{100 + 0.10(100)^2}{875 - 100 - 0.05(100)^2} = 4;$ ELASTIC

26. $p + 0.01x = 50$

(A) $0.01x = 50 - p,\quad x = \dfrac{50}{0.01} - \dfrac{1}{0.01}p$

$\qquad\qquad\qquad = 5,000 - 100p,\ 0 \le p \le 50$

(B) $E(p) = -\dfrac{p(-100)}{5,000 - 100p} = \dfrac{p}{50 - p}$

(C) $E(10) = \dfrac{10}{50 - 10} = 0.25;\ (0.25)(5\%) = 1.25\%$ increase

(D) $E(45) = \dfrac{45}{50 - 45} = 9;\ 9(5\%) = 45\%$ increase

(E) $E(25) = \dfrac{25}{50 - 25} = 1;\ 1(5\%) = 5\%$ increase

28. $0.025x + p = 50$

(A) $0.025x = 50 - p$, $x = \dfrac{50}{0.025} - \dfrac{1}{0.025}p = 2{,}000 - 40p$, $0 \le p \le 50$

(B) $R(p) = px = p(2{,}000 - 40p) = 2{,}000p - 40p^2$

(C) $E(p) = \dfrac{-p(-40)}{2{,}000 - 40p} = \dfrac{40p}{2{,}000 - 40p} = \dfrac{p}{50 - p}$

(D) $E(p) > 1$ if $\dfrac{p}{50 - p} > 1$ or $p > 50 - p$ or $p > 25$.

Thus, Elastic on $(25, 50)$ and Inelastic on $(0, 25)$.

(E) Inelastic on $(0, 25)$ implies revenue increase on $(0, 25)$.
Elastic on $(25, 50)$ implies revenue decrease on $(25, 50)$.

(F) Since $p = \$10 < \$25$, a decrease in price results in decrease in revenue.

(G) Since $p = \$40 > \$25$, a decrease in price results in increase in revenue.

30. $x = f(p) = 5(p - 60)^2$

$E(p) = \dfrac{-pf'(p)}{f(p)} = \dfrac{-p[10(p - 60)]}{5(p - 60)^2} = -\dfrac{2p}{p - 60} = \dfrac{2p}{60 - p}$

$E(p) > 1$, $\dfrac{2p}{60 - p} > 1$ or $2p > 60 - p$ or $3p > 60$ or $p > 20$.

Thus, Elastic on $(20, 60)$ and Inelastic on $(0, 20)$.

32. $x = f(p) = \sqrt{324 - 2p}$ $\qquad$ $324 - 2p \ge 0$ $\quad$ or $\quad$ $0 \le p \le 162$

$E(p) = \dfrac{-pf'(p)}{f(p)} = \dfrac{-p\left[\dfrac{1}{2}(-2)(324 - 2p)^{-1/2}\right]}{(324 - 2p)^{1/2}} = \dfrac{p}{324 - 2p}$

$E(p) = \dfrac{p}{324 - 2p} > 1$ implies that $p > 108$. Thus, Elastic on $(108, 162)$
and Inelastic on $(0, 108)$.

34. $x = f(p) = \sqrt{3{,}600 - 2p^2}$, $3{,}600 - 2p^2 \ge 0$, $0 \le p \le 30\sqrt{2}$

$E(p) = \dfrac{-pf'(p)}{f(p)} = \dfrac{-p\left[\dfrac{1}{2}(-4p)(3{,}600 - 2p^2)^{-1/2}\right]}{(3{,}600 - 2p^2)^{1/2}} = \dfrac{2p^2}{3{,}600 - 2p^2}$

$E(p) = \dfrac{2p^2}{3{,}600 - 2p^2} > 1$ implies that $2p^2 > 3{,}600 - 2p^2$

or $4p^2 > 3{,}600$ or $p^2 > 900$ or $30 < p < 30\sqrt{2}$

Therefore, Elastic on $(30, 30\sqrt{2})$ and Inelastic on $(0, 30)$.

36. $x = f(p) = 10(16 - p)$, $0 \leq p \leq 16$

$R(p) = px = p[10(16 - p)] = 160p - 10p^2$.

$R(p)$ is a parabola and its graph over $[0, 16]$ is given below.

<u>Note</u>: $R'(p) > 0$
($R(p)$ increasing)
corresponds to Inelastic and
$R'(p) < 0$
($R(p)$ decreasing)
corresponds to Elastic.

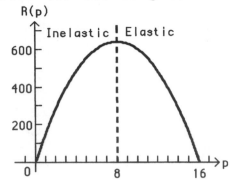

38. $x = f(p) = 10(p - 9)^2$

$R(p) = px = 10p(p - 9)^2$

$R'(p) = 10(p - 9)^2 + 20p(p - 9) = 10(p - 9)[p - 9 + 2p]$
$\qquad\qquad\qquad\qquad\qquad\qquad = 10(p - 9)(3p - 9)$

Critical value in the interval $(0, 9)$ is $p = 3$.

$R'(p) > 0$ for $3p - 9 < 0$ or $p < 3$ and $R'(p) < 0$ for $3p - 9 > 0$ or $p > 3$.
(Note that $p - 9 \leq 0$).

The graph of $R(p)$ is:

<u>Note</u>: $R'(p) > 0$ on $(0, 3)$,
thus Inelastic.
$R'(p) < 0$ on $(3, 9)$,
thus Elastic.

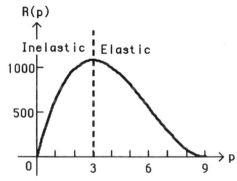

40. $x = f(p) = 30 - 5\sqrt{p} \geq 0$ implies $0 \leq p \leq 36$

$(30 - 5\sqrt{p} \geq 0$ or $\sqrt{p} \leq 6$ or $p \leq 36)$

$R(p) = px = p(30 - 5\sqrt{p}) = 30p - 5p^{3/2}$

$R'(p) = 30 - \dfrac{15}{2}p^{1/2} > 0$ if $30 > \dfrac{15}{2}p^{1/2}$ or

$p^{1/2} < 4$ or $p < 16$. Thus $R'(p) > 0$ (or Inelastic) on $(0, 16)$ and
$R'(p) < 0$ (Elastic) on $(16, 36)$.

The graph of $R(p)$ is:

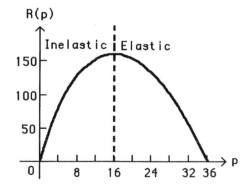

42. $p = g(x) = 30 - 0.05x$

$g'(x) = -0.05$

$E(x) = -\dfrac{g(x)}{xg'(x)} = -\dfrac{30 - 0.05x}{-0.05x} = \dfrac{600}{x} - 1$

For $x = 400$, $E(400) = \dfrac{600}{400} - 1 = \dfrac{3}{2} - 1 = \dfrac{1}{2}$.

44. $p = g(x) = 20 - \sqrt{x}$

$g'(x) = -\dfrac{1}{2\sqrt{x}}$

$E(x) = -\dfrac{20 - \sqrt{x}}{x\left(-\dfrac{1}{2\sqrt{x}}\right)} = \dfrac{20 - \sqrt{x}}{\dfrac{1}{2}\sqrt{x}} = \dfrac{2(20 - \sqrt{x})}{\sqrt{x}}$

For $x = 100$, $E(100) = \dfrac{2(20 - 10)}{10} = 2$

46. $x = f(p) = Ae^{-kp}$

$E(p) = \dfrac{-pf'(p)}{f(p)} = \dfrac{-p\left[-kAe^{-kp}\right]}{Ae^{-kp}} = \dfrac{kApe^{-kp}}{Ae^{-kp}} = kp$

48. $(0.40)(15) = \$6$ per day

50. $x = 2{,}000 - 400p$

$E(p) = \dfrac{-p(-400)}{2{,}000 - 400p} = \dfrac{p}{5 - p}$

$E(3) = \dfrac{3}{5 - 3} = \dfrac{3}{2} > 1$

Thus, 10% increase in the price will result in a decrease in revenue.

52. $R(p) = 800p - 1000p^2$

$R'(p) = 800 - 2000p > 0$ if $p < 0.40$, so for $p = \$0.60$, $R'(p) < 0$ (i.e. $R(p)$ is decreasing) so a 10% price decrease will cause an increase in revenue.

54. From Problem 51, we have

$R(p) = p(800 - 1{,}000p) = 800p - 1{,}000p^2$

$R'(p) = 800 - 2{,}000p = 0$, $p = \dfrac{800}{2{,}000} = 0.40$

$R''(p) = -2{,}000 < 0$ for all p.

Thus, $p = \$0.40$ will maximize the revenue from selling fries.

56. $f(t) = 1.47t + 25.5$

$f'(t) = 1.47$

$$\frac{f'(t)}{f(t)}(100) = \frac{1.47}{1.47t + 25.5}(100)$$

$$= \frac{147}{1.47t + 25.5}$$

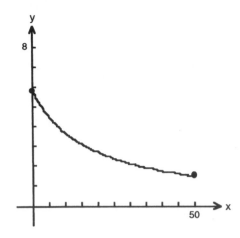

58. $a(t) = 19.6 - 6.0 \ln t$

$$a'(t) = -\frac{6}{t}$$

$$\frac{a'(t)}{a(t)}(100) = \frac{-\frac{6}{t}}{19.6 - 6.0 \ln t}(100) = \frac{-600}{19.6t - 6t \ln t}$$

For $t = 12$, we have $\dfrac{-600}{19.6(12) - 6(12) \ln 12} = -10.66$, so -0.011 assaults

annually per 1,000 population age 12 or over.

EXERCISE 5-5

2. $-2x + 6y - 4 = 0$

(A) Implicit differentiation:

$$\frac{d}{dx}(-2x) + \frac{d}{dx}(6y) + \frac{d}{dx}(-4) = \frac{d}{dx}(0)$$

$$-2 + 6y' - 0 = 0$$

$$y' = \frac{2}{6} = \frac{1}{3}$$

(B) $6y = 2x + 4$

$$y = \frac{1}{3}x + \frac{2}{3}$$

$$y' = \frac{1}{3}$$

4. $2x^3 + 5y - 2 = 0$

(A) Implicit differentiation:

$$\frac{d}{dx}(2x^3) + \frac{d}{dx}(5y) + \frac{d}{dx}(-2) = \frac{d}{dx}(0)$$

$$6x^2 + 5y' + 0 = 0$$

$$5y' = -6x^2$$

$$y' = -\frac{6}{5}x^2$$

(B) $5y = -2x^3 + 2$

$$y = -\frac{2}{5}x^3 + \frac{2}{5}$$

$$y' = -\frac{6}{5}x^2$$

6. $5x^3 - y - 1 = 0$

$$\frac{d}{dx}(5x^3) + \frac{d}{dx}(-y) + \frac{d}{dx}(-1) = \frac{d}{dx}(0)$$

$$15x^2 - y' + 0 = 0$$

$$y' = 15x^2$$

$$y'\Big|_{(1,4)} = 15(1)^2 = 15$$

8. $y^2 + x^3 + 4 = 0$

$$\frac{d}{dx}(y^2) + \frac{d}{dx}(x^3) + \frac{d}{dx}(4) = \frac{d}{dx}(0)$$

$$2yy' + 3x^2 + 0 = 0$$

$$2yy' = -3x^2$$

$$y' = -\frac{3x^2}{2y}$$

$$y'\Big|_{(-2,2)} = -\frac{3(-2)^2}{2(2)} = -\frac{12}{4} = -3$$

10. $y^2 - y - 4x = 0$

$$\frac{d}{dx}(y^2) - \frac{d}{dx}(y) - \frac{d}{dx}(4x) = \frac{d}{dx}(0)$$

$$2yy' - y' - 4 = 0$$

$$y'(2y - 1) = 4$$

$$y' = \frac{4}{2y - 1}$$

$$y'\Big|_{(0,1)} = \frac{4}{2(1) - 1} = 4$$

12. $3xy - 2x - 2 = 0$

$$\frac{d}{dx}(3xy) - \frac{d}{dx}(2x) - \frac{d}{dx}(2) = \frac{d}{dx}(0)$$

$$3y + 3xy' - 2 - 0 = 0$$

$$3xy' = 2 - 3y$$

$$y' = \frac{2 - 3y}{3x}$$

$$y' \text{ at } (2, 1) = \frac{2 - 3(1)}{3(2)} = -\frac{1}{6}$$

14. $2y + xy - 1 = 0$

$$\frac{d}{dx}(2y) + \frac{d}{dx}(xy) - \frac{d}{dx}(1) = \frac{d}{dx}(0)$$

$$2y' + y + xy' - 0 = 0$$

$$y'(x + 2) = -y$$

$$y' = -\frac{y}{x + 2}$$

$$y' \text{ at } (-1, 1) = -\frac{1}{-1 + 2} = -1$$

16. $2x^3y - x^3 + 5 = 0$

$$\frac{d}{dx}(2x^3y) - \frac{d}{dx}(x^3) + \frac{d}{dx}(5) = \frac{d}{dx}(0)$$

$$6x^2y + 2x^3y' - 3x^2 + 0 = 0$$

$$2x^3y' = 3x^2 - 6x^2y$$

$$y' = \frac{3x^2 - 6x^2y}{2x^3} = \frac{3(1 - 2y)}{2x}$$

$$y' \text{ at } (-1, 3) = \frac{3(1 - 2(3))}{2(-1)} = \frac{-15}{-2} = \frac{15}{2}$$

18. $x^2 - y = 4e^y$

$\dfrac{d}{dx}(x^2) - \dfrac{d}{dx}(y) = \dfrac{d}{dx}(4e^y)$

$2x - y' = 4e^y y'$

$y'(1 + 4e^y) = 2x$

$y' = \dfrac{2x}{1 + 4e^y}$

y' at $(2, 0) = \dfrac{2(2)}{1 + 4e^0} = \dfrac{4}{5}$

20. $\ln y = 2y^2 - x$

$\dfrac{d}{dx}(\ln y) = \dfrac{d}{dx}(2y^2) - \dfrac{d}{dx}(x)$

$\dfrac{1}{y} \cdot y' = 4yy' - 1$

$y' = 4y^2 y' - y$

$y'(4y^2 - 1) = y$

$y' = \dfrac{y}{4y^2 - 1}$

y' at $(2, 1) = \dfrac{1}{4(1)^2 - 1} = \dfrac{1}{3}$

22. $xe^y - y = x^2 - 2$

$\dfrac{d}{dx}(xe^y) - \dfrac{d}{dx}(y) = \dfrac{d}{dx}(x^2) - \dfrac{d}{dx}(2)$

$e^y + xe^y \cdot y' - y' = 2x - 0$

$y'(xe^y - 1) = 2x - e^y$

$y' = \dfrac{2x - e^y}{xe^y - 1}$

y' at $(2, 0) = \dfrac{2(2) - e^0}{2e^0 - 1} = \dfrac{4 - 1}{2 - 1} = 3$

24. $x^3 - tx^2 - 4 = 0$

$\dfrac{d}{dt}(x^3) - \dfrac{d}{dt}(tx^2) - \dfrac{d}{dt}(4) = \dfrac{d}{dt}(0)$

$3x^2 x' - x^2 - 2txx' - 0 = 0$

$x'(3x^2 - 2tx) = x^2$

$x' = \dfrac{x^2}{x(3x - 2t)} = \dfrac{x}{3x - 2t}$

x' at $(-3, -2) = \dfrac{-2}{3(-2) - 2(-3)} = \dfrac{-2}{0}$, so

x' is not defined at $(-3, -2)$

26. $(x - 1)^2 + (y - 1)^2 = 1$.

Differentiating implicitly, we have:

$\dfrac{d}{dx}(x - 1)^2 + \dfrac{d}{dx}(y - 1)^2 = \dfrac{d}{dx}(1)$

$2(x - 1) + 2(y - 1)y' = 0$

$y' = -\dfrac{x - 1}{y - 1}$

To find the points on the graph where $x = 0.2$, we solve the given equation for y:

$(y - 1)^2 = 1 - (x - 1)^2$

$y - 1 = \pm\sqrt{1 - (x - 1)^2}$

$y = 1 \pm \sqrt{1 - (x - 1)^2}$

Now, when $x = 0.2$, $y = 1 + \sqrt{1 - 0.64} = 1 + \sqrt{0.36}$
$$= 1 + 0.6$$
$$= 1.6$$
and $y = 1 - \sqrt{0.36} = 1 - 0.6 = 0.4$. Thus, the points are $(0.2, 1.6)$ and $(0.2, 0.4)$. These values can be verified on the graph.

$$y'\Big|_{(0.2, 1.6)} = -\frac{0.2 - 1}{1.6 - 1} = \frac{0.8}{0.6} = \frac{4}{3}$$

$$y'\Big|_{(0.2, 0.4)} = -\frac{0.2 - 1}{0.4 - 1} = -\frac{0.8}{0.6} = -\frac{4}{3}$$

28. $3x + xy + 1 - 0$
When $x = -1$, $3(-1) + (-1)y + 1 = 0$, so $y = -2$. Thus, we want to find the equation of the tangent line at $(-1, -2)$.

First, find y'.

$$\frac{d}{dx}(3x) + \frac{d}{dx}(xy) + \frac{d}{dx}(1) = \frac{d}{dx}(0)$$
$$3 + y + xy' + 0 = 0$$
$$xy' = -(y + 3)$$
$$y' = -\frac{y + 3}{x}$$
$$y'\Big|_{(-1, -2)} = -\frac{-2 + 3}{-1} = 1$$

Thus, the slope of the tangent line at $(-1, -2)$ is $m = 1$. The equation of the line through $(-1, -2)$ with slope $m = 1$ is:
$$y + 2 = (x + 1)$$
$$y = x - 1$$

30. $xy^2 - y - 2 = 0$
When $x = 1$, $y^2 - y - 2 = 0$
$$(y + 1)(y - 2) = 0$$
$$y = -1 \text{ or } 2$$

Thus, we have to find the equations of the tangent lines at $(1, -1)$ and $(1, 2)$. First find y':

$$\frac{d}{dx}(xy^2) - \frac{d}{dx}(y) - \frac{d}{dx}(0) = \frac{d}{dx}(0)$$
$$y^2 + 2xyy' - y' - 0 = 0$$
$$y'(2xy - 1) = -y^2$$
$$y' = \frac{y^2}{1 - 2xy}$$
$$y'\Big|_{(1, -1)} = \frac{(-1)^2}{1 - 2(1)(-1)} = \frac{1}{3}$$

The equation of the tangent line at $(1, -1)$ with $m = \frac{1}{3}$ is:

$$y + 1 = \frac{1}{3}(x - 1)$$

$$y = \frac{1}{3}x - \frac{4}{3}$$

$$y'\big|_{(1,2)} = \frac{(2)^2}{1 - 2(1)(2)} = -\frac{4}{3} \quad [\text{slope at } (1, 2)]$$

Thus, the equation of the tangent line at $(1, 2)$ with $m = -\frac{4}{3}$ is:

$$y - 2 = -\frac{4}{3}(x - 1)$$

$$y = -\frac{4}{3}x + \frac{10}{3}$$

32. Since y appears in two places as polynomial of degree one and as exponent we cannot express y as an explicit function of x. We need to use implicit differentiation to find the slope of the tangent line to the graph of the equation at the point $(0, 1)$.

$$x^3 + y + xe^y = 1$$

$$\frac{d}{dx}(x^3) + \frac{d}{dx}(y) + \frac{d}{dx}(xe^y) = \frac{d}{dx}(1)$$

$$3x^2 + y' + e^y + xe^y \cdot y' = 0$$

$$y'(xe^y + 1) = -(e^y + 3x^2)$$

$$y' = -\frac{e^y + 3x^2}{xe^y + 1}$$

$$y'\big|_{(0,1)} = -\frac{e^1 + 3(0)^2}{0e^1 + 1} = -e$$

34. $(y - 3)^4 - x = y$

$$\frac{d}{dx}(y - 3)^4 - \frac{d}{dx}(x) = \frac{d}{dx}(y)$$

$$4(y - 3)^3 y' - 1 = y'$$

$$y'[4(y - 3)^3 - 1] = 1$$

$$y' = \frac{1}{4(y - 3)^3 - 1}$$

$$y'\big|_{(-3,4)} = \frac{1}{4(4 - 3)^3 - 1} = \frac{1}{3}$$

36. $(2x - y)^4 - y^3 = 8$

$$\frac{d}{dx}(2x - y)^4 - \frac{d}{dx}(y^3) = \frac{d}{dx}(8)$$

$$4(2x - y)^3(2 - y') - 3y^2 y' = 0$$

$$[4(2x - y)^3 + 3y^2]y' = 8(2x - y)^3$$

$$y' = \frac{8(2x - y)^3}{4(2x - y)^3 + 3y^2}$$

$$y'\Big|_{(-1,-2)} = \frac{8(2(-1) - (-2))^3}{4(2(-1) - (-2))^3 + 3(-2)^2}$$

$$= \frac{8(0)^3}{4(0)^3 + 12} = 0$$

38. $6\sqrt{y^3 + 1} - 2x^{3/2} - 2 = 0$

$$6(y^3 + 1)^{1/2} - 2x^{3/2} - 2 = 0$$

$$\frac{d}{dx}(6(y^3 + 1)^{1/2}) - \frac{d}{dx}(2x^{3/2}) - \frac{d}{dx}(2) = \frac{d}{dx}(0)$$

$$6\left(\frac{1}{2}\right)(y^3 + 1)^{-1/2}(3y^2 y') - 3x^{1/2} - 0 = 0$$

$$9y^2(y^3 + 1)^{-1/2}y' = 3x^{1/2}$$

$$y' = \frac{x^{1/2}}{3y^2(y^3 + 1)^{-1/2}} = \frac{x^{1/2}(y^3 + 1)^{1/2}}{3y^2}$$

$$y'\Big|_{(4,2)} = \frac{4^{1/2}(2^3 + 1)^{1/2}}{3(2)^2} = \frac{(2)(3)}{12} = \frac{1}{2}$$

40. $e^{xy} - 2x = y + 1$

$$\frac{d}{dx}(e^{xy}) - \frac{d}{dx}(2x) = \frac{d}{dx}(y) + \frac{d}{dx}(1)$$

$$e^{xy}(y + xy') - 2 = y' + 0$$

$$ye^{xy} + xy'e^{xy} - 2 = y'$$

$$y'(xe^{xy} - 1) = 2 - ye^{xy}$$

$$y' = \frac{2 - ye^{xy}}{xe^{xy} - 1}; \quad y'\Big|_{(0,0)} = \frac{2 - 0e^0}{0e^0 - 1} = -2$$

42. First find the point(s) on the graph of the equation with $y = -1$:
Setting $y = -1$, we have

$$(-1)^3 - x(-1) - x^3 = 2$$

$$-1 + x - x^3 = 2$$

$$x^2 - x + 3 = 0$$

Graphing this equation on a graphing utility, we get $x \approx -1.67$.

Now, differentiate implicitly to find the slope of the tangent line at the point $(-1.67, -1)$:

$$\frac{d}{dx}(y^3) - \frac{d}{dx}(xy) - \frac{d}{dx}(x^3) = \frac{d}{dx}(2)$$

$$3y^2 y' - y - xy' - 3x^2 = 0$$

$$(3y^2 - x)y' = y + 3x^2$$

$$y' = \frac{y + 3x^2}{3y^2 - x}$$

$$y'\Big|_{(-1.67,-1)} = \frac{-1 + 3(-1.67)^2}{3(-1)^2 - (-1.67)} \approx 1.58$$

Tangent line: $y + 1 = 1.58(x + 1.67)$ or
$$y = 1.58x + 1.64$$

44. $x = p^3 - 3p^2 + 200$

$$\frac{d}{dx}(x) = \frac{d}{dx}(p^3) - \frac{d}{dx}(3p^2) + \frac{d}{dx}(200)$$

$$1 = 3p^2\frac{dp}{dx} - 6p\frac{dp}{dx} + 0$$

$$1 = 3p(p - 2)\frac{dp}{dx}$$

Thus,
$$p' = \frac{dp}{dx} = \frac{1}{3p(p - 2)}.$$

46. $x = \sqrt[3]{1,500 - p^3} = (1,500 - p^3)^{1/3}$

$$\frac{dx}{dx} = \frac{d}{dx}(1,500 - p^3)^{1/3}$$

$$1 = \frac{1}{3}(1,500 - p^3)^{-2/3}\left(-3p^2\frac{dp}{dx}\right)$$

$$3(1,500 - p^3)^{2/3} = -3p^2\frac{dp}{dx}$$

$$p' = \frac{dp}{dx} = -\frac{(-1,500 - p^3)^{2/3}}{p^2} \quad \text{or} \quad p' = -\frac{x^2}{p^2}$$

48. $(L + m)(V + n) = k$

$$\frac{d}{dL}((L + m)(V + n)) = \frac{d}{dL}(k)$$

$$V + n + (L + m)\frac{dV}{dL} = 0$$

$$\frac{dV}{dL} = -\frac{(V + n)}{(L + m)}$$

2. $y = x^3 - 3$

Differentiating with respect to t:

$$\frac{dy}{dt} = 3x^2 \frac{dx}{dt}$$

Given: $\frac{dx}{dt} = -2$ when $x = 2$. Thus, we have

$$\frac{dy}{dt} = 3(2)^2(-2) = -24$$

4. $x^2 + y^2 = 4$

Differentiating with respect to t:

$$2x\frac{dx}{dt} + 2y\frac{dy}{dt} = 0$$

Given: $\frac{dy}{dt} = 5$ when $x = 1.2$ and $y = -1.6$. Therefore

$$2(1.2)\frac{dx}{dt} + 2(-1.6)(5) = 0$$

$$2.4\frac{dx}{dt} = 16$$

$$\frac{dx}{dt} = \frac{16}{2.4} = \frac{160}{24} = \frac{20}{3}$$

6. $x^2 - 2xy - y^2 = 7$

Differentiating with respect to t:

$$2x\frac{dx}{dt} - 2\frac{dx}{dt}y - 2x\frac{dy}{dt} - 2y\frac{dy}{dt} = 0$$

Given: $\frac{dy}{dt} = -1$ when $x = 2$ and $y = -1$. Therefore

$$2(2)\frac{dx}{dt} - 2\frac{dx}{dt}(-1) - 2(2)(-1) - 2(-1)(-1) = 0$$

$$4\frac{dx}{dt} + 2\frac{dx}{dt} + 4 - 2 = 0$$

$$6\frac{dx}{dt} = -2$$

$$\frac{dx}{dt} = -\frac{1}{3}$$

8. $4x^2 + 9y^2 = 36$

Differentiate with respect to t:

$$8x\frac{dx}{dt} + 18y\frac{dy}{dt} = 0$$

Given: $\frac{dy}{dt} = -2$ when $x = 3$ and $y = 0$. Therefore

$$8(3)\frac{dx}{dt} + 18(0)(-2) = 0$$

$$24\frac{dx}{dt} = 0$$

$$\frac{dx}{dt} = 0$$

The x coordinate does not change at that moment.

10. z = rope

From the triangle,
$$x^2 + y^2 = z^2$$
or $x^2 + 16 = z^2$, since $y = 4$.

$y = 4$

x

Differentiate with respect to t:
$$2x\frac{dx}{dt} = 2z\frac{dz}{dt}$$
or $\quad x\frac{dx}{dt} = z\frac{dz}{dt}$

Given: $\dfrac{dx}{dt} = -3.05$ when $x = 10$ and $z = \sqrt{100 + 16} \approx 10.77$.

Therefore,
$$10(-3.05) = 10.77\frac{dz}{dt}$$
$$\frac{dz}{dt} = -\frac{30.5}{10.77} \approx -2.83 \text{ feet per second.}$$

12. Circumference: $C = 2\pi R$
$$\frac{dC}{dt} = 2\pi\frac{dR}{dt}$$
Given: $\dfrac{dR}{dt} = 2$ ft/sec
$$\frac{dC}{dt} = 2\pi(2) = 4\pi$$
$$\approx 12.56 \text{ ft/sec}$$

14. Surface area: $S = 4\pi R^2$
$$\frac{dS}{dt} = 8\pi R\frac{dR}{dt}$$
Given: $\dfrac{dR}{dt} = 3$ cm/min
$$\frac{dR}{dt} = 8\pi R(3) = 24\pi R$$
$$\frac{dS}{dt}\bigg|_{R = 10 \text{ cm}} = 240\pi$$
$$\approx 753.6 \text{ cm}^2/\text{min}$$

16. $VP = k$

Differentiating with respect to t:
$$\frac{dV}{dt}P + V\frac{dP}{dt} = 0$$
Given: $\dfrac{dV}{dt} = -5$ in^3/sec, $V = 1,000$ in^3, $P = 40$ pounds per square inch.

Thus, we have $(-5)(40) + 1,000\dfrac{dP}{dt} = 0$
$$\frac{dP}{dt} = \frac{200}{1,000} = 0.2$$

Pressure increases at 0.2 pound per square inch per second.

18. By the Pythagorean theorem,
$$z^2 + (300)^2 + y^2 \qquad (1)$$
Differentiating with respect to t:
$$z\frac{dz}{dt} = y\frac{dy}{dt}$$

Therefore, $\dfrac{dz}{dt} = \dfrac{y}{z}\dfrac{dy}{dt}$. Given: $\dfrac{dy}{dt} = 5$. Thus, $\dfrac{dz}{dt} = \dfrac{5y}{z}$.

From (1), $z^2 = (300)^2 + y^2 = (300)^2 + (400)^2 = 250,000$ when $y = 400$.
Thus, $z = 500$ when $y = 400$, and
$$\frac{dz}{dt}\bigg|_{(400,500)} = \frac{5(400)}{500} = 4 \text{ m/sec}$$

20. y = length of shadow
x = distance of man from light
z = distance of tip of shadow from light

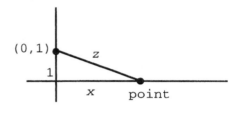

We want to compute $\dfrac{dy}{dt}$. Triangles ABE and CDE are similar

triangles; thus, the ratios of corresponding sides are equal.

Therefore, $\dfrac{z}{20} = \dfrac{y}{5}$ or $\dfrac{x+y}{20} = \dfrac{y}{5}$ [<u>Note</u>: $z = x + y$]

or $x + y = 4y$ or $y = \dfrac{1}{3}x$

Differentiating with respect to t:

$\dfrac{dy}{dt} = \dfrac{1}{3}\dfrac{dx}{dt}$

Given: $\dfrac{dx}{dt} = 5$. Thus, $\dfrac{dy}{dt} = \dfrac{5}{3}$ ft/sec.

22. Observe that
$$z^2 = x^2 + 1$$
Differentiating with respect to t:

$$z\dfrac{dz}{dt} = x\dfrac{dx}{dt}$$

$$x = \dfrac{z\dfrac{dz}{dt}}{\dfrac{dx}{dt}}$$

Given: $\dfrac{dx}{dt} = 5$, $z = \sqrt{x^2 + 1}$.

Thus, $x = \dfrac{1}{5}\sqrt{x^2 + 1}\,\dfrac{dz}{dt}$ (1)

From (1), for $\dfrac{dz}{dt} = 2$, we have:

$x = \dfrac{2}{5}\sqrt{x^2 + 1}$ or $x^2 = \dfrac{4(x^2 + 1)}{25}$ or

$21x^2 = 4$, $x^2 = \dfrac{4}{21}$, $x \approx 0.4364$

From (1), for $\dfrac{dz}{dt} = 4$, we have

$x = \dfrac{4}{5}\sqrt{x^2 + 1}$ or $25x^2 = 16(x^2 + 1)$

$9x^2 = 16$, $x^2 = \dfrac{16}{9}$, $x = \dfrac{4}{3} = 1.3333$

From (1), for $\dfrac{dz}{dt} = 5$, we have

$x = \sqrt{x^2 + 1}$ which is impossible.

Therefore, the distance from $(0, 1)$ is never increasing at ≥ 5 units per second.

24. $x^3 + y^2 = 1;\ \dfrac{dy}{dt} = 2,\ \dfrac{dx}{dt} = 1$

Differentiating with respect to t:

$3x^2 \dfrac{dx}{dt} + 2y\dfrac{dy}{dt} = 0$ [<u>Note</u>: this equation has a solution

for x only when $y \le 0$.]

or

$3x^2(1) + 2y(2) = 0$

or

$3x^2 + 4y = 0$

From $x^3 + y^2 = 1$, $y = -\sqrt{1 - x^3}$ and hence

$3x^2 - 4\sqrt{1 - x^3} = 0$

$\qquad\qquad 3x^2 = 4\sqrt{1 - x^3}$

$\qquad\qquad 9x^4 = 16(1 - x^3)$

$9x^4 + 16x^3 - 16 = 0$

Using a graphing utility, we find $x \approx 0.875$ and $x \approx -2$.

Therefore the points at which the x coordinate increasing at a rate of 1 unit per second are: $(0.875, -0.574)$ and $(-2, -3)$.

[<u>Note</u>: For $x = 0.875$, $y = -\sqrt{1 - x^3} = -0.574$ and for $x = -2$,

$y = -\sqrt{1 - x^3} = -3$.]

26. $C = 72{,}000 + 60x$ (1)

$R = 200x - \dfrac{x^2}{30}$ (2)

$P = R - C$ (3)

(A) Differentiating (1) with respect to t:

$\dfrac{dC}{dt} = 60\dfrac{dx}{dt}$

Thus, $\dfrac{dC}{dt} = 60(500)$ $\left(\dfrac{dx}{dt} = 500\right)$

$\qquad\qquad = \$30{,}000$ per week.

Costs are increasing at \$30,000 per week at this production level.

(B) Differentiating (2) with respect to t:

$\dfrac{dR}{dt} = 200\dfrac{dx}{dt} - \dfrac{1}{15}x\dfrac{dx}{dt}$

$\qquad = \left(200 - \dfrac{x}{15}\right)\dfrac{dx}{dt}$

Thus, $\dfrac{dR}{dt} = \left(200 - \dfrac{1{,}500}{15}\right)(500)$ $\left(x = 1{,}500, \dfrac{dx}{dt} = 500\right)$

$\qquad\qquad = \$50{,}000$ per week.

Revenue is increasing at \$50,000 per week at this production level.

(C) Differentiating (3) with respect to t:
$$\frac{dP}{dt} = \frac{dR}{dt} - \frac{dC}{dt}$$
Thus, from parts (A) and (B), we have:
$$\frac{dP}{dt} = 50,000 - 30,000 = \$20,000$$
Profits are increasing at \$20,000 per week at this production level.

28. $S = 50,000 - 20,000e^{-0.0004x}$
Differentiating implicitly with respect to t, we have
$$\frac{dS}{dt} = -20,000e^{-0.0004x}(-0.0004)\frac{dx}{dt}$$
$$= 8e^{-0.0004x}\frac{dx}{dt}$$
Now, for $x = 2,000$ and $\frac{dx}{dt} = 300$, we have
$$\frac{dS}{dt} = 8e^{-0.0004(2000)}(300)$$
$$= 2,400e^{-0.8} \approx 1,078$$
Thus, sales are increasing at the rate of \$1,078 per week.

30. Price p and demand x are related by the equation
$$x^2 + 2xp + 25p^2 = 74,500 \qquad (1)$$
Differentiating implicitly with respect to t, we have
$$2x\frac{dx}{dt} + 2\frac{dx}{dt}p + 2x\frac{dp}{dt} + 50p\frac{dp}{dt} = 0 \qquad (2)$$

(A) From (2), $\dfrac{dx}{dt} = \dfrac{-(x + 25p)\dfrac{dp}{dt}}{x + p}$

Setting $p = 30$ in (1), we get
$$x^2 + 60x + 22,500 = 74,500$$
or $\quad x^2 + 60x - 52,000 = 0$

Thus, $x = -30 \pm \sqrt{(30)^2 + 52,000}$
$$= -30 \pm 230 = 200, -260$$
Since $x \geq 0$, $x = 200$

Now, for $x = 200$, $p = 30$ and $\dfrac{dp}{dt} = 2$, we have
$$\frac{dx}{dt} = \frac{-(200 + 25(30))(2)}{200 + 30} = -\frac{1,900}{230} \approx -8.26$$
The demand is decreasing at the rate of 8.26 units/month.

(B) From (2), $\dfrac{dp}{dt} = \dfrac{(x + p)\dfrac{dx}{dt}}{x + 25p}$

Setting $x = 150$ in (1), we get

$(150)^2 + 2(150)p + 25p^2 = 74,500$

$22,500 + 300p + 25p^2 = 74,500$

or $\qquad p^2 + 12p - 2,080 = 0$

and $\qquad p = -6 \pm \sqrt{36 + 2080} = -6 \pm 46 = 40, -52$

Since $p \geq 0$, $p = 40$.

Now, for $x = 150$, $p = 40$ and $\dfrac{dx}{dt} = -6$, we have

$\dfrac{dp}{dt} = -\dfrac{(150 + 40)\,(-6)}{150 + 25(40)} \approx 0.99$

Thus, the price is increasing at the rate of $0.99 per month.

32. $T = 6\left(1 + \dfrac{1}{\sqrt{x}}\right) = 6(1 + x^{-1/2})$

Differentiating with respect to t:

$\dfrac{dT}{dt} = 6\left(-\dfrac{1}{2}\right)x^{-3/2}\left(\dfrac{dx}{dt}\right) = -3x^{-3/2}\dfrac{dx}{dt}$

or

$\dfrac{dT}{dt} = -\dfrac{3}{x^{3/2}} \cdot \dfrac{dx}{dt}$

Given: $\dfrac{dx}{dt} = 6$, $x = 36$. Therefore,

$\dfrac{dT}{dt} = -\dfrac{3}{(36)^{3/2}}(6) = -\dfrac{18}{216} = -\dfrac{1}{12}$ of a minute/hour.

6 INTEGRATION

2. $\int x^5 dx = \dfrac{1}{6}x^6 + C$ [using Indefinite Integral Formula]

Check: $\left(\dfrac{1}{6}x^6 + C\right)' = \dfrac{1}{6} \cdot 6x^5 + 0 = x^5$

4. $\int x^{-4} dx = -\dfrac{1}{3}x^{-3} + C$ [using Indefinite Integral Formula]

Check: $\left(-\dfrac{1}{3}x^{-3} + C\right)' = -\dfrac{1}{3} \cdot (-3)x^{-4} + 0 = x^{-4}$

6. $\int -10\ dx = -10x + C$ [using Indefinite Integral Formula]

Check: $(-10x + C)' = -10 + 0 = -10$

8. $\int 3u^6 du = \dfrac{3}{7}u^7 + C$ [using Indefinite Integral Formula]

Check: $\left(\dfrac{3}{7}u^7 + C\right)' = \dfrac{3}{7} \cdot 7u^6 + 0 = 3u^6$

10. $\int e^3 du = e^3 x + C$ [using Indefinite Integral Formula]

Check: $(e^3 x + C)' = e^3 + 0 = e^3$

12. $\int (5 - 4t)\,dt = \int 5\,dt - \int 4t\ dt = 5t - 2t^2 + C$ [using Indefinite Integral Formula]

Check: $(5t - 2t^2 + C)' = 5 - 2(2t) + 0 = 5 - 4t$

14. $\int 12e^t dt = 12e^t + C$ [using Indefinite Integral Formula]

Check: $(12e^t + C)' = 12e^t + 0 = 12e^t$

16. $\int 4z^{-1} dz = 4\ \ln|z| + C$ [using Indefinite Integral Formula]

Check: $(4\ \ln|z| + C)' = 4 \cdot \dfrac{1}{z} + 0 = 4z^{-1}$

18. $\int 8t^{2/3} dt = \dfrac{24}{5}t^{5/3} + C$ [using Indefinite Integral Formula]

Check: $\left(\dfrac{24}{5}t^{5/3} + C\right)' = \dfrac{24}{5} \cdot \dfrac{5}{3}t^{2/3} + 0 = 8t^{2/3}$

20. $\int 2x^{-5/2} dx = -\dfrac{4}{3}x^{-3/2} + C$ [using Indefinite Integral Formula]

Check: $\left(-\dfrac{4}{3}x^{-3/2} + C\right)' = \left(-\dfrac{4}{3}\right)\left(-\dfrac{3}{2}\right)x^{-5/2} + 0 = 2x^{-5/2}$

22. $\int(3\sqrt{x} - x^{-1})\,dx = \int(3x^{1/2} - x^{-1})\,dx = \int 3x^{1/2}\,dx - \int x^{-1}\,dx$

$$= 2x^{3/2} - \ln|x| + C \quad \text{[using Indefinite Integral Formula]}$$

Check: $(2x^{3/2} - \ln|x| + C)' = 2 \cdot \dfrac{3}{2}x^{1/2} - \dfrac{1}{x} + 0 = 3\sqrt{x} - x^{-1}$

24. $\dfrac{dx}{dt} = 42t^5$

$$x = \int 42t^5\,dt = \dfrac{42}{6}t^6 + C = 7t^6 + C$$

26. $\dfrac{dy}{dx} = 3x^2 - 4x^3$

$$y = \int(3x^2 - 4x^3)\,dx = \int 3x^2\,dx - \int 4x^3\,dx$$

$$= x^3 - x^4 + C$$

28. $\dfrac{dA}{dt} = 3 - 12t^3 - 9t^5$

$$A = \int(3 - 12t^3 - 9t^5)\,dt = \int 3\,dt - \int 12t^3\,dt - \int 9t^5\,dt$$

$$= 3t - \dfrac{12}{4}t^4 - \dfrac{9}{6}t^6 + C$$

$$= 3t - 3t^4 - \dfrac{3}{2}t^6 + C$$

30. $\dfrac{dy}{dx} = x - e^x$

$$y = \int(x - e^x)\,dx = \int x\,dx - \int e^x\,dx$$

$$= \dfrac{1}{2}x^2 - e^x + C$$

32. $\dfrac{du}{dv} = \dfrac{4}{v} + \dfrac{v}{4}$

$$du = \int\left(\dfrac{4}{v} + \dfrac{v}{4}\right)dv = \int \dfrac{4}{v}\,dv + \int \dfrac{v}{4}\,dv$$

$$= 4\,\ln|v| + \dfrac{1}{4} \cdot \dfrac{1}{2}v^2 + C$$

$$= 4\,\ln|v| + \dfrac{1}{8}v^2 + C$$

34. (A) True; $\dfrac{d}{dx}(x^4 + x^2) = 4x^3 + 2x$ and

$$\int(4x^3 + 2x)\,dx = \dfrac{4}{4}x^4 + \dfrac{2}{2}x^2 + C = x^4 + x^2 + C$$

(B) False; $\int x^2\,dx = \dfrac{1}{3}x^3 + C_1$ and hence

$$\dfrac{d}{dx}\left(\int x^2\,dx\right) = x^2 \text{ which is equal to } x^2 + C \text{ only if } C = 0.$$

36. No, since one graph cannot be obtained from another by a vertical translation.

38. Yes, since one graph can be obtained from another by a vertical translation.

40. $\int x^2 (1 + x^3)\, dx = \int (x^2 + x^5)\, dx = \int x^2 dx + \int x^5 dx$

$$= \frac{1}{3}x^3 + \frac{1}{6}x^6 + C \quad \text{[using Indefinite Integral Formula]}$$

Check: $\left(\frac{1}{3}x^3 + \frac{1}{6}x^6 + C\right)' = \frac{1}{3} \cdot 3x^2 + \frac{1}{6} \cdot 6x^5 + 0 = x^2 + x^5 = x^2(1 + x^3)$

42. $\int (1 + x)(1 - x)\, dx = \int (1 - x^2)\, dx = \int 1\, dx - \int x^2 dx$

$$= x - \frac{1}{3}x^3 + C \quad \text{[using Indefinite Integral Formula]}$$

Check: $\left(x - \frac{1}{3}x^3 + C\right)' = 1 - \frac{1}{3} \cdot 3x^2 + 0 = 1 - x^2 = (1 + x)(1 - x)$

44. $\int \dfrac{dt}{\sqrt[3]{t}} = \int \dfrac{dt}{t^{1/3}} = \int t^{-1/3}\, dt$

$$= \frac{1}{-\frac{1}{3} + 1} t^{(-1/3)+1} + C = \frac{3}{2} t^{2/3} + C$$

Check: $\left(\dfrac{3}{2} t^{2/3} + C\right)' = \dfrac{3}{2}\left(\dfrac{2}{3}\right) t^{(2/3)-1} + 0 = t^{-1/3} = \dfrac{1}{t^{1/3}} = \dfrac{1}{\sqrt[3]{t}}$

46. $\int \dfrac{6\, dm}{m^2} = 6 \int m^{-2}\, dm$

$$= 6(-m^{-1}) + C = -\frac{6}{m} + C$$

Check: $(-6m^{-1} + C)' = (-6)(-1)m^{-2} + 0 = 6m^{-2} = \dfrac{6}{m^2}$

48. $\int \dfrac{1 - y^2}{3y}\, dy = \int \dfrac{1}{3y}\, dy - \int \dfrac{y^2}{3y}\, dy$

$$= \frac{1}{3}\int \frac{1}{y}\, dy - \frac{1}{3}\int y\, dy$$

$$= \frac{1}{3}\ln|y| - \frac{1}{3} \cdot \frac{1}{2}y^2 + C$$

$$= \frac{1}{3}\ln|y| - \frac{1}{6}y^2 + C$$

Check: $\left(\dfrac{1}{3}\ln|y| - \dfrac{1}{6}y^2 + C\right)' = \dfrac{1}{3} \cdot \dfrac{1}{y} - \dfrac{1}{6}(2y) + 0 = \dfrac{1}{3y} - \dfrac{y}{3} = \dfrac{1 - y^2}{3y}$

50. $\int \dfrac{e^t - t}{2}\, dt = \int \left(\dfrac{e^t}{2} - \dfrac{t}{2}\right) dt = \int \dfrac{e^t}{2}\, dt - \int \dfrac{t}{2}\, dt$

$$= \frac{1}{2}e^t - \frac{t^2}{4} + C \quad \text{[using Indefinite Integral Formula]}$$

Check: $\left(\dfrac{1}{2}e^t - \dfrac{t^2}{4} + C\right)' = \dfrac{1}{2}e^t - \dfrac{2t}{4} + 0 = \dfrac{e^t}{2} - \dfrac{t}{2} = \dfrac{e^t - t}{2}$

52. $\displaystyle\int\left(4x^3 + \frac{2}{x^3}\right)dx = 4\int x^3\ dx + 2\int x^{-3}\ dx$

$$= 4\left(\frac{x^4}{4}\right) + 2\left(\frac{1}{-2}\,x^{-2}\right) + C$$

$$= x^4 - x^{-2} + C$$

Check: $(x^4 - x^{-2} + C)' = 4x^3 - (-2)x^{-3} + 0 = 4x^3 + 2x^{-3} = 4x^3 + \dfrac{2}{x^3}$

54. $\displaystyle\int\left(\frac{6}{x^4} - \frac{2}{x^3} + 1\right)dx = 6\int x^{-4}\ dx - 2\int x^{-3}\ dx + \int dx$

$$= 6\left(\frac{x^{-3}}{-3}\right) - 2\left(\frac{x^{-2}}{-2}\right) + x + C$$

$$= -2x^{-3} + x^{-2} + x + C$$

Check: $(-2x^{-3} + x^{-2} + x + C)' = (-2)(-3x^{-4}) + (-2)x^{-3} + 1$

$$= 6x^{-4} - 2x^{-3} + 1 = \frac{6}{x^4} - \frac{2}{x^3} + 1$$

56. $\displaystyle\int\left(\frac{2}{\sqrt[3]{x}} - \sqrt[3]{x^2}\right)dx = \int\left(\frac{2}{x^{1/3}} - x^{2/3}\right)dx$

$$= 2\int x^{-1/3}\ dx - \int x^{2/3}\ dx$$

$$= 2\left(\frac{x^{2/3}}{\frac{2}{3}}\right) - \left(\frac{x^{5/3}}{\frac{5}{3}}\right) + C$$

$$= 3x^{2/3} - \frac{3}{5}x^{5/3} + C$$

Check: $\left(3x^{2/3} - \dfrac{3}{5}\,x^{5/3} + C\right)' = 3\left(\dfrac{2}{3}\right)x^{-1/3} - \dfrac{3}{5}\left(\dfrac{5}{3}\right)x^{2/3}$

$$= 2x^{-1/3} - x^{2/3} = \frac{2}{x^{1/3}} - \sqrt[3]{x^2} = \frac{2}{\sqrt[3]{x}} - \sqrt[3]{x^2}$$

58. $\displaystyle\int\left(\frac{12}{x^5} - \frac{1}{\sqrt[3]{x^2}}\right)dx = \int\left(12x^{-5} - \frac{1}{x^{2/3}}\right)dx$

$$= 12\int x^{-5}\ dx - \int x^{-2/3}\ dx$$

$$= 12\left(\frac{x^{-4}}{-4}\right) - \left(\frac{x^{1/3}}{\frac{1}{3}}\right) + C$$

$$= -3x^{-4} - 3x^{1/3} + C$$

Check: $(-3x^{-4} - 3x^{1/3} + C)' = (-3)(-4)x^{-5} - 3\left(\dfrac{1}{3}\right)x^{-2/3}$

$$= 12x^{-5} - x^{-2/3} = \frac{12}{x^5} - \frac{1}{x^{2/3}} = \frac{12}{x^5} - \frac{1}{\sqrt[3]{x^2}}$$

60. $\int \dfrac{e^x - 3x^2}{2}\,dx = \int\left(\dfrac{e^x}{2} - \dfrac{3x^2}{2}\right)dx$

$\qquad\qquad = \dfrac{1}{2}\int e^x\,dx - \dfrac{3}{2}\int x^2\,dx$

$\qquad\qquad = \dfrac{1}{2}e^x - \dfrac{3}{2}\left(\dfrac{x^3}{3}\right) + C$

$\qquad\qquad = \dfrac{1}{2}e^x - \dfrac{1}{2}x^3 + C$

Check: $\left(\dfrac{1}{2}e^x - \dfrac{1}{2}x^3 + C\right)' = \dfrac{1}{2}e^x - \dfrac{1}{2}(3x^2) + 0$

$\qquad\qquad\qquad\qquad = \dfrac{1}{2}e^x - \dfrac{3x^2}{2} = \dfrac{e^x - 3x^2}{2}$

62. $\int \dfrac{(1 + z^2)^2}{z}\,dz = \int \dfrac{(1 + 2z^2 + z^4)}{z}\,dz$

$\qquad\qquad = \int\left(\dfrac{1}{z} + 2z + z^3\right)dz$

$\qquad\qquad = \int \dfrac{1}{z}\,dz + 2\int z\,dz + \int z^3\,dz$

$\qquad\qquad = \ln|z| + 2\left(\dfrac{z^2}{2}\right) + \dfrac{z^4}{4} + C$

$\qquad\qquad = \ln|z| + z^2 + \dfrac{z^4}{4} + C$

Check: $\left(\ln|z| + z^2 + \dfrac{z^4}{4} + C\right)' = \dfrac{1}{z} + 2z + \dfrac{1}{4}(4z^3) + 0$

$\qquad\qquad\qquad\qquad = \dfrac{1}{z} + 2z + z^3 = \dfrac{1 + 2z^2 + z^4}{z} = \dfrac{(1 + z^2)^2}{z}$

64. $\int\left(\dfrac{2}{3x^2} - \dfrac{5}{4x^3}\right)dx = \int \dfrac{2}{3x^2}\,dx - \int \dfrac{5}{4x^3}\,dx$

$\qquad\qquad = \int \dfrac{2}{3}x^{-2}\,dx - \int \dfrac{5}{4}x^{-3}\,dx$

$\qquad\qquad = -\dfrac{2}{3}x^{-1} + \dfrac{5}{8}x^{-2} + C \quad \text{[using I.I.F.]}$

Check: $\left(-\dfrac{2}{3}x^{-1} + \dfrac{5}{8}x^{-2} + C\right)' = -\dfrac{2}{3}\cdot(-1)x^{-2} + \dfrac{5}{8}\cdot(-2)x^{-3} + 0$

$\qquad\qquad\qquad\qquad = \dfrac{2}{3}x^{-2} - \dfrac{5}{4}x^{-3}$

$\qquad\qquad\qquad\qquad = \dfrac{2}{3x^2} - \dfrac{5}{4x^3}$

66. $\dfrac{dy}{dx} = 5 - 4x$

$y = \int (5 - 4x)\,dx = \int 5\,dx - \int 4x\,dx = 5x - 2x^2 + C$

Given $y(0) = 20$: $20 = 5(0) - 2(0)^2 + C$.
Hence, $C = 20$ and $y = 5x - 2x^2 + 20$.

68. $R'(x) = 600 - 0.6x$

$R(x) = \int (600 - 0.6x)\,dx = \int 600\,dx - 0.6\int x\,dx$

$$= 600x - 0.6\left(\dfrac{x^2}{2}\right) + C = 600x - 0.3x^2 + C$$

Given $R(0) = 0$: $0 = 600(0) - 0.3(0)^2 + C$. Hence, $C = 0$ and
$R(x) = 600x - 0.3x^2$.

70. $\dfrac{dR}{dt} = \dfrac{100}{t^2}$

$R = \int \dfrac{100}{t^2}\,dt = \int 100 t^{-2}\,dt = 100\left(\dfrac{t^{-1}}{-1}\right) + C = -100 t^{-1} + C$

Given $R(1) = 400$: $400 = -100(1)^{-1} + C = -100 + C$. Hence, $C = 500$ and
$R = -100 t^{-1} + 500 = 500 - \dfrac{100}{t}$

72. $\dfrac{dy}{dx} = 3x^{-1} + x^{-2}$

$y = \int (3x^{-1} + x^{-2})\,dx = 3\int x^{-1}\,dx + \int x^{-2}\,dx$

$$= 3\ln|x| + \left(\dfrac{x^{-1}}{-1}\right) + C = 3\ln|x| - x^{-1} + C$$

Given $y(1) = 1$: $1 = 3\ln|1| - (1)^{-1} + C$. Hence, $C = 2$ and
$y = 3\ln|x| - x^{-1} + 2$.

74. $\dfrac{dy}{dt} = 5e^t - 4$

$y = \int (5e^t - 4)\,dt = \int 5e^t\,dt - \int 4\,dt = 5e^t - 4t + C$

Given $y(0) = -1$: $-1 = 5e^0 - 4(0) + C$. Hence, $C = -6$ and
$y = 5e^t - 4t - 6$.

76. $\dfrac{dy}{dx} = 12x^2 - 12x$

$$y = \int (12x^2 - 12x)\,dx = 12\int x^2\,dx - 12\int x\,dx$$

$$= 12\left(\frac{x^3}{3}\right) - 12\left(\frac{x^2}{2}\right) + C = 4x^3 - 6x^2 + C$$

Given $y(1) = 3$: $3 = 4(1)^3 - 6(1)^2 + C$. Hence, $C = 5$ and $y = 4x^3 - 6x^2 + 5$.

78. $\displaystyle\int \frac{x^{-1} - x^4}{x^2}\,dx = \int\left(\frac{x^{-1}}{x^2} - \frac{x^4}{x^2}\right)dx$

$$= \int (x^{-3} - x^2)\,dx = \int x^{-3}\,dx - \int x^2\,dx$$

$$= \frac{x^{-2}}{-2} - \frac{x^3}{3} + C = -\frac{1}{2}x^{-2} - \frac{1}{3}x^3 + C$$

80. $\displaystyle\int \frac{1 - 3x^4}{x^2}\,dx = \int\left(\frac{1}{x^2} - \frac{3x^4}{x^2}\right)dx$

$$= \int (x^{-2} - 3x^2)\,dx = \int x^{-2}\,dx - 3\int x^2\,dx$$

$$= \frac{x^{-1}}{-1} - 3\left(\frac{x^3}{3}\right) + C$$

$$= -x^{-1} - x^3 + C$$

82. $\displaystyle\int \frac{1 - xe^x}{x}\,dx = \int\left(\frac{1}{x} - \frac{xe^x}{x}\right)dx$

$$= \int (x^{-1} - e^x)\,dx = \int x^{-1}\,dx - \int e^x\,dx = \ln|x| - e^x + C$$

84. $\dfrac{dR}{dx} = \dfrac{1 - x^4}{x^3}$

$$R = \int\left(\frac{1 - x^4}{x^3}\right)dx = \int\left(\frac{1}{x^3} - \frac{x^4}{x^3}\right)dx$$

$$= \int (x^{-3} - x)\,dx = \int x^{-3}\,dx - \int x\,dx$$

$$= \frac{x^{-2}}{-2} - \frac{x^2}{2} + C$$

$$= -\frac{1}{2}x^{-2} - \frac{1}{2}x^2 + C$$

Given $R(1) = 4$: $4 = -\dfrac{1}{2}(1)^{-2} - \dfrac{1}{2}(1)^2 + C$. Hence, $C = 5$ and

$$R = -\frac{1}{2}x^{-2} - \frac{1}{2}x^2 + 5.$$

86. $\dfrac{dx}{dt} = \dfrac{\sqrt{t^3} - t}{\sqrt{t^3}}$

$$x = \int\left(\dfrac{\sqrt{t^3} - t}{\sqrt{t^3}}\right)dt = \int\left(1 - \dfrac{t}{\sqrt{t^3}}\right)dt$$

$$= \int\left(1 - \dfrac{t}{t^{3/2}}\right)dt$$

$$= \int(1 - t^{-1/2})\,dt$$

$$= \int dt - \int t^{-1/2}\,dt$$

$$= t - \dfrac{t^{1/2}}{1/2} + C = t - 2t^{1/2} + C$$

Given $x(9) = 4$: $4 = 9 - 2\sqrt{9} + C$. Hence, $C = 1$ and $x = t - 2\sqrt{t} + 1$.

88. $p'(x) = \dfrac{10}{x^3}$

$$p(x) = \int\dfrac{10}{x^3}dx = \int 10x^{-3}\,dx = 10\left(\dfrac{x^{-2}}{-2}\right) + C = -5x^{-2} + C$$

Given $p(1) = 15$: $15 = -5(1)^{-2} + C$. Hence, $C = 20$ and $p(x) = -5x^{-2} + 20$.

90. $\dfrac{d}{dx}\left(\displaystyle\int \dfrac{\ln t}{t}\,dt\right) = \dfrac{\ln t}{t} \quad \left(\dfrac{d}{dx}\left(\displaystyle\int f(x)dx\right) = f(x)\right)$

92. $\displaystyle\int \dfrac{d}{du}(e^{u^2})\,du = e^{u^2} + C \quad \left(\displaystyle\int F'(x)dx = F(x) + C\right)$

94. $\dfrac{d}{dx}(e^x + C) = e^x + 0 = e^x$

96. $\dfrac{d}{dx}(\ln|x| + C) = \dfrac{d}{dx}(\ln(-x) + C) \quad$ since $x < 0$

$$= \dfrac{-1}{-x} + 0 = \dfrac{1}{x}$$

100. $f'(t) = 0.004t + 0.062$

$$f(t) = \int f'(t)\,dt = \int(0.004t + 0.062)\,dt$$

$$= \int 0.004t\,dt + \int 0.062\,dt$$

$$= 0.004\left(\dfrac{t^2}{2}\right) + 0.062t + C$$

$$= 0.002t^2 + 0.062t + C$$

Given: $f(38) = 6.89$: $6.89 = 0.002(38)^2 + 0.062(38) + C$.
Hence, $C = 1.65$ and $f(t) = 0.002t^2 + 0.062t + 1.65$.

In 2020 (or for $t = 60$), $f(60) = 0.002(60)^2 + 0.062(60) + 1.65 = 12.57$.
Therefore, the U.S. consumption of renewable energy in 2020 is 12.57 quadrillion BTU.

102. (A) $R'(x) > 0$ for $0 < x < 500$ and $R'(x) < 0$ for $500 < x < 1,000$.
Therefore, the graph of $R(x)$ is rising from 0 to 500 and falling from 500 to 1,000. $R'(x)$ is decreasing, so $R''(x) < 0$ and hence the graph of $R(x)$ is concave downward on $(0, 1,000)$. It has a local maximum at $x = 500$.

(B) $\dfrac{R'(x) - 100}{0 - 100} = \dfrac{x - 0}{500 - 0}$ or $R'(x) = 100 - 0.2x$

(C) $R(x) = \displaystyle\int R'(x)\,dx = \int (100 - 0.2x)\,dx$

$$= \int 100\,dx - \int 0.2\,x\,dx$$

$$= 100x - 0.2\left(\frac{x^2}{2}\right) + C$$

$$= 100x - 0.1x^2 + C$$

Given $R(0) = 0$: $0 = 100(0) - 0.1(0)^2 + C$. Hence, $C = 0$ and $R(x) = 100x - 0.1x^2$.

(D) $p(x) = \dfrac{R(x)}{x} = 100 - 0.1x$

Given $x = 700$: $p(700) = 100 - 0.1(700)$
$= 100 - 70 = 30$.

So the price is \$30 per digital sports watch when there are 700 demands.

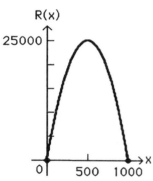

104. $S'(t) = 500t^{1/4}$

$S(t) = \displaystyle\int S'(t)\,dt = \int 500t^{1/4}\,dt = 500\int t^{1/4}\,dt$

$$= 500\left(\frac{1}{1 + \frac{1}{4}}\right)t^{1 + (1/4)} + C$$

$$= 500\left(\frac{4}{5}\right)t^{5/4} + C$$

$$= 400t^{5/4} + C$$

Given $S(0) = 0$: $0 = 400(0)^{5/4} + C$. Hence, $C = 0$ and $S(t) = 400t^{5/4}$.

We need to solve the following equation for t:
$20,000 = 400t^{5/4}$ or $t^{5/4} = 50$
$$t = 50^{4/5} \approx 23 \text{ months}$$

106. $S'(t) = 500t^{1/4} + 300$

$$S(t) = \int(500t^{1/4} + 300)\,dt = 500\int t^{1/4}\,dt + 300\int dt$$
$$= 400t^{5/4} + 300t + C$$

Given $S(0) = 0$: This implies that $C = 0$ and hence $S(t) = 400t^{5/4} + 300t$.
For $S(t) = 20,000$, we have
$$20,000 = 400t^{5/4} + 300t$$

Using a graphing utility, we obtain $t \approx 17.83$ months.

108. $L'(x) = 2,000x^{-1/3}$

$$L(x) = \int g(x)\,dx = \int 2,000x^{-1/3}\,dx = 2,000\int x^{-1/3}\,dx$$
$$= 2,000\left(\frac{x^{(-1/3)+1}}{-\frac{1}{3}+1}\right) + C$$
$$= 2,000\left(\frac{3}{2}x^{2/3}\right) + C = 3,000x^{2/3} + C$$

Given $L(18) = 12,000$: $12,000 = 3,000(8)^{2/3} + C$.   Hence,
$C = 0$ and $L(x) = 3,000x^{2/3}$.
$L(27) = 3,000(27)^{2/3} = 3,000(9) = 27,000$ labor hours.

110. $\dfrac{dA}{dt} = -4t^{-3}$, $1 \leq t \leq 10$

$$A = \int -4t^{-3}\,dt = -4\left(\frac{t^{-2}}{-2}\right) + C = 2t^{-2} + C$$

Given $A(1) = 2$: $2 = 2(1)^{-2} + C$. Hence, $C = 0$ and $A = 2t^{-2}$.

For $t = 10$, $A(10) = 2(10)^{-2} = \dfrac{2}{100} = 0.02$ square centimeters.

112. $V'(t) = \dfrac{15}{t}$, $1 \leq t \leq 5$

$$V(t) = \int \frac{15}{t}\,dt = 15\int t^{-1}\,dt = 15 \ln t + C$$

Given: $V(1) = 15$: $15 = 15 \ln 1 + C$. Hence, $C = 15$ and
$V(t) = 15 \ln t + 15$, $1 \leq t \leq 5$.

After 4 hours of study,
$$V(4) = 15 \ln 4 + 15 \approx 36 \text{ words.}$$

2. $\int (6x - 1)^3(6)\,dx$

Let $u = 6x - 1$, then $du = 6\,dx$ and

$$\int (6x - 1)^3(6)\,dx = \int u^3\,du = \frac{u^4}{4} + C \quad \text{[using I.I.F.]}$$

$$= \frac{(6x - 1)^4}{4} + C$$

Check: $\dfrac{d}{dx}\left[\dfrac{(6x - 1)^4}{4} + C\right] = \dfrac{1}{4}(4)(6x - 1)^3(6) + 0$

$$= (6x - 1)^3(6)$$

4. $\int (x^6 + 1)^4(6x^5)\,dx$

Let $u = x^6 + 1$, then $du = 6x^5\,dx$ and

$$\int (x^6 + 1)^4(6x^5)\,dx = \int u^4\,du = \frac{u^5}{5} + C \quad \text{[using I.I.F.]}$$

$$= \frac{(x^6 + 1)^5}{5} + C$$

Check: $\dfrac{d}{dx}\left[\dfrac{(x^6 + 1)^5}{5} + C\right] = \dfrac{1}{5}(5)(x^6 + 1)^4(6x^5) + 0$

$$= (x^6 + 1)^4(6x^5)$$

6. $\int (4x^2 - 3)^{-6}(8x)\,dx$

Let $u = 4x^2 - 3$, then $du = 8x\,dx$ and

$$\int (4x^2 - 3)^{-6}(8x)\,dx = \int u^{-6}\,du = -\frac{u^{-5}}{5} + C \quad \text{[using I.I.F.]}$$

$$= -\frac{(4x^2 - 3)^{-5}}{5} + C$$

Check: $\dfrac{d}{dx}\left[-\dfrac{(4x^2 - 3)^{-5}}{5} + C\right] = \left(-\dfrac{1}{5}\right)(-5)(4x^2 - 3)^{-6}(8x) + 0$

$$= (4x^2 - 3)^{-6}(8x)$$

8. $\int e^{x^3}(3x^2)\,dx$

Let $u = x^3$, then $du = 3x^2\,dx$ and

$$\int e^{x^3}(3x^2)\,dx = \int e^u\,du = e^u + C \quad \text{[using I.I.F.]}$$

$$= e^{x^3} + C$$

Check: $\dfrac{d}{dx}(e^{x^3} + C) = e^{x^3}(3x^2) + 0 = e^{x^3}(3x^2)$

10. $\int \dfrac{1}{5x-7}(5)\,dx = \int (5x-7)^{-1}(5)\,dx$

Let $u = (5x-7)$, then $du = 5dx$ and
$$\int (5x-7)^{-1}(5)\,dx = \int u^{-1}du = \ln|u| + C \quad \text{[using I.I.F.]}$$
$$= \ln|5x-7| + C$$

Check: $\dfrac{d}{dx}(\ln|5x-7| + C) = \dfrac{5}{5x-7} + 0 = (5x-7)^{-1}(5)$

12. $\int (x^2+9)^{-1/2}(2x)\,dx$

Let $u = x^2 + 9$, then $du = 2x\,dx$ and
$$\int (x^2+9)^{-1/2}(2x)\,dx = \int u^{-1/2}du = 2u^{1/2} + C \quad \text{[using I.I.F.]}$$
$$= 2(x^2+9)^{1/2} + C$$

Check: $\dfrac{d}{dx}[2(x^2+9)^{1/2}] = (2)\left(\dfrac{1}{2}\right)(x^2+9)^{-1/2}(2x) + 0 = (x^2+9)^{-1/2}(2x)$

14. $\int (x-3)^{-4}\,dx$

Let $u = x - 3$, then $du = dx$ and
$$\int (x-3)^{-4}\,dx = \int u^{-4}du = \dfrac{1}{-4+1}u^{-4+1} + C \quad \text{[using I.I.F.]}$$
$$= -\dfrac{1}{3}u^{-3} + C$$
$$= -\dfrac{1}{3}(x-3)^{-3} + C$$

Check: $\dfrac{d}{dx}\left[-\dfrac{1}{3}(x-3)^{-3} + C\right] = -\dfrac{1}{3}(-3)(x-3)^{-4}(1) = (x-3)^{-4}$

16. $\int (5t+1)^3\,dt$

Let $u = 5t + 1$, then $du = 5\,dt$ and $dt = \dfrac{1}{5}du$ and
$$\int (5t+1)^3\,dt = \int u^3 \dfrac{1}{5}du = \dfrac{1}{5}\int u^3\,du$$
$$= \dfrac{1}{5} \cdot \dfrac{u^4}{4} + C \quad \text{[using I.I.F.]}$$
$$= \dfrac{1}{20}(5t+1)^4 + C$$

Check: $\dfrac{d}{dt}\left[\dfrac{1}{20}(5t+1)^4 + C\right] = \dfrac{1}{20}(4)(5t+1)^3(5) = (5t+1)^3$

18. $\int (t^3 + 4)^{-2} \, t^2 \, dt$

Let $u = t^3 + 4$, then $du = 3t^2 \, dt$, $t^2 \, dt = \dfrac{1}{3} \, du$ and

$$\int (t^3 + 4)^{-2} \, t^2 \, dt = \int u^{-2} \frac{1}{3} du = \frac{1}{3} \int u^{-2} \, du$$

$$= \frac{1}{3} \cdot \frac{1}{-2 + 1} u^{-2+1} + C$$

$$= -\frac{1}{3} u^{-1} + C \qquad \text{[using I.I.F.]}$$

$$= -\frac{1}{3} (t^3 + 4)^{-1} + C$$

Check: $\dfrac{d}{dt}\left[-\dfrac{1}{3}(t^3 + 4)^{-1} + C \right] = -\dfrac{1}{3}(-1)(t^3 + 4)^{-2}(3t^2)$

$$= (t^3 + 4)^{-2}(t^2) = (t^3 + 4)^{-2} \, t^2$$

20. $\int e^{-0.01x} \, dx$

Let $u = -0.01x$, then $du = -0.01 \, dx$, $dx = -100 \, du$ and
$\int e^{-0.01x} \, dx = \int e^u (-100) \, du = -100 \int e^u \, du$

$$= -100 e^u + C \qquad \text{[using I.I.F.]}$$
$$= -100 e^{-0.01x} + C$$

Check: $\dfrac{d}{dx}[-100 e^{-0.01x} + C] = (-100) e^{-0.01x}(-0.01) = e^{-0.01x}$

22. $\int \dfrac{x}{1 + x^2} dx$

Let $u = 1 + x^2$, then $du = 2x \, dx$, $x \, dx = \dfrac{1}{2} \, du$ and

$$\int \frac{x}{1 + x^2} dx = \int \frac{1}{u} \cdot \frac{1}{2} du = \frac{1}{2} \int \frac{1}{u} \, du$$

$$= \frac{1}{2} \ln|u| + C \qquad \text{[using I.I.F.]}$$

$$= \frac{1}{2} \ln(1 + x^2) + C$$

Check: $\dfrac{d}{dx}\left[\dfrac{1}{2} \ln(1 + x^2) + C \right] = \dfrac{1}{2} \cdot \dfrac{1}{1 + x^2}(2x) = \dfrac{x}{1 + x^2}$

24. $\int \dfrac{3}{2 - t} dt$

Let $u = 2 - t$, then $du = -dt$, $dt = -du$ and

$$\int \frac{3}{u}(-du) = -3 \int \frac{1}{u} \, du = -3 \ln|u| + C \qquad \text{[using I.I.F.]}$$

$$= -3 \ln|2 - t| + C$$

Check: $\dfrac{d}{dt}[-3 \ln|2 - t| + C] = -3 \cdot \dfrac{1}{2 - t}(-1) = \dfrac{3}{2 - t}$

26. $\int \dfrac{t^2}{(t^3 - 2)^5}\, dt$

Let $u = t^3 - 2$, then $du = 3t^2\, dt$, and

$$\int \frac{t^2}{(t^3 - 2)^5}\, dt = \int (t^3 - 2)^{-5}\, \frac{3}{3}\, t^2\, dt = \int u^{-5}\, \frac{1}{3}\, du$$

$$= \frac{1}{3} \int u^{-5}\, du = \frac{1}{3} \cdot \frac{1}{-5 + 1} u^{-5+1} + C$$

$$= -\frac{1}{12} u^{-4} + C$$

$$= -\frac{1}{12} (t^3 - 2)^{-4} + C$$

Check: $\dfrac{d}{dt}\left[-\dfrac{1}{12}(t^3 - 2)^{-4} + C \right] = -\dfrac{1}{12}(-4)(t^3 - 2)^{-5}(3t^2)$

$$= (t^3 - 2)^{-5} t^2 = \frac{t^2}{(t^3 - 2)^5}$$

28. $\int \dfrac{x}{(5 - 2x^2)^5}\, dx$

Let $u = 5 - 2x^2$, then $du = -4x\, dx$ and

$$\int \frac{x}{(5 - 2x^2)^5}\, dx = \int (5 - 2x^2)^{-5}\, x\, dx$$

$$= \int (5 - 2x^2)^{-5}\, \frac{-4}{-4} x\, dx$$

$$= \int u^{-5}\, \frac{1}{-4}\, du$$

$$= -\frac{1}{4} \int u^{-5}\, du = -\frac{1}{4} \cdot \frac{1}{-5 + 1} u^{-5+1} + C$$

$$= \frac{1}{16} u^{-4} + C$$

$$= \frac{1}{16} (5 - 2x^2)^{-4} + C$$

Check: $\dfrac{d}{dx}\left[\dfrac{1}{16}(5 - 2x^2)^{-4} + C \right] = \dfrac{1}{16}(-4)(5 - 2x^2)^{-5}(-4x)$

$$= (5 - 2x^2)^{-5}(x)$$

$$= \frac{x}{(5 - 2x^2)^5}$$

30. $\int x\sqrt{x-9}\,dx = \int x(x-9)^{1/2}\,dx$

Let $u = (x-9)$, then $du = dx$ and $x = u + 9$.

$$\int x\sqrt{x-9}\,dx = \int (u+9)u^{1/2}\,du$$

$$= \int (u^{3/2} + 9u^{1/2})\,du$$

$$= \frac{u^{5/2}}{5/2} + \frac{9u^{3/2}}{3/2} + C$$

$$= \frac{2}{5}u^{5/2} + 6u^{3/2} + C$$

$$= \frac{2}{5}(x-9)^{5/2} + 6(x-9)^{3/2} + C$$

Check: $\dfrac{d}{dx}\left[\dfrac{2}{5}(x-9)^{5/2} + 6(x-9)^{3/2} + C\right]$

$$= \frac{2}{5}\left(\frac{5}{2}\right)(x-9)^{3/2}(1) + 6\left(\frac{3}{2}\right)(x-9)^{1/2}(1)$$

$$= (x-9)^{3/2} + 9(x-9)^{1/2}$$

$$= (x-9)\sqrt{x-9} + 9\sqrt{x-9}$$

$$= x\sqrt{x-9} - 9\sqrt{x-9} + 9\sqrt{x-9}$$

$$= x\sqrt{x-9}$$

32. $\int \dfrac{x}{\sqrt{x+5}}\,dx = \int x(x+5)^{-1/2}\,dx$

Let $u = x + 5$, then $du = dx$ and $x = u - 5$.

$$\int \frac{x}{\sqrt{x+5}}\,dx = \int (u-5)u^{-1/2}\,du$$

$$= \int (u^{1/2} - 5u^{-1/2})\,du$$

$$= \frac{u^{3/2}}{3/2} - \frac{5u^{1/2}}{1/2} + C$$

$$= \frac{2}{3}u^{3/2} - 10u^{1/2} + C$$

$$= \frac{2}{3}(x+5)^{3/2} - 10(x+5)^{1/2} + C$$

Check: $\dfrac{d}{dx}\left[\dfrac{2}{3}(x+5)^{3/2} - 10(x+5)^{1/2} + C\right]$

$$= \frac{2}{3}\left(\frac{3}{2}\right)(x+5)^{1/2} - 10\left(\frac{1}{2}\right)(x+5)^{-1/2}$$

$$= (x+5)^{1/2} - 5(x+5)^{-1/2}$$

$$= (x+5)^{1/2} - \frac{5}{(x+5)^{1/2}} = \frac{(x+5)-5}{(x+5)^{1/2}} = \frac{x}{\sqrt{x+5}}$$

34. $\int x(x + 6)^8 \, dx$

Let $u = x + 6$, then $du = dx$ and $x = u - 6$.

$$\int x(x + 6)^8 \, dx = \int (u - 6) u^8 \, du$$

$$= \int (u^9 - 6u^8) \, du$$

$$= \frac{u^{10}}{10} - \frac{6u^9}{9} + C$$

$$= \frac{1}{10} (x + 6)^{10} - \frac{2}{3} (x + 6)^9 + C$$

Check: $\dfrac{d}{dx} \left[\dfrac{1}{10} (x + 6)^{10} - \dfrac{2}{3} (x + 6)^9 + C \right]$

$$= \frac{1}{10} (10)(x + 6)^9 (1) - \frac{2}{3} (9)(x + 6)^8 (1)$$

$$= (x + 6)^9 - 6(x + 6)^8$$

$$= (x + 6)^8 [(x + 6) - 6] = (x + 6)^8 (x)$$

$$= x(x + 6)^8$$

36. Let $u = 1 - e^{-x}$, then $du = -e^{-x}(-1) \, dx = e^{-x} \, dx$.

$$\int e^{-x} (1 - e^{-x})^4 \, dx = \int (1 - e^{-x})^4 e^{-x} \, dx$$

$$= \int u^4 \, du = \frac{u^5}{5} + C$$

$$= \frac{1}{5} (1 - e^{-x})^5 + C$$

Check: $\dfrac{d}{dx} \left[\dfrac{1}{5} (1 - e^{-x})^5 + C \right] = \dfrac{1}{5} (5)(1 - e^{-x})^4 (e^{-x})(-1)$

$$= (1 - e^{-x})^4 e^{-x}$$

$$= e^{-x} (1 - e^{-x})^4$$

38. Let $u = x^3 - 3x + 7$, then $du = (3x^2 - 3) \, dx = 3(x^2 - 1) \, dx$.

$$\int \frac{x^2 - 1}{x^3 - 3x + 7} \, dx = \int (x^3 - 3x + 7)^{-1} \frac{3}{3} (x^2 - 1) \, dx$$

$$= \int u^{-1} \frac{1}{3} \, du = \frac{1}{3} \int u^{-1} \, du$$

$$= \frac{1}{3} \ln|u| + C$$

$$= \frac{1}{3} \ln|x^3 - 3x + 7| + C$$

Check: $\dfrac{d}{dx} \left[\dfrac{1}{3} \ln|x^3 - 3x + 7| + C \right] = \dfrac{1}{3} \cdot \dfrac{1}{x^3 - 3x + 7} (3x^2 - 3)$

$$= \frac{1}{3} \cdot \frac{3(x^2 - 1)}{x^3 - 3x + 7} = \frac{x^2 - 1}{x^3 - 3x + 7}$$

40. Let $u = x^3 - 3x + 7$, then $du = (3x^2 - 3)\,dx = 3(x^2 - 1)\,dx$.

$$\int \frac{x^2 - 1}{(x^3 - 3x + 7)^2}\,dx = \int (x^3 - 3x + 7)^{-2}\,\frac{3}{3}(x^2 - 1)\,dx$$

$$= \int u^{-2}\,\frac{1}{3}\,du = \frac{1}{3}\int u^{-2}\,du$$

$$= \frac{1}{3} \cdot \frac{u^{-1}}{-1} + C$$

$$= -\frac{1}{3}u^{-1} + C$$

$$= -\frac{1}{3}(x^3 - 3x + 7)^{-1} + C$$

Check: $\dfrac{d}{dx}\left[-\dfrac{1}{3}(x^3 - 3x + 7)^{-1} + C\right] = -\dfrac{1}{3}(-1)(x^3 - 3x + 7)^{-2}(3x^2 - 3)$

$$= \frac{1}{3}(x^3 - 3x + 7)^{-2}\,3(x^2 - 1)$$

$$= (x^3 - 3x + 7)^{-2}(x^2 - 1)$$

$$= \frac{x^2 - 1}{(x^3 - 3x + 7)^2}$$

42. (A) Differentiate $F(x) = \ln|x^2 + 5| + C$ to see if you get the integrand
$$f(x) = \frac{x}{x^2 + 5}$$

(B) Wrong: $\dfrac{d}{dx}[\ln|x^2 + 5| + C] = \dfrac{2x}{x^2 + 5} \neq \dfrac{x}{x^2 + 5}$

(C) Let $u = x^2 + 5$, then $du = 2x\,dx$.

$$\int \frac{x}{x^2 + 5}\,dx = \int (x^2 + 5)^{-1}\,\frac{2}{2}x\,dx = \int u^{-1}\,\frac{1}{2}\,du$$

$$= \frac{1}{2}\int u^{-1}\,du$$

$$= \frac{1}{2}\ln|u| + C$$

$$= \frac{1}{2}\ln|x^2 + 5| + C$$

Check: $\dfrac{d}{dx}\left[\dfrac{1}{2}\ln|x^2 + 5| + C\right] = \dfrac{1}{2} \cdot \dfrac{1}{x^2 + 5}(2x) = \dfrac{x}{x^2 + 5}$

44. (A) Differentiate $F(x) = e^{4x-5} + C$ to see if you get the integrand
$$f(x) = e^{4x-5}$$

(B) Wrong: $\dfrac{d}{dx}[e^{4x-5} + C] = e^{4x-5}(4) \neq e^{4x-5}$

(C) Let $u = 4x - 5$, then $du = 4\ dx$.

$$\int e^{4x-5}\ dx = \int e^{4x-5}\ \frac{4}{4}dx = \int e^u\ \frac{1}{4}du$$

$$= \frac{1}{4}\int e^u\ du$$

$$= \frac{1}{4}e^u + C$$

$$= \frac{1}{4}e^{4x-5} + C$$

Check: $\dfrac{d}{dx}\left[\dfrac{1}{4}\ e^{4x-5} + C\right] = \dfrac{1}{4}e^{4x-5}(4) = e^{4x-5}$

46. (A) Differentiate $F(x) = (x^2 - 3)^{-5} + C$ to see if you get the integrand
$f(x) = (-10x)(x^2 - 3)^{-4}$

(B) Wrong: $\dfrac{d}{dx}[(x - 3)^{-5} + C] = (-5)(x^2 - 3)^{-6}(2x) = (-10x)(x^2 - 3)^{-6}$

$$\neq (-10x)(x^2 - 3)^{-4}$$

(C) Let $u = x^2 - 3$, then $du = 2x\ dx$

$$\int(-10x)(x^2 - 3)^{-4}\ dx = -5\int(x^2 - 3)^{-4}(2x)\ dx = -5\int u^{-4}\ du$$

$$= -5 \cdot \frac{1}{-4 + 1}u^{-4+1} + C = \frac{5}{3}u^{-3} + C$$

$$= \frac{5}{3}(x^2 - 3)^{-3} + C$$

Check: $\dfrac{d}{dx}\left[\dfrac{5}{3}(x^2 - 3)^{-3} + C\right] = \dfrac{5}{3}(-3)(x^2 - 3)^{-4}(2x)$

$$= (-10x)(x^2 - 3)^{-4}$$

48. Let $u = 2x^3 + 1$, then $du = 6x^2\ dx$.

$$\int x^2\sqrt{2x^3 + 1}\ dx = \int(2x^3 + 1)^{1/2}\ \frac{6}{6}x^2\ dx$$

$$= \int u^{1/2}\ \frac{1}{6}du = \frac{1}{6}\int u^{1/2}\ du$$

$$= \frac{1}{6} \cdot \frac{u^{3/2}}{\frac{3}{2}} + C$$

$$= \frac{1}{9}u^{3/2} + C$$

$$= \frac{1}{9}(2x^3 + 1)^{3/2} + C$$

Check: $\dfrac{d}{dx}\left[\dfrac{1}{9}(2x^3 + 1)^{3/2} + C\right] = \dfrac{1}{9}\left(\dfrac{3}{2}\right)(2x^3 + 1)^{1/2}(6x^2) = x^2\sqrt{2x^3 + 1}$

50. Let $u = x^2 + 2$, then $du = 2x\,dx$.

$$\int x(x^2 + 2)^2\,dx = \int (x^2 + 2)^2 \frac{2}{2}x\,dx$$

$$= \int u^2 \frac{1}{2}du = \frac{1}{2}\int u^2\,du$$

$$= \frac{1}{2} \cdot \frac{u^3}{3} + C$$

$$= \frac{1}{6}(x^2 + 2)^3 + C$$

Check: $\dfrac{d}{dx}\left[\dfrac{1}{6}(x^2 + 2)^3 + C\right] = \dfrac{1}{6}(3)(x^2 + 2)^2(2x) = x(x^2 + 2)^2$

52. $\int (x^2 + 2)^2\,dx = \int (x^4 + 4x^2 + 4)\,dx$

$$= \frac{1}{5}x^5 + \frac{4}{3}x^3 + 4x + C$$

Check: $\dfrac{d}{dx}\left[\dfrac{1}{5}x^5 + \dfrac{4}{3}x^3 + 4x + C\right] = \dfrac{1}{5}(5x^4) + \dfrac{4}{3}(3x^2) + 4$

$$= x^4 + 4x^2 + 4 = (x^2 + 2)^2$$

54. Let $u = 4x^3 - 1$, then $du = 12x^2\,dx$.

$$\int \frac{x^2}{\sqrt{4x^3 - 1}}\,dx = \int \frac{x^2}{(4x^3 - 1)^{1/2}}\,dx = \int (4x^3 - 1)^{-1/2} \frac{12}{12}x^2\,dx$$

$$= \int u^{-1/2} \frac{1}{12}\,du$$

$$= \frac{1}{12}\int u^{-1/2}\,du$$

$$= \frac{1}{12} \cdot \frac{u^{1/2}}{\frac{1}{2}} + C$$

$$= \frac{1}{6}(4x^3 - 1)^{1/2} + C$$

Check: $\dfrac{d}{dx}\left[\dfrac{1}{6}(4x^3 - 1)^{1/2} + C\right] = \dfrac{1}{6}\left(\dfrac{1}{2}\right)(4x^3 - 1)^{-1/2}(12x^2)$

$$= (4x^3 - 1)^{-1/2}(x^2)$$

$$= \frac{x^2}{(4x^3 - 1)^{1/2}} = \frac{x^2}{\sqrt{4x^3 - 1}}$$

56. Let $u = 1 + e^x$, then $du = e^x\,dx$.

$$\int \frac{e^x}{1 + e^x}\,dx = \int (1 + e^x)^{-1} e^x\,dx = \int u^{-1}\,du$$

$$= \ln|u| + C$$

$$= \ln(1 + e^x) + C$$

Check: $\dfrac{d}{dx}[\ln(1 + e^x) + C] = \dfrac{1}{1 + e^x}(e^x) = \dfrac{e^x}{1 + e^x}$

58. Let $u = \ln x$, then $du = \dfrac{1}{x}dx$.

$$\int \frac{1}{x \ln x}dx = \int (\ln x)^{-1}\,\frac{1}{x}dx = \int u^{-1}\,du$$
$$= \ln|u| + C$$
$$= \ln|\ln x| + C$$

Check: $\dfrac{d}{dx}[\ln|\ln x| + C] = \dfrac{1}{\ln x}\left(\dfrac{1}{x}\right) = \dfrac{1}{x \ln x}$

60. $\dfrac{dm}{dn} = 10n(n^2 - 8)^7$

Let $u = (n^2 - 8)$, then $du = 2n\,dn$.

$$m = \int 10n(n^2 - 8)^7\,dn = 10\int (n^2 - 8)^7\,\frac{2}{2}n\,dn$$
$$= 10\int u^7\,\frac{1}{2}\,du$$
$$= 5\int u^7\,du$$
$$= 5 \cdot \frac{u^8}{8} + C$$
$$= \frac{5}{8}(n^2 - 8)^8 + C$$

62. $\dfrac{dy}{dx} = \dfrac{5x^2}{(x^3 - 7)^4}$

Let $u = x^3 - 7$, then $du = 3x^2\,dx$.

$$y = \int \frac{5x^2}{(x^3 - 7)^4}dx = \int (x^3 - 7)^{-4}(5x^2)\,dx$$
$$= 5\int (x^3 - 7)^{-4}\,\frac{3}{3}x^2\,dx$$
$$= 5\int u^{-4}\,\frac{1}{3}u\,du$$
$$= \frac{5}{3}\int u^{-4}\,du = \frac{5}{3} \cdot \frac{u^{-3}}{-3} + C$$
$$= -\frac{5}{9}u^{-3} + C = -\frac{5}{9}(x^3 - 7)^{-3} + C$$

64. $\dfrac{dm}{dt} = \dfrac{\ln(t - 5)}{t - 5}$

Let $u = \ln(t - 5)$, then $du = \dfrac{1}{t - 5}dt$.

$$m = \int \frac{\ln(t - 5)}{t - 5}dt = \int \ln(t - 5)\,\frac{1}{t - 5}dt$$
$$= \int u\,du = \frac{u^2}{2} + C = \frac{1}{2}[\ln(t - 5)]^2 + C$$

66. Let $v = au + b$, then $dv = a\,du$.

$$\int \frac{1}{au + b}\,du = \int (au + b)^{-1}\frac{a}{a}\,du = \int v^{-1}\frac{1}{a}\,dv \qquad (a \neq 0)$$

$$= \frac{1}{a}\int v^{-1}\,dv$$

$$= \frac{1}{a}\ln|v| + C$$

$$= \frac{1}{a}\ln|au + b| + C$$

Check: $\dfrac{d}{dx}\left[\dfrac{1}{a}\ln|au + b| + C\right] = \dfrac{1}{a}\cdot\dfrac{1}{au + b}\,(a)$

$$= \frac{1}{au + b}$$

68. $p'(x) = \dfrac{300}{(3x + 25)^2}$

Let $u = 3x + 25$, then $du = 3\,dx$.

$$p(x) = \int \frac{300}{(3x + 25)^2}\,dx = 300\int (3x + 25)^{-2}\,dx$$

$$= 300\int (3x + 25)^{-2}\frac{3}{3}\,dx$$

$$= 300\int u^{-2}\frac{1}{3}\,du = 100\int u^{-2}\,du$$

$$= 100\cdot\frac{u^{-1}}{-1} + C = -100u^{-1} + C$$

$$p(x) = -100(3x + 25)^{-1} + C = -\frac{100}{3x + 25} + C$$

Given: $p(75) = 1.6$:

$$1.6 = -\frac{100}{3(75) + 25} + C$$

$$1.6 = -\frac{100}{250} + C = -0.4 + C \quad\text{or}\quad C = 2 \quad\text{and}$$

$$p(x) = -\frac{100}{3x + 25} + 2$$

Now, $1.75 = -\dfrac{100}{3x + 25} + 2$

$$\frac{100}{3x + 25} = 0.25$$

$$0.25(3x + 25) = 100$$

$$3x + 25 = 400$$

$$3x = 375$$

$$x = 125$$

Thus, the demand is 125 bottles when the price is \$1.75.

70. $R'(x) = 40 - 0.02x + \dfrac{200}{x + 1}$

$R(x) = \displaystyle\int\left(40 - 0.02x + \dfrac{200}{x + 1}\right)dx$

$= \displaystyle\int 40\ dx - \int 0.02x\ dx + 200\int\dfrac{1}{x + 1}dx$

$= 40x - 0.02\left(\dfrac{x^2}{2}\right) + 200\ \ln(x + 1) + C \quad (u = x + 1,\ du = dx)$

$= 40x - 0.01x^2 + 200\ \ln(x + 1) + C$

Now, $R(0) = 0$. Thus, $C = 0$ and

$\qquad R(x) = 40x - 0.01x^2 + 200\ \ln(x + 1)$

$R(1,000) = 40(1,000) - 0.01(1,000)^2 + 200\ \ln(1,000 + 1)$

$\qquad\qquad = \$31,381.75$

72. $S'(t) = 20 - 20e^{-0.05t},\ 0 \le t \le 24$

(A) $S(t) = \displaystyle\int(20 - 20e^{-0.05t})\,dt$

$= \displaystyle\int 20\ dt - 20\int e^{-0.05t}\ dt$

$= 20t - 20\left(\dfrac{1}{-0.05}\right)e^{-0.05t} + C$

$= 20t + 400e^{-0.05t} + C$

Given: $S(0) = 0$: $0 = 0 + 400 + C$

$\qquad\qquad\qquad\qquad C = -400$

Total sales at time t:

$\qquad S(t) = 20t + 400e^{-0.05t} - 400,\ 0 \le t \le 24$

(B) $S(12) = 20(12) + 400e^{-0.05(12)} - 400 \approx 60$
Total estimated sales for the first twelve months: $60 million.

(C) On a graphing utility solve

$\qquad 20t + 400e^{-0.05t} - 400 = 100$

or

$\qquad 20t + 400e^{-0.05t} = 500$

The result is: $t \approx 16.02$ months.

74. (A) $R(t) = \dfrac{120t}{t^2 + 1} + 3, \ 0 \leq t \leq 20$

$R'(t) = 120\left(\dfrac{t^2 + 1 - 2t^2}{(t^2 + 1)^2}\right) = \dfrac{120(1 - t^2)}{(t^2 + 1)^2}$

$R'(t) = 0$ when $t = 1$.

Sign chart for $R'(t)$:

Test Numbers	
t	$R'(t)$
0	120 (+)
2	$-\frac{72}{5}$ (−)

Thus, the rate of production is greatest at $t = 1$.

(B) $Q(t) = \int R(t)\,dt = \int\left(\dfrac{120t}{t^2 + 1} + 3\right)dt$

$\qquad = 120\int\dfrac{t}{t^2 + 1}\,dt + \int 3\ dt$

$\qquad = 60\ \ln(t^2 + 1) + 3t + C$

$Q(0) = 0: \ 0 = 0 + 0 + C$ and
$Q(t) = 60\ \ln(t^2 + 1) + 3t$
$Q(5) = 60\ \ln(5^2 + 1) + 3(5) = 60\ \ln(26) + 15$
$\qquad\qquad\qquad\qquad\qquad \approx 210.5$ thousand barrels

(C) $Q(t) = 250$ thousands. Now, we need to solve:
$250 = 60\ \ln(t^2 + 1) + 3t$
Using a graphing utility we obtain $t \approx 6.7$ years.

76. $A'(t) = -0.9e^{-0.1t}, \ t \geq 0$

$A(t) = \int -0.9e^{-0.1t}\ dt = -0.9\int e^{-0.1t}\ dt$

$\qquad\qquad\qquad = -0.9\left(\dfrac{1}{-0.1}\right)e^{-0.1t} + C$

$\qquad\qquad\qquad = 9e^{-0.1t} + C$

Given $A(0) = 9: \ 9 = 9e^{-0.1(0)} + C$ or $9 = 9 + C$
$\qquad\qquad\qquad\qquad\qquad\qquad\qquad\qquad C = 0$

Thus, $A(t) = 9e^{-0.1t}$.
Now, $A(5) = 9e^{-0.1(5)} \approx 5.46$ square centimeters.

78. $\dfrac{dR}{dt} = \dfrac{60}{\sqrt{t + 9}}, \quad t \geq 0$

$R = \displaystyle\int \dfrac{60}{\sqrt{t + 9}}\, dt = 60\displaystyle\int (t + 9)^{-1/2}\, dt$

$\qquad\qquad = 60\left(\dfrac{(t + 9)^{1/2}}{\frac{1}{2}}\right) + C \quad (u = t + 9, \; du = dt)$

$\qquad\qquad = 120(t + 9)^{1/2} + C$

Given $R(0) = 0$: $0 = 120(0 + 9)^{1/2} + C$ or $C = -360$, and

$\qquad\qquad R(t) = 120(t + 9)^{1/2} - 360$

Now, $R(16) = 120(16 + 9)^{1/2} - 360$

$\qquad\qquad = 120(25)^{1/2} - 360$

$\qquad\qquad = 120(5) - 360$

$\qquad\qquad = 600 - 360 = 240$ feet.

80. $N'(t) = 12e^{-0.06t}, \quad 0 \leq t \leq 15$

$N(t) = \displaystyle\int 12e^{-0.06t}\, dt = (12)\left(\dfrac{1}{-0.06}\right)e^{-0.06t} + C$

$\qquad\qquad = -200e^{-0.06t} + C$

Given $N(0) = 0$: $0 = -200e^{-0.06(0)} + C = -200 + C$ or $C = 200$ and

$\qquad\qquad N(t) = -200e^{-0.06t} + 200$

$\qquad$ or

$\qquad\qquad N(t) = 200(1 - e^{-0.06t}), \quad 0 \leq t \leq 15$

Now, $N(15) = 200(1 - e^{-0.06(15)}) \approx 118$ words per minute.

EXERCISE 6-3
___

2. $\dfrac{dy}{dx} = 3x^{-2}$

$y = \dfrac{3}{-2 + 1}x^{-2+1} + C = -3x^{-1} + C \quad$ (General solution)

4. $\dfrac{dy}{dx} = e^{0.1x}$

$y = \dfrac{1}{0.1}e^{0.1x} + C = 10e^{0.1x} + C \quad$ (General solution)

6. $\dfrac{dy}{dx} = 8x^{-1}$

$y = 8 \ln|x| + C \quad$ (General solution)

8. $\dfrac{dy}{dx} = \sqrt{x} = x^{1/2}$

$y = \dfrac{x^{3/2}}{3/2} + C = \dfrac{2}{3}x^{3/2} + C$

Given $y(0) = 0$: $0 = \dfrac{2}{3}(0)^{3/2} + C$ or $C = 0$ and

the particular solution is: $y = \dfrac{2}{3}x^{3/2}$.

10. $\frac{dy}{dx} = e^{(x-3)}$

$y = e^{(x-3)} + C$

Given $y(3) = -5$: $-5 = e^{(3-3)} + C = 1 + C$ or $C = -6$

and the particular solution is: $y = e^{(x-3)} - 6$.

12. $\frac{dy}{dx} = \frac{1}{4(3-x)}$

$y = -\frac{1}{4} \ln|3 - x| + C$

Given $y(0) = 1$: $1 = -\frac{1}{4} \ln|3 - 0| + C$ or $C = 1 + \frac{1}{4} \ln 3$

and the particular solution is:

$y = -\frac{1}{4} \ln|3 - x| + 1 + \frac{1}{4} \ln 3$

14. Figure (a). When $x = 0$, $\frac{dy}{dx} = -0 = 0$ for any y. When $x = -1$, $\frac{dy}{dx} = -(-1) = 1$ for any y. When $x = 1$, $\frac{dy}{dx} = -1$ for any y.

These facts are consistent with the slope-field in Figure (a); they are not consistent with the slope-field in Figure (b).

16. $\frac{dy}{dx} = -x$

$\int \frac{dy}{dx} dx = \int (-x)\, dx$

General solution: $y = -\frac{1}{2} x^2 + C$

Given $y(0) = 3$: $-\frac{1}{2}(0)^2 + C = 3$

$C = 3$

Particular solution: $y = -\frac{1}{2} x^2 + 3$

18.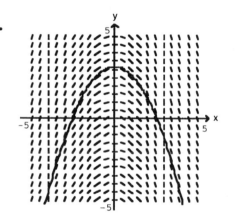

20. $\frac{dy}{dt} = -3y$

$\int \frac{1}{y} \frac{dy}{dt} dt = \int -3\, dt$

$\int \frac{1}{y} dy = \int -3\, dt$

$\ln |y| = -3t + K$ [K an arbitrary constant]

$|y| = e^{-3t+K} = e^K e^{-3t}$

$|y| = Ce^{-3t}$ [$C = e^K$]

If we assume $y > 0$, we get

General solution: $y = Ce^{-3t}$

22. $\dfrac{dy}{dx} = 0.1y, \quad y(0) = -2.5$

$\displaystyle\int \dfrac{1}{y}\dfrac{dy}{dx}\,dx = \int 0.1\,dx$

$\displaystyle\int \dfrac{1}{y}\,dy = \int 0.1\,dx$

$\ln\,|y| = 0.1x + K \qquad (K \text{ an arbitrary constant})$

$|y| = e^{0.1x+K} = e^K e^{0.1x}$

$|y| = Ce^{0.1x} \qquad (C = e^K)$

If we assume $y < 0$, we get

General solution: $y = -Ce^{0.1x}$

Given $y(0) = -2.5$: $-2.5 = -Ce^{0.1(0)} = -C$ or $C = 2.5$

and the particular solution is: $y = -2.5e^{0.1x}$

24. $\dfrac{dx}{dt} = 4t$

$x = \dfrac{4t^2}{2} + C = 2t^2 + C \quad$ (General solution)

26. $\dfrac{dx}{dt} = 4x$

$\displaystyle\int \dfrac{1}{x}\dfrac{dx}{dt}\,dt = \int 4\,dt$

$\displaystyle\int \dfrac{1}{x}\,dx = \int 4\,dt$

$\ln|x| = 4t + K \quad [K \text{ an arbitrary constant}]$

$|x| = e^{4t+K} = e^K e^{4t}$

$|x| = Ce^{4t} \quad [C = e^K]$

If we assume $x > 0$, we get General solution: $x = Ce^{4t}$.

28. Figure (B). When $y = -1$, the slope $\dfrac{dy}{dx} = -1 + 1 = 0$ for any x.

When $y = 1$, the slope $\dfrac{dy}{dx} = 1 + 1 = 2$ for any x; and so on. Both are consistent with the slope-field graph in Figure (B).

30. $y = Ce^x - 1$

$\dfrac{dy}{dx} = \dfrac{d}{dx}[Ce^x - 1] = Ce^x$

From the original equation,

$Ce^x = y + 1$

Thus, we have

$\dfrac{dy}{dx} = y + 1$

and $y = Ce^x - 1$ is a solution of the differential equation for any number C.

Given $y(0) = 0$: $0 = Ce^0 - 1 = C - 1$

$C = 1$

Particular solution: $y = e^x - 1$

32.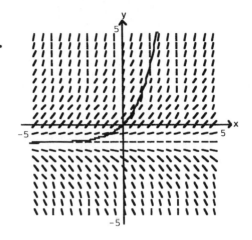

34.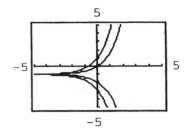

36. $y = 5,250e^{0.12t}$
$0 \leq t \leq 10, \ 0 \leq y \leq 20,000$

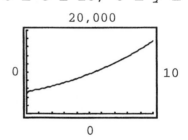

38. $p = 1,000e^{-0.08x}$
$0 \leq x \leq 40, \ 0 \leq p \leq 1,000$

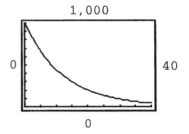

40. $N = 1,000(1 - e^{-0.07t})$
$0 \leq t \leq 70, \ 0 \leq N \leq 1,000$

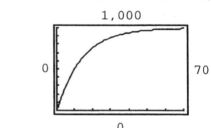

42. $N = \dfrac{400}{1 + 99e^{-0.4t}}$
$0 \leq t \leq 30, \ 0 \leq N \leq 400$

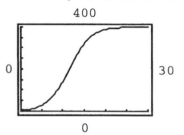

44. $y = \dfrac{M}{1 + ce^{-kMt}} = \dfrac{M}{2}$. Thus,

$1 + ce^{-kMt} = 2$ or $ce^{-kMt} = 1$ or

$e^{-kMt} = \dfrac{1}{c} = c^{-1}$. Take natural log from both sides.

$-kMt = -\ln c$ or $t = \dfrac{\ln c}{kM}$.

46. r = continuous compound growth rate is not constant, as can be seen from Problem 45.

48. $\dfrac{dA}{dt} = 0.12A, \ A(0) = 5,250$

This is an unlimited growth model. Thus,
$A(t) = 5,250e^{0.12t}$

50. $\dfrac{dA}{dt} = rA$, $A(0) = 5{,}000$

This is an unlimited growth model. Thus,

$A(t) = 5{,}000e^{rt}$

Since $A(5) = 7{,}460$, we solve $5{,}000e^{5r} = 7{,}460$ for r.

$$e^{5r} = \dfrac{7{,}460}{5{,}000}$$

$$5r = \ln\!\left(\dfrac{7{,}460}{5{,}000}\right)$$

$$r = \dfrac{1}{5}\ln\!\left(\dfrac{7{,}460}{5{,}000}\right) \approx 0.08$$

Thus, $A(t) = 5{,}000e^{0.08t}$.

52. (A) $\dfrac{dp}{dx} = rp$, $p(0) = 10$

This is an unlimited growth model. Thus,

$p(x) = 10e^{rx}$

Since $p(50) = 12.84$, we have

$12.84 = 10e^{50r}$

$e^{50r} = 1.284$

$50r = \ln(1.284)$

$r = \dfrac{1}{50}\ln(1.284) \approx 0.005$

Therefore, $p(x) = 10e^{0.005x}$.

(B) $p(100) = 10e^{0.005(100)} = 10e^{0.5}$
$\approx \$16.49$ per unit

(C)

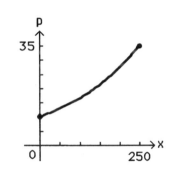

54. $\dfrac{dN}{dt} = k(L - N)$; $N(0) = 0$

(A) $N(10) = 0.1L$
Approximately 10% of the possible viewers will have been exposed after 10 days.

(B) $\dfrac{dN}{dt} = k(L - N)$; $N(0) = 0$

This is a limited growth model. Thus,

$N(t) = L(1 - e^{-kt})$

Since $N(10) = 0.1L$, we have

$0.1L = L(1 - e^{-10k})$

$1 - e^{-10k} = 0.1$

$e^{-10k} = 0.9$

$-10k = \ln(0.9)$

$k = -\dfrac{1}{10}\ln(0.9) \approx 0.011$

Therefore,

$N(t) = L(1 - e^{-0.011t})$

(C) Solve $L(1 - e^{-0.011t}) = 0.5L$:
$$1 - e^{-0.011t} = 0.5$$
$$e^{-0.011t} = 0.5$$
$$-0.011t = \ln(0.5)$$
$$t = -\frac{\ln(0.5)}{0.011} \approx 63 \text{ days}$$

(D)
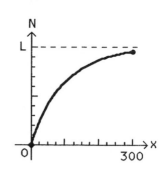

56. $\frac{dP}{dt} = -aP, \ P(0) = P_0$

This is an exponential decay model. Thus,
$$P(t) = P_0 e^{-at}$$

58. (A) $N(0) = \dfrac{1,000}{1 + 999e^{-0.4(10)}} \approx 52 \text{ people}$

$N(20) = \dfrac{1,000}{1 + 999e^{-0.4(20)}} \approx 749 \text{ people}$

(B) Solve $\dfrac{1,000}{2} = \dfrac{1,000}{1 + 999e^{-0.4t}}$ for t. Thus,

$$1 + 999e^{-0.4t} = 2$$
$$999e^{-0.4t} = 1$$
$$e^{-0.4t} = \frac{1}{999}$$
$$-0.4t = \ln\left(\frac{1}{999}\right)$$
$$t = -\frac{1}{0.4}\ln\left(\frac{1}{999}\right) = \frac{\ln(999)}{0.4} \approx 17 \text{ days}$$

(C) $\lim\limits_{t\to\infty} N(t) = \lim\limits_{t\to\infty} \dfrac{1,000}{1 + 999e^{-0.4t}}$

$$= \frac{1,000}{1} = 1,000$$

(D)
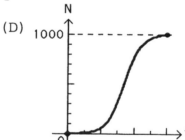

60. Using the exponential decay model, we have $\dfrac{dy}{dt} = -ky, \ y(0) = 100, \ k > 0$
where $y = y(t)$ is the amount of DDT present at time t. Therefore,
$$y(t) = 100e^{-kt}$$
Since $y(5) = 75$, we solve:
$$75 = 100e^{-5k}$$
for k to find the continuous compound decay rate:
$$75 = 100e^{-5k}$$
$$e^{-5k} = 0.75$$
$$-5k = \ln(0.75)$$
$$k = -\frac{1}{5}\ln(0.75) \approx 0.057536$$

62. $N(t) = 100(1 - e^{-0.02t})$

$N'(t) = 100(-e^{-0.02t})(-0.02)$

$\quad\quad = 2e^{-0.02t}$

$N'(10) = 2e^{-0.02(10)} = 2e^{-0.2} \approx 1.64$ words per minute/hour of practice

$N'(40) = 2e^{-0.02(40)} = 2e^{-0.8} \approx 0.9$ words per minute/hour of practice

64. $\dfrac{dS}{dR} = \dfrac{k}{R}$

$S = k\displaystyle\int \dfrac{1}{R}\,dR = k \ln R + C$

Given: $S(R_0) = 0$: $0 = k \ln R_0 + C$ or $C = -k \ln R_0$.

Thus,

$\quad S = k \ln R - k \ln R_0$

$\quad\quad = k(\ln R - \ln R_0) = k \ln \dfrac{R}{R_0}$

66. Solve

$$\dfrac{400}{2} = \dfrac{400}{1 + 399e^{-0.4t}} \quad \text{for } t.$$

$2 = 1 + 399e^{-0.4t}$

$399e^{-0.4t} = 1$

$e^{-0.4t} = \dfrac{1}{399}$

$-0.4t = \ln\left(\dfrac{1}{399}\right) = -\ln(399)$

$t = \dfrac{\ln(399)}{0.4} \approx 15$ minutes

EXERCISE 6-4

2.

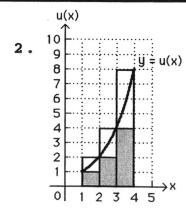
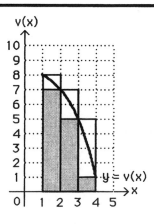

4. For Figure (C):

$$L_3 = u(1) \cdot 1 + u(2) \cdot 1 + u(3) \cdot 1$$
$$= 1 + 2 + 4 = 7$$
$$R_3 = u(2) \cdot 1 + u(3) \cdot 1 + u(4) \cdot 1$$
$$= 2 + 4 + 8 = 14$$

For Figure (D):

$$L_3 = v(1) \cdot 1 + v(2) \cdot 1 + v(3) \cdot 1$$
$$= 8 + 7 + 5 = 20$$
$$R_3 = v(2) \cdot 1 + v(3) \cdot 1 + v(4) \cdot 1$$
$$= 7 + 5 + 1 = 13$$

6. $L_3 \leq \int_1^4 u(x)dx \leq R_3$, $R_3 \leq \int_1^4 v(x)dx \leq L_3$; since $u(x)$ is increasing on [1, 4], L_3 underestimates the area and R_3 overestimates the area; since $v(x)$ is decreasing on [1, 4], L_3 overestimates the area and R_3 underestimates the area.

8. For Figure (C):

Error bound for L_3 and R_3:

$$\text{Error} \leq |u(4) - u(1)| \left(\frac{4-1}{3} \right) = |8 - 1| = 7$$

For Figure (D):

Error bound for L_3 and R_3:

$$\text{Error} \leq |v(4) - v(1)| \left(\frac{4-1}{3} \right) = |1 - 8| = 7$$

10. $f(x) = 25 - 3x^2$; $\Delta x = 3$;

Given $c_i = \dfrac{x_{i-1} + 2x_i}{3}$

$$c_1 = \frac{0 + 2(3)}{3} = 2, \quad c_2 = \frac{3 + 2(6)}{3} = 5, \quad c_3 = \frac{6 + 2(9)}{3} = 8, \quad c_4 = \frac{9 + 2(12)}{3} = 11$$

$$S_4 = \Delta x \{f(c_1) + f(c_2) + f(c_3) + f(c_4)\}$$
$$= 3\{13 - 50 - 167 - 338\} = -1,626$$

12. $f(x) = 25 - 3x^2$; $\Delta x = 2$;

Given $c_i = \dfrac{x_{i-1} + x_i}{2}$

$$c_1 = -4, \quad c_2 = -2, \quad c_3 = 0, \quad c_4 = 2, \quad c_5 = 4$$
$$S_5 = \Delta x \{f(c_1) + f(c_2) + f(c_3) + f(c_4) + f(c_5)\}$$
$$= 2\{-23 + 13 + 25 + 13 - 23\} = 10$$

14. $f(x) = x^2 - 5x - 6$; $\Delta x = 1$.
  Given: $c_1 = 0.2$, $c_2 = 1.5$, $c_3 = 2.8$
  $S_3 = \Delta x\{f(c_1) + f(c_2) + f(c_3)\}$
    $= 1 \cdot \{-6.96 - 11.25 - 12.16\} = -30.37$

16. $f(x) = x^2 - 5x - 6$; $\Delta x = 1$.
  Given: $c_1 = 2$, $c_2 = 2$, $c_3 = 4$, $c_4 = 4$, $c_5 = 6$, $c_6 = 6$
  $S_6 = \Delta x\{f(c_1) + f(c_2) + f(c_3) + f(c_4) + f(c_5) + f(c_6)\}$
    $= 1 \cdot \{-12 - 12 - 10 - 10 + 0 + 0\} = -44$

18. $\int_0^C f(x)\,dx = \text{Area } C = 5.333$

20. $\int_b^d f(x)\,dx = -(\text{Area } B) + (\text{Area } C) - (\text{Area } D)$
    $= -2.475 + 5.333 - 1.792 = 1.066$

22. $\int_0^d f(x)\,dx = (\text{Area } C) - (\text{Area } D) = 5.333 - 1.792 = 3.541$

24. $\int_d^a f(x)\,dx = -\int_a^d f(x)\,dx = -\{(\text{Area } A) - (\text{Area } B) + (\text{Area } C) - (\text{Area } D)\}$
    $= -\{1.408 - 2.475 + 5.333 - 1.792\} = -2.474$

26. $\int_c^a f(x)\,dx = -\int_a^c f(x)\,dx = -\{(\text{Area } A) - (\text{Area } B) + (\text{Area } C)\}$
    $= -\{1.408 - 2.475 + 5.333\} = -4.266$

28. $\int_c^b f(x)\,dx = -\int_b^c f(x)\,dx = -\{-(\text{Area } D) + (\text{Area } C)\}$
    $= -\{-2.475 + 5.333\} = -2.858$

30. $\int_1^4 3x^2\,dx = 3\int_1^4 x^2\,dx = 3(21) = 63$

32. $\int_1^4 (7x - 2x^2)\,dx = \int_1^4 7x\,dx - \int_1^4 2x^2\,dx$
    $= 7\int_1^4 x\,dx - 2\int_1^4 x^2\,dx$
    $= 7(7.5) - 2(21) = 52.5 - 42 = 10.5$

34. $\int_1^4 (4x^2 - 9x)\,dx = \int_1^4 4x^2\,dx - \int_1^4 9x\,dx$
    $= 4\int_1^4 x^2\,dx - 9\int_1^4 x\,dx$
    $= 4(21) - 9(7.5) = 16.5$

36. $\int_1^5 -4x^2\,dx = \int_1^4 -4x^2\,dx + \int_4^5 -4x^2\,dx$
    $= -4\int_1^4 x^2\,dx - 4\int_4^5 x^2\,dx$
    $= -4(21) - 4\left(\dfrac{61}{3}\right) = -84 - \dfrac{244}{3} = -\dfrac{496}{3}$

38. $\int_5^5 (10 - 7x + x^2) \, dx = 0$

40. $\int_4^1 x(1 - x) \, dx = -\int_1^4 x(1 - x) \, dx$

$$= -\int_1^4 (x - x^2) \, dx$$

$$= -\int_1^4 x \, dx - \int_1^4 -x^2 \, dx$$

$$= -\int_1^4 x \, dx + \int_1^4 x^2 \, dx$$

$$= -7.5 + 21 = 13.5$$

42. (A) False. See function $v(x)$ in problem 4.
(B) False. See function $u(x)$ in problem 4.

44. $h(x)$ is an increasing function; $\Delta x = 100$

$R_{10} = h(100)100 + h(200)100 + h(300)100 + h(400)100 + h(500)100$

$\qquad\qquad + h(600)100 + h(700)100 + h(800)100 + h(900)100$

$\qquad\qquad + h(1000)100 = 336,100 \text{ ft}^2.$

Error bound for R_{10}:

Error $\leq |h(1000) - h(0)| \left(\dfrac{1000 - 0}{10} \right) = |500 - 0|(100) = 50,000$

To choose n so that Error ≤ 1000, we have

$(500) \left(\dfrac{1000}{n} \right) \leq 1000 \quad \text{or} \quad n \geq 500$

46. $f(x) = 0.25x^2 - 4$ on $[1, 6]$

$\quad L_5 = f(1)\Delta x + f(2)\Delta x + f(3)\Delta x + f(4)\Delta x + f(5)\Delta x$

where $\Delta x = 1$.
Thus,

$\quad L_5 = [-3.75 - 3 - 1.75 + 0 + 2.25](1) = -6.25$

$\quad R_5 = f(2)\Delta x + f(3)\Delta x + f(4)\Delta x + f(5)\Delta x + f(6)\Delta x$

where $\Delta x = 1$.
Thus,

$\quad R_5 = [-3 - 1.75 + 0 + 2.25 + 5](1) = 2.5$

Error bound for L_5 and R_5:

Error $\leq |f(6) - f(1)| \left(\dfrac{6 - 1}{5} \right) = |5 - (-3.75)| = 8.75$

Geometrically, the definite integral over the interval $[1, 6]$ is the sum of the areas between the curve and the x-axis from $x = 1$ to $x = 6$, with the areas below the x-axis counted negatively and those above the x-axis counted positively.

48. $f(x) = \dfrac{3}{1 + 2e^{-x}}$

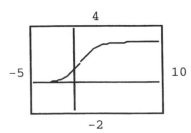

Thus, f is increasing on $(-\infty, \infty)$.

50. $f(x) = e^{x^2}$

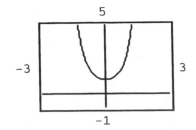

Thus, f is decreasing on $(-\infty, 0]$ and increasing on $[0, \infty)$.

52. $\displaystyle\int_0^{10} \ln(x^2 + 1)\, dx;\ \ f(x) = \ln(x^2 + 1)$

$$|I - L_n| \le |f(10) - f(0)|\left(\dfrac{10 - 0}{n}\right) \le 0.5$$

$$|\ln(101) - \ln 1|\dfrac{10}{n} \le 0.5$$

$$n \ge \dfrac{10\ln(101)}{0.5} \approx 93$$

54. $\displaystyle\int_1^4 x^x\, dx;\ \ f(x) = x^x$

$$|I - R_n| = |f(4) - f(1)|\left(\dfrac{4 - 1}{n}\right) \le 0.5$$

$$|4^4 - 1^1|\left(\dfrac{3}{n}\right) \le 0.5$$

$$n \ge \dfrac{3(255)}{0.5} \approx 1{,}530$$

56. $L_4 = [N(20) + N(40) + N(60) + N(80)]\Delta t$
  $= [51 + 68 + 76 + 81](20) = 5{,}520$ units
$R_4 = [N(40) + N(60) + N(80) + N(100)]\Delta t$
  $= [68 + 76 + 81 + 84](20) = 6{,}180$ units
Thus, $5{,}520 \le \displaystyle\int_{20}^{100} N(t)\, dt \le 6{,}180$.
Error bound for L_4 or R_4 is $6{,}180 - 5{,}520 = 660$.

58. $L_5 = [A'(5) + A'(6) + A'(7) + A'(8) + A'(9)]\Delta t,\ \Delta t = 1$
  $= [0.55 + 0.49 + 0.45 + 0.40 + 0.36] = 2.25$
$R_5 = [A'(6) + A'(7) + A'(8) + A'(9) + A'(10)]\Delta t,\ \Delta t = 1$
  $= [0.49 + 0.45 + 0.40 + 0.36 + 0.33] = 2.03$
Error bound for L_5 and R_5:
Error $\le |2.03 - 2.25| = 0.22$

60. $[0, 6]$, $\Delta x = 2$

$L_3 = [N'(0) + N'(2) + N'(4)]\Delta x$

$\quad = [29 + 26 + 23](2) = 156$

$R_3 = [N'(2) + N'(4) + N'(6)]\Delta x$

$\quad = [26 + 23 + 21](2) = 140$

$R_3 = 140 \le \int_0^6 N'(x)\,dx \le 156 = L_3$

EXERCISE 6-5

2. $F(x) = 9x + 120$

(A) $F(15) - F(10) = 255 - 210 = 45$

(B) $F'(x) = 9$

$\quad$ Area $= 9 \times 5 = 45$

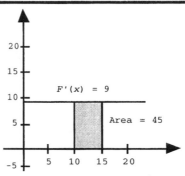

4. $F(x) = x^2 + 30x + 210$

(A) $F(15) - F(10) = 225 + 450 - 100 - 300 = 275$

(B) $F'(x) = 2x + 30$

$\quad$ Area $= \dfrac{5}{2}\{60 + 50\} = 275$

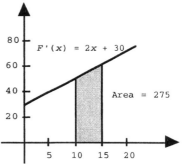

6. $\int_1^2 3x^2\,dx = 3 \cdot \dfrac{x^3}{3}\Big|_1^2 = 2^3 - 1^3 = 7$

8. $\int_{12}^{20} dx = x\Big|_{12}^{20} = 20 - 12 = 8$

10. $\int_1^3 (6x + 5)\,dx = (3x^2 + 5x)\Big|_1^3 = (3(3)^2 + 5(3)) - (3(1)^2 + 5(1))$

$\qquad\qquad = (27 + 15) - (3 + 5)$

$\qquad\qquad = 42 - 8 = 34$

12. $\int_{-1}^2 (x^2 - 4x)\,dx = \left(\dfrac{1}{3}x^3 - 2x^2\right)\Big|_{-1}^2 = \left(\dfrac{1}{3}(2)^3 - 2(2)^2\right) - \left(\dfrac{1}{3}(-1)^3 - 2(-1)^2\right)$

$\qquad\qquad = \left(\dfrac{8}{3} - 8\right) - \left(-\dfrac{1}{3} - 2\right)$

$\qquad\qquad = \dfrac{8}{3} - 8 + \dfrac{1}{3} + 2 = -3$

14. $\int_0^2 30x^5\,dx = 5x^6\Big|_0^2 = 5(2)^6 - 5(0)^6 = 320$

16. $\int_{-1}^{1} e^{5x} dx = \frac{1}{5}e^{5x} \Big|_{-1}^{1} = \frac{1}{5}e^5 - \frac{1}{5}e^{-5}$

18. $\int_{1}^{2} \frac{dx}{x} = \ln|x| \Big|_{1}^{2} = \ln 2 - \ln 1 = \ln 2 - 0 \approx 0.693$

20. $\int_{2}^{5} 3x^{-2} dx = -3x^{-1} \Big|_{2}^{5} = -3(5)^{-1} + 3(2)^{-1} = -\frac{3}{5} + \frac{3}{2} = \frac{-6 + 15}{10} = \frac{9}{10}$

22. $\int_{0}^{4} 9x^{1/2} dx = 6x^{3/2} \Big|_{0}^{4} = 6(4)^{3/2} - 6(0)^{3/2} = 6(2^2)^{3/2} = 6(2)^3 = 48$

24. $\int_{1}^{2} (5 - 16x^{-3}) dx = (5x + 8x^{-2}) \Big|_{1}^{2} = (5(2) + 8(2)^{-2}) - (5(1) + 8(1)^{-2})$

$$= 12 - 13 = -1$$

26. $\int_{4}^{25} \frac{2}{\sqrt{x}} dx = \int_{4}^{25} 2x^{-1/2} dx = 4x^{1/2} \Big|_{4}^{25} = 4(25)^{1/2} - 4(4)^{1/2} = 20 - 8 = 12$

28. $\int_{0}^{1} 32(x^2 + 1)^7 x \, dx$

Let $u = x^2 + 1$, then $du = 2x \, dx$.

$\int 32(x^2 + 1)^7 x \, dx = 32 \int (x^2 + 1)^7 \frac{2}{2}x \, dx = 16 \int u^7 \, du = 2u^8 + C$

$$= 2(x^2 + 1)^8 + C$$

Thus,

$\int_{0}^{1} 32(x^2 + 1)^7 x \, dx = 2(x^2 + 1)^8 \Big|_{0}^{1} = 2(1^2 + 1)^8 - 2(0^2 + 1)^8$

$$= 2^9 - 2 = 512 - 2 = 510$$

30. $\int_{2}^{8} \frac{1}{x + 1} dx$

Let $u = x + 1$, then $du = dx$.

$\int \frac{1}{x + 1} dx = \int \frac{1}{u} du = \ln|u| + C = \ln|x + 1| + C$

Thus,

$\int_{2}^{8} \frac{1}{x + 1} dx = \ln|x + 1| \Big|_{2}^{8} = \ln 9 - \ln 3 = \ln \frac{9}{3} = \ln 3 \approx 1.099$

32. $\int_{-10}^{25} e^{-0.01x} dx$

Let $u = -0.01x$, then $du = -0.01dx$.

$\int e^{-0.01x} dx = \int e^{-0.01} \frac{-0.01}{-0.01} dx = -100 \int e^u \, du = -100e^u + C$

$$= -100e^{-0.01x} + C$$

$\int_{-10}^{25} e^{-0.01x} dx = -100e^{-0.01x} \Big|_{-10}^{25}$

$$= -100e^{-0.25} + 100e^{0.1} = 100(e^{0.1} - e^{-0.25}) \approx 32.637$$

34. $\int_e^{e^2} \frac{(\ln t)^2}{t} dt$

Let $u = \ln t$, the $du = \frac{1}{t} dt$. Thus,

$$\int \frac{(\ln t)^2}{t} dt = \int u^2 \, du = \frac{1}{3} u^3 + C = \frac{1}{3} (\ln t)^3 + C$$

$$\int_e^{e^2} \frac{(\ln t)^2}{t} dt = \frac{1}{3} (\ln t)^3 \Big|_e^{e^2} = \frac{1}{3} (\ln e^2)^3 - \frac{1}{3} (\ln e)^3$$

$$= \frac{1}{3} (2 \ln e)^3 - \frac{1}{3} (\ln e)^3$$

$$= \frac{8}{3} - \frac{1}{3} = \frac{7}{3} \approx 2.333$$

36. $\int_0^4 x\sqrt{4 - x} \, dx$

Let $u = 4 - x$, then $du = -dx$ and $x = 4 - u$.

$$\int x\sqrt{4 - x}\, dx = \int (4 - u) u^{1/2} (-du) = \int (-4u^{1/2} + u^{3/2})\, du$$

$$= (-4) \frac{u^{3/2}}{\frac{3}{2}} + \frac{u^{5/2}}{\frac{5}{2}} + C$$

$$= -\frac{8u^{3/2}}{3} + \frac{2u^{5/2}}{5} + C$$

$$= -\frac{8}{3} (4 - x)^{3/2} + \frac{2}{5} (4 - x)^{5/2} + C$$

$$\int_0^4 x\sqrt{4 - x}\, dx = \left[-\frac{8}{3} (4 - x)^{3/2} + \frac{2}{5} (4 - x)^{5/2} \right] \Big|_0^4$$

$$= \frac{8}{3} (4)^{3/2} - \frac{2}{5} (4)^{5/2}$$

$$= \frac{64}{3} - \frac{64}{5} = \frac{128}{15} \approx 8.533$$

38. $\int_0^1 xe^{x^2} dx$

Let $u = x^2$, then $du = 2x\, dx$.

$$\int xe^{x^2} dx = \int e^{x^2} \frac{2}{2} x\, dx = \frac{1}{2} \int e^u \, du$$

$$= \frac{1}{2} e^u + C$$

$$= \frac{1}{2} e^{x^2} + C$$

$$\int_0^1 xe^{x^2} dx = \frac{1}{2} e^{x^2} \Big|_0^1$$

$$= \frac{1}{2} e - \frac{1}{2} e^0 = \frac{1}{2} (e - 1) \approx 0.859$$

40. $\int_{-2}^{-1} \dfrac{x}{x^2 + 1}\, dx$

Let $u = x^2 + 1$, then $du = 2x\, dx$.

$$\int \dfrac{x}{x^2 + 1}\, dx = \int \dfrac{x}{x^2 + 1} \cdot \dfrac{2}{2}x\, dx = \dfrac{1}{2}\int \dfrac{1}{u}\, du$$

$$= \dfrac{1}{2}\ln|u| + C$$

$$= \dfrac{1}{2}\ln(x^2 + 1) + C$$

$$\int_{-2}^{-1} \dfrac{x}{x^2 + 1}\, dx = \dfrac{1}{2}\ln(x^2 + 1)\Big|_{-2}^{-1}$$

$$= \dfrac{1}{2}\ln 2 - \dfrac{1}{2}\ln 5 = \dfrac{1}{2}(\ln 2 - \ln 5) \approx -0.458$$

42. $g(x) = 2x + 7$ on $[0, 5]$

(A) Ave $g(x) = \dfrac{1}{5 - 0}\int_0^5 (2x + 7)\, dx$

$$= \dfrac{1}{5}(x^2 + 7x)\Big|_0^5$$

$$= \dfrac{1}{5}(5^2 + 7(5))$$

$$= \dfrac{1}{5}(25 + 35) = 12$$

(B)

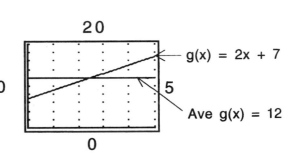

44. $g(t) = 4t - 3t^2$ on $[-2, 2]$

(A) Ave $g(t) = \dfrac{1}{2 - (-2)}\int_{-2}^{2} (4t - 3t^2)\, dt$

$$= \dfrac{1}{4}(2t^2 - t^3)\Big|_{-2}^{2}$$

$$= \dfrac{1}{4}(8 - 8) - \dfrac{1}{4}(8 + 8)$$

$$= 0 - 4 = -4$$

(B)

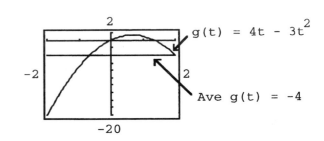

46. $g(x) = \sqrt{x + 1}$ on $[3, 8]$

(A) Ave $g(x) = \dfrac{1}{8 - 3}\int_3^8 \sqrt{x + 1}\, dx$

$$= \dfrac{1}{5}\int_3^8 (x + 1)^{1/2}\, dx$$

$$= \dfrac{2}{15}(x + 1)^{3/2}\Big|_3^8$$

$$= \dfrac{2}{15}[(9)^{3/2} - (4)^{3/2}]$$

$$= \dfrac{2}{15}[27 - 8]$$

$$= \dfrac{38}{15} \approx 2.53$$

(B)

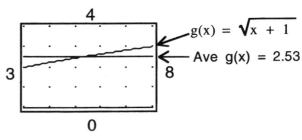

48. $f(x) = 64e^{0.08x}$ on $[0, 10]$

(A) Ave $f(x) = \dfrac{1}{10 - 0} \displaystyle\int_0^{10} 64e^{0.08x}\, dx$ (B)

$\qquad\qquad\qquad = \dfrac{64}{10}\left(\dfrac{1}{0.08}\, e^{0.08x}\right)\Big|_0^{10}$

$\qquad\qquad\qquad = 80(e^{0.08} - 1)$

$\qquad\qquad\qquad \approx 98.04$

$f(x) = 64e^{0.08x}$

Ave $f(x) = 98.04$

50. $\displaystyle\int_0^1 x\sqrt{3x^2 + 2}\, dx = \int_0^1 x(3x^2 + 2)^{1/2}\, dx$

Let $u = 3x^2 + 2$, then $du = 6x\, dx$.

$\displaystyle\int x(3x^2 + 2)^{1/2}\, dx = \int (3x^2 + 2)^{1/2}\, \dfrac{6}{6}x\, dx = \dfrac{1}{6}\int u^{1/2}\, du$

$\qquad\qquad\qquad\qquad\qquad = \dfrac{1}{6} \cdot \dfrac{u^{3/2}}{\frac{3}{2}} + C$

$\qquad\qquad\qquad\qquad\qquad = \dfrac{u^{3/2}}{9} + C$

$\qquad\qquad\qquad\qquad\qquad = \dfrac{(3x^2 + 2)^{3/2}}{9} + C$

$\displaystyle\int_0^1 x\sqrt{3x^2 + 2}\, dx = \left(\dfrac{(3x^2 + 2)^{3/2}}{9}\right)\Big|_0^1$

$\qquad\qquad\qquad\quad = \dfrac{(3 + 2)^{3/2}}{9} - \dfrac{(2)^{3/2}}{9}$

$\qquad\qquad\qquad\quad = \dfrac{(5^{3/2} - 2^{3/2})}{9} = \dfrac{1}{9}(5^{3/2} - 2^{3/2})$

52. $\displaystyle\int_1^2 \dfrac{x + 1}{2x^2 + 4x + 4}\, dx = \int_1^2 (2x^2 + 4x + 4)^{-1}(x + 1)\, dx$

Let $u = 2x^2 + 4x + 4$, then $du = (4x + 4)\, dx = 4(x + 1)\, dx$.

$\displaystyle\int (2x^2 + 4x + 4)^{-1}(x + 1)\, dx = \int (2x^2 + 4x + 4)^{-1}\, \dfrac{4}{4}(x + 1)\, dx$

$\qquad\qquad\qquad\qquad\qquad = \int \dfrac{1}{4}u^{-1}\, du = \dfrac{1}{4}\ln|u| + C$

$\qquad\qquad\qquad\qquad\qquad = \dfrac{1}{4}\ln|2x^2 + 4x + 4| + C$

$\displaystyle\int_1^2 \dfrac{x + 1}{2x^2 + 4x + 4}\, dx = \left(\dfrac{1}{4}\ln|2x^2 + 4x + 4|\right)\Big|_1^2$

$\qquad\qquad\qquad\qquad = \dfrac{1}{4}\ln(20) - \dfrac{1}{4}\ln(10) = \dfrac{1}{4}\ln\left(\dfrac{20}{10}\right) = \dfrac{1}{4}\ln 2$

54. $\displaystyle\int_6^7 \frac{\ln(t-5)}{t-5}\,dt$

Let $u = \ln(t-5)$, then $du = \dfrac{1}{t-5}\,dt$.

$$\int \frac{\ln(t-5)}{t-5}\,dt = \int u\,du = \frac{u^2}{2} + C = \frac{(\ln(t-5))^2}{2} + C$$

$$\int_6^7 \frac{\ln(t-5)}{t-5}\,dt = \left[\frac{(\ln(t-5))^2}{2}\right]\Bigg|_6^7$$

$$= \frac{(\ln 2)^2}{2} - \frac{(\ln 1)^2}{2} = \frac{(\ln 2)^2}{2} = \frac{1}{2}(\ln 2)^2$$

56. $\displaystyle\int_{-1}^1 e^{x^2}\,dx \approx 2.925$

```
fnInt(e^(X²),X,-
1,1)
        2.925303492
■
```

58. $\displaystyle\int_0^3 \sqrt{9-x^2}\,dx \approx 7.069$

```
fnInt(√(9-X²),X,
0,3)
        7.068583805
■
```

62. $C'(x) = 500 - \dfrac{x}{3}$ on $[0, 600]$

The increase in cost from a production level of 0 bikes per month to a production level of 600 bikes per month is given by:

$$\int_0^{600}\left(500 - \frac{x}{3}\right)dx = \left(500x - \frac{1}{6}x^2\right)\Bigg|_0^{600}$$

$$= 500(600) - \frac{1}{6}(600)^2$$

$$= 300{,}000 - 60{,}000$$

$$= \$240{,}000$$

64. Total maintenance costs from the end of the second year to the end of the seventh year:

$$M(7) - M(2) = \int_2^7 (90x^2 + 5{,}000)\,dx = (30x^3 + 5{,}000x)\Bigg|_2^7$$

$$= (30(7)^3 + 5{,}000(7)) - (30(2)^3 + 5{,}000(2))$$

$$= 45{,}290 - 10{,}240 = \$35{,}050$$

66. (A)

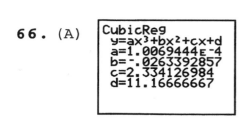

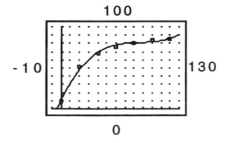

(B) Let $q(t)$ be the quadratic regression model found in part (A). The number of units assembled by a new employee during the second 60 days on the job is given (approximately) by
$$\int_{60}^{120} q(t)\, dt \approx 4.893$$

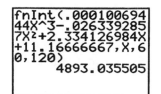

```
fnInt(.000100694
44X^3-.026339285
7X²+2.334126984X
+11.16666667,X,6
0,120)
      4893.035505
```

68. To obtain the useful life, set $C'(t) = R'(t)$ and solve for t.
$$3 = 15e^{-0.1t}$$
$$e^{0.1t} = 5$$
$$0.1t = \ln 5$$
$$t = 10 \ln 5 \approx 16 \text{ years}$$

The total profit accumulated during the useful life is:
$$
\begin{aligned}
P(16) - P(0) &= \int_0^{16} [R'(t) - C'(t)]\, dt \\
&= \int_0^{16} (15e^{-0.1t} - 3)\, dt \\
&= \left(-\frac{15}{0.1} e^{-0.1t} - 3t \right)\Big|_0^{16} \\
&= -150e^{-1.6} - 48 + 150 \\
&= 102 - 150e^{-1.6} \approx 71.716 \text{ or } \$76,716
\end{aligned}
$$

70. $C(x) = 20,000 + 10x$

(A) Average cost per unit:
$$\overline{C}(x) = \frac{C(x)}{x} = \frac{20,000}{x} + 10$$
$$\overline{C}(1,000) = \frac{20,000}{1,000} + 10 = \$30$$

(B) Ave $C(x) = \dfrac{1}{1,000} \displaystyle\int_0^{1,000} (20,000 + 10x)\, dx$
$$= \frac{1}{1,000} (20,000x + 5x^2)\Big|_0^{1,000}$$
$$= \$25,000$$

(C) $\overline{C}(1,000)$ is the average cost per unit at a production level of 1,000 units; Ave $C(x)$ is the average value of the total cost as production increases from 0 units to 1,000 units.

72. (A)

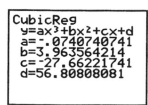

```
CubicReg
 y=ax³+bx²+cx+d
 a=-.0740740741
 b=3.963564214
 c=-27.66221741
 d=56.80808081
```

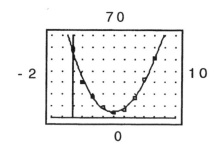

(B) Let $q(x)$ be the cubic regression model found in part (A). The increase in cost in going from a production level of 1 thousand watches per month to 7 thousand watches per month is given (approximately) by

$$\int_1^7 q(x)\,dx \approx 84.357 \text{ or } \$84,357$$

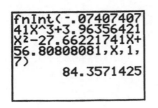

```
fnInt(-.07407407
41X^3+3.96356421
X²-27.66221741X+
56.80808081,X,1,
7)
         84.3571425
```

74. Average price:

$$\text{Ave } D(x) = \frac{1}{600 - 400}\int_{400}^{600}\frac{1,000}{x}\,dx$$

$$= \frac{1}{200}\,(1,000\,\ln|x|)\Big|_{400}^{600}$$

$$= 5(\ln 600 - \ln 400) = 5\,\ln\left(\frac{3}{2}\right) \approx \$2.03$$

76. $g(x) = 2,000x^{-1/3}$ and $L'(x) = g(x)$.

The number of labor hours to assemble the 9th through the 27th control units is:

$$L(27) - L(8) = \int_8^{27} g(x)\,dx = \int_8^{27} 2,000x^{-1/3}\,dx$$

$$= 2,000\left(\frac{x^{2/3}}{2/3}\right)\Big|_8^{27}$$

$$= 3,000\,(x^{2/3})\Big|_8^{27}$$

$$= 3,000\,(9 - 4)$$

$$= 15,000 \text{ labor hours}$$

78. (A) The inventory function is obtained by finding the equation of the line joining $(0, 1,200)$ and $(4, 0)$.

Slope: $m = \dfrac{0 - 1,200}{4 - 0} = -300$, y intercept: $b = 1,200$

Thus, the equation of the line is: $I = -300t + 1,200$

(B) The average of I over $[0, 4]$ is given by:

$$\text{Ave } I(t) = \frac{1}{4 - 0}\int_0^4 I(t)\,dt = \frac{1}{4}\int_0^4 (-300t + 1,200)\,dt$$

$$= \frac{1}{4}(-150t^2 + 1,200t)\Big|_0^4$$

$$= \frac{1}{4}(-150(4)^2 + 1,200(4))$$

$$= 600 \text{ units}$$

80. Rate of production: $R(t) = \dfrac{120t}{t^2 + 1} + 3, \ 0 \le t \le 20$

Total production from year N to year M is given by:

$$P = \int_N^M R(t)\,dt = \int_N^M \left(\frac{120t}{t^2 + 1} + 3\right)dt$$

$$= 120\int_N^M \frac{t}{t^2 + 1}\,dt + \int_N^M 3\ dt$$

$$= 60\left(\ln(t^2 + 1)\right)\Big|_N^M + (3t)\Big|_N^M$$

$$= 60(\ln(M^2 + 1) - \ln(N^2 + 1)) + 3(M - N)$$

$$= 60\ \ln\left(\frac{M^2 + 1}{N^2 + 1}\right) + 3(M - N)$$

Thus, for total production during the first 5 years, let $M = 5$ and $N = 0$.

$$P = 60\ \ln\left(\frac{26}{1}\right) + 3(5 - 0) = 60\ \ln(26) + 15 \approx 210 \text{ thousand barrels}$$

For the total production from the end of the 5th year to the end of the 10th year, let $M = 10$ and $N = 5$.

$$P = 60\ \ln\left(\frac{101}{26}\right) + 3(10 - 5) = 60\ \ln\left(\frac{101}{26}\right) + 15 \approx 96 \text{ thousand barrels}$$

82. $A'(t) = -0.9e^{-0.1t}$

The change during the first five days is given by:

$$A(5) - A(0) = \int_0^5 -0.9e^{-0.1t}\ dt$$

$$= -0.9\left(\frac{e^{-0.1t}}{-0.1}\right)\Big|_0^5$$

$$= 9(e^{-0.1t})\Big|_0^5$$

$$= 9(e^{-0.5} - 1) \approx -3.54 \text{ square centimeters}$$

The change during the second five days, i.e., from the 5th day to the 10th day, is given by:

$$A(10) - A(5) = \int_5^{10} -0.9e^{-0.1t}\ dt$$

$$= 9(e^{-0.1t})\Big|_5^{10}$$

$$= 9(e^{-1} - e^{-0.5}) \approx -2.15 \text{ square centimeters}$$

84. $C(t) = \dfrac{0.14t}{t^2 + 1}$

Average concentration during the first hour after injection is given by:

$$\frac{1}{1 - 0}\int_0^1 \frac{0.14t}{t^2 + 1}dt = 0.07(\ln(t^2 + 1))\Big|_0^1$$

$$= 0.07 \ln 2 \approx 0.0485$$

Average concentration during the first two hours after the injection is given by:

$$\frac{1}{2 - 0}\int_0^2 \frac{0.14t}{t^2 + 1}dt = \frac{0.07}{2}\ln(t^2 + 1)\Big|_0^2$$

$$= \frac{0.07}{2}\ln 5 = 0.035 \ln 5 \approx 0.056$$

86. The average number of children in the city over the six year time period is given by:

$$\frac{1}{6 - 0}\int_0^6 N(t)\,dt = \frac{1}{6}\int_0^6 \left(-\frac{1}{4}t^2 + t + 4\right)dt$$

$$= \frac{1}{6}\left(-\frac{1}{12}t^3 + \frac{t^2}{2} + 4t\right)\Big|_0^6$$

$$= \frac{1}{6}\left(-\frac{1}{12}(6)^3 + \frac{(6)^2}{2} + 4(6)\right)$$

$$= -\frac{6^2}{12} + \frac{6}{2} + 4$$

$$= -3 + 3 + 4 = 4 \text{ million}$$

2. $A = \int_a^b f(x)dx$

4. $A = \int_0^b [-F(x)]dx$

6. The area of the shaded region in Figure (c) is the same as the area of the region between the curve $y = -h(x)$ and the x-axis from $x = a$ to $x = b$ (the mirror image of the shaded region with respect to the x-axis). But the latter region is above the x-axis, and its area is given by $\int_a^b [-h(x)]dx$.

8. $A = \int_{-2}^1 -[2x - 4]\,dx$

$= \int_{-2}^1 (-2x + 4]\,dx = (-x^2 + 4x)\Big|_{-2}^1$

$= 3 - (-4 - 8)$

$= 15$

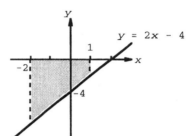

10. $A = \int_{-2}^0 (3x^2 + 1)\,dx = (x^3 + x)\Big|_{-2}^0$

$= -(-8 - 2)$

$= 10$

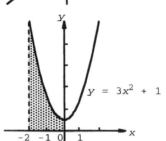

12. $A = \int_{-2}^1 (-x^3 + 2)\,dx = \left(-\frac{1}{4}x^4 + 2x\right)\Big|_{-2}^1$

$= \left(-\frac{1}{4} + 2\right) - \left(-\frac{16}{4} - 4\right)$

$= -\frac{1}{4} + 2 + \frac{16}{4} + 4 = 9.75$

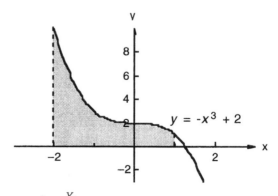

14. $A = \int_{-2}^1 e^{-x}\,dx = (-e^{-x})\Big|_{-2}^1$

$= -e^{-1} + e^2$

$= e^2 - e^{-1} \approx 7.021$

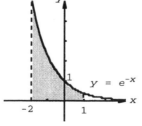

16. $A = \int_{0.1}^{1} -\left(-\frac{1}{t}\right) dt = \int_{0.1}^{1} \frac{1}{t} dt = \ln|t| \Big|_{0.1}^{1}$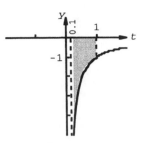

$\qquad = \ln 1 - \ln(0.1)$

$\qquad \approx 0 - (-2.303)$

$\qquad \approx 2.303$

18. $A = \int_{c}^{d} [-f(x)] dx$ $\qquad$ **20.** $A = \int_{a}^{b} [-f(x)] dx + \int_{b}^{c} f(x) dx$

22. $A = \int_{a}^{b} [f(x) - g(x)] dx$ $\quad$ **24.** $A = \int_{b}^{c} [g(x) - f(x)] dx + \int_{c}^{d} [f(x) - g(x)] dx$

26. Find the x-intercepts b and c by solving $f(x) = 0$. Then observe that $f(x) \leq 0$ on $[a, b]$, $f(x) \geq 0$ on $[b, c]$, and $f(x) \leq 0$ on $[c, d]$. Thus,

$$\text{Area} = \int_{a}^{b} [-f(x)] dx + \int_{b}^{c} f(x) dx + \int_{c}^{d} [-f(x)] dx$$

28. $A = A_1 + A_2 = \int_{-1}^{1} (-x + 1) dx + \int_{1}^{2} -(-x + 1) dx$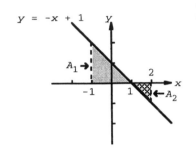

$\qquad = \left(-\frac{1}{2} x^2 + x\right)\Big|_{-1}^{1} + \left(\frac{1}{2} x^2 - x\right)\Big|_{1}^{2}$

$\qquad = \left(-\frac{1}{2} + 1\right) - \left(-\frac{1}{2} - 1\right) + (2 - 2) - \left(\frac{1}{2} - 1\right)$

$\qquad = 2.5$

30. $A = A_1 + A_2 = \int_{0}^{2} (4 - x^2) dx + \int_{2}^{4} -(4 - x^2) dx$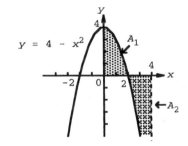

$\qquad = \left(4x - \frac{1}{3} x^3\right)\Big|_{0}^{2} + \left(-4x + \frac{1}{3} x^3\right)\Big|_{2}^{4}$

$\qquad = \left(8 - \frac{8}{3}\right) + \left(-16 + \frac{64}{3}\right) - \left(-8 + \frac{8}{3}\right)$

$\qquad = 16$

32. $A = A_1 + A_2 = \int_{-2}^{0} (-x^2 - 2x) dx + \int_{0}^{1} -(-x^2 - 2x) dx$

$\qquad = \left(-\frac{1}{3} x^3 - x^2\right)\Big|_{-2}^{0} + \left(\frac{1}{3} x^3 + x^2\right)\Big|_{0}^{1}$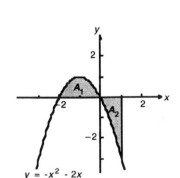

$\qquad = -\left(\frac{8}{3} - 4\right) + \left(\frac{1}{3} + 1\right) = -\frac{8}{3} + 4 + \frac{1}{3} + 1 = \frac{8}{3}$

$\qquad \approx 2.667$

34. $A = \int_{-1}^{2} [(2x + 6) - 3] dx = \int_{-1}^{2} (2x + 3) dx$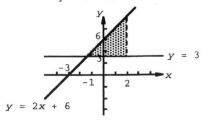

$\qquad = (x^2 + 3x)\Big|_{-1}^{2}$

$\qquad = 10 - (-2) = 12$

36. $A = \int_{-3}^{3} [9 - x^2]\,dx = \left(9x - \dfrac{1}{3}x^3\right)\Big|_{-3}^{3}$

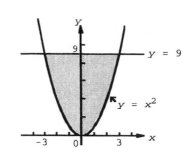

$$= (18) - (-18)$$

$$= 36$$

38. $A = \int_{-2}^{2} [3 - (x^2 - 1)]\,dx$

$$= \int_{-2}^{2} (4 - x^2)\,dx = \left(4x - \dfrac{1}{3}x^3\right)\Big|_{-2}^{2}$$

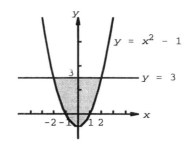

$$= \left(\dfrac{16}{3}\right) - \left(-\dfrac{16}{3}\right)$$

$$= \dfrac{32}{3} \approx 10.667$$

40. $A = \int_{-2}^{1} [(x^2 - 1) - (x - 2)]\,dx$

$$= \int_{-2}^{1} (x^2 - x + 1)\,dx = \left(\dfrac{1}{3}x^3 - \dfrac{1}{2}x^2 + x\right)\Big|_{-2}^{1}$$

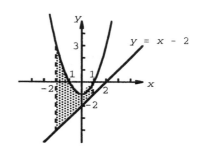

$$= \left(\dfrac{5}{6}\right) - \left(-\dfrac{20}{3}\right) = \dfrac{45}{6} = 7.5$$

42. $A = \int_{0.5}^{1} \left[\dfrac{1}{x} - (-e^x)\right]dx$

$$= \int_{0.5}^{1} \left(\dfrac{1}{x} + e^x\right)dx$$

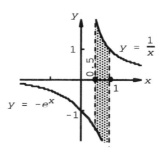

$$= (\ln|x| + e^x)\Big|_{0.5}^{1}$$

$$= e^1 - (\ln(0.5) + e^{0.5})$$

$$\approx 1.763$$

44. The graphs of $y = 3 - 2x^2$ and $y = 2x^4 - 4x$ are shown at the right. The x-coordinates of the points of intersection are: $x_1 = -0.5$, $x_2 = 1.5$.

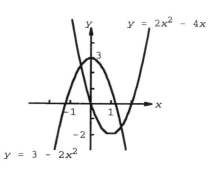

$$A = \int_{-0.5}^{1.5} [(3 - 2x^2) - (2x^2 - 4x)]\,dx$$

$$= \int_{-0.5}^{1.5} (3 - 4x^2 + 4x)\,dx$$

$$= \left(3x - \dfrac{4}{3}x^3 + 2x^2\right)\Big|_{-0.5}^{1.5}$$

$$= \left(3(1.5) - \dfrac{4}{3}(1.5)^3 + 2(1.5)^2\right) - \left(3(-0.5) - \dfrac{4}{3}(-0.5)^3 + 2(-0.5)^2\right)$$

$$\approx 5.333$$

46. The graphs of $y = x - 4.25$ and $y = -\dfrac{1}{x}$ are shown below.

The x-coordinates of the points of intersection are: $x_1 = 0.25$, $x_2 = 4$.

$$A = \int_{0.25}^{4} \left[-\frac{1}{x} - (x - 4.25) \right] dx$$

$$= \left(-\ln|x| - \frac{1}{2}x^2 + 4.25x \right) \Big|_{0.5}^{4}$$

$$\approx 5.196$$

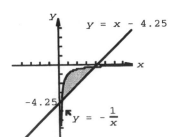

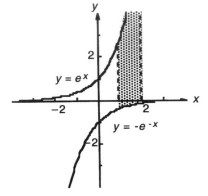

48. The graphs of $y = e^x$ and $y = -e^{-x}$ are shown at the right.

$$A = \int_{1}^{2} (e^x + e^{-x}) \, dx$$

$$= (e^x - e^{-x}) \Big|_{1}^{2}$$

$$= (e^2 - e^{-2}) - (e - e^{-1})$$

$$= \frac{e^4 - e^3 + e - 1}{e^2} = 4.903$$

50. The graphs are given at the right. To find the points of intersection, solve:

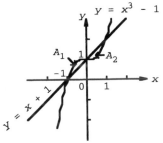

$x^3 + 1 = x + 1$

$x^3 - x = 0$ or $x(x^2 - 1) = 0$ or

$x(x - 1)(x + 1) = 0$

$\qquad\qquad x = -1, 0, 1$

Thus, the points of intersection are $(-1, 0)$, $(0, 1)$, and $(1, 2)$.

$A = A_1 + A_2$

$$= \int_{-1}^{0} [(x^3 + 1) - (x + 1)] \, dx + \int_{0}^{1} [(x + 1) - (x^3 + 1)] \, dx$$

$$= \int_{-1}^{0} (x^3 - x) \, dx + \int_{0}^{1} (x - x^3) \, dx$$

$$= \left(\frac{x^4}{4} - \frac{x^2}{2} \right) \Big|_{-1}^{0} + \left(\frac{x^2}{2} - \frac{x^4}{4} \right) \Big|_{0}^{1}$$

$$= 0.5$$

52. The graphs are given at the right. To find the points of intersection, solve:

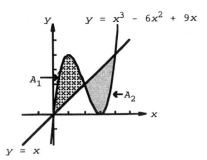

$\qquad x^3 - 6x^2 + 9x = x$

$\qquad x^3 - 6x^2 + 8x = 0$

$\qquad x(x^2 - 6x + 8) = 0$

$\qquad x(x - 2)(x - 4) = 0$

$\qquad\qquad\qquad x = 0, \ x = 2, \ x = 4$

Thus, $(0, 0)$, $(2, 2)$, $(4, 4)$ are the points of intersection.

$$A = A_1 + A_2$$

$$= \int_0^2 [(x^3 - 6x^2 + 9x - (x)] dx + \int_2^4 [(x) - (x^3 - 6x^2 + 9x)] dx$$

$$= \int_0^2 (x^3 - 6x^2 + 8x) dx + \int_2^4 (-x^3 + 6x^2 - 8x) dx$$

$$= \left(\frac{x^4}{4} - 2x^3 + 4x^2\right)\Big|_0^2 + \left(-\frac{x^4}{4} + 2x^3 - 4x^2\right)\Big|_2^4$$

$$= (4) - (0) + (0) - (-4) = 8$$

54. The graphs are given at the right. To find the points of intersection, solve:

$$x^4 - 6x^2 = 4x^2 - 9$$
$$x^4 - 10x^2 + 9 = 0$$
$$(x^2 - 1)(x^2 - 9) = 0$$
$$(x - 1)(x + 1)(x - 3)(x + 3) = 0$$
$$x = -3, -1, 1, 3$$

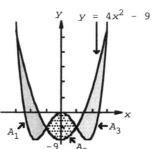

$$A = A_1 + A_2 + A_3$$

$$= \int_{-3}^{-1} [(4x^2 - 9) - (x^4 - 6x^2)] dx + \int_{-1}^{1} [(x^4 - 6x^2) - (4x^2 - 9)] dx$$

$$+ \int_{1}^{3} [(4x^2 - 9) - (x^4 - 6x^2)] dx$$

$$= \int_{-3}^{-1} (10x^2 - 9 - x^4) dx + \int_{-1}^{1} [x^4 - 10x^2 + 9] dx + \int_{1}^{3} [10x^2 - 9 - x^4] dx$$

$$= \left(\frac{10}{3} x^3 - 9x - \frac{x^5}{5}\right)\Big|_{-3}^{-1} + \left(\frac{x^5}{5} - \frac{10x^3}{3} + 9x\right)\Big|_{-1}^{1} + \left(\frac{10x^3}{3} - 9x - \frac{x^5}{5}\right)\Big|_{1}^{3} \approx 52.267$$

56. The graphs are given below. The x-coordinates of the points of intersection are: $x_1 = -1.5$, $x_2 = 0$, $x_3 = 0.5$.

$$A = A_1 + A_2$$

$$= \int_{-1.5}^{0} [(2x^3 + 2x^2 - x) - (-2x^3 - 2x^2 + 2x)] dx$$

$$+ \int_{0}^{0.5} [(-2x^3 - 2x^2 + 2x) - (2x^3 + 2x^2 - x)] dx$$

$$= \int_{-1.5}^{0} (4x^3 + 4x^2 - 3x) dx + \int_{0}^{0.5} (-4x^3 - 4x^2 + 3x) dx$$

$$= \left(x^4 + \frac{4x^3}{3} - \frac{3x^2}{2}\right)\Big|_{-1.5}^{0} + \left(-x^4 - \frac{4x^3}{3} + \frac{3x^2}{2}\right)\Big|_{0}^{0.5}$$

$$= 2.8125 + 0.1458\overline{3} \approx 2.958$$

58. The graphs are given at the right. The x-coordinates of the points of intersection are: $x_1 \approx -2.340$, $x_2 \approx -0.425$.

$$A = \int_{-2.340}^{-0.425} [2 - (x + 1)^2 - e^{x+1}]\,dx$$

$$= \left(2x - \frac{(x + 1)^3}{3} - e^{x+1} \right) \Bigg|_{-2.340}^{-0.425}$$

$$\approx 1.452$$

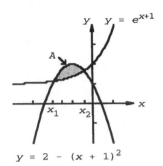

$y = e^{x+1}$

A

$y = 2 - (x + 1)^2$

60. The graphs are given at the right. The x-coordinates of the points of intersection are: $x_1 \approx -2.743$, $x_2 \approx -0.851$, $x_3 \approx 0.392$.

$$A = A_1 + A_2$$

$$= \int_{-2.743}^{-0.851} [(x^3 + 3x^2) - (2 - e^x)]\,dx$$

$$+ \int_{-0.851}^{0.392} [(2 - e^x) - (x^3 + 3x^2)]\,dx$$

$$\approx 2.579 + 0.882 = 3.461$$

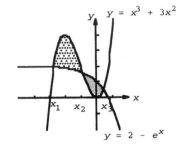

$y = x^3 + 3x^2$

$y = 2 - e^x$

62. $y = x^2 + 3x + 1;\ y = e^{e^x};\ -3 \le x \le 0$

The graphs of $y_1 = x^2 + 3x + 1$ and $y_2 = e^{e^x}$ are:

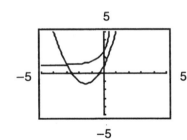

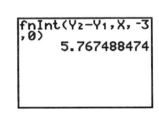

```
fnInt(Y₂-Y₁,X,-3
,0)
        5.767488474
```

Thus, $A = \int_{-3}^{0} [e^{e^x} - (x^2 + 3x + 1)]\,dx \approx 5.767$

64. $y = \ln(\ln x);\ y = 0.01x$

The graphs of $y_1 = \ln(\ln x)$ and $y_2 = 0.01x$ are:

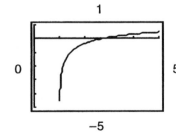

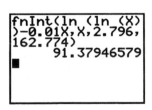

```
fnInt(ln (ln (X)
)-0.01X,X,2.796,
162.774)
        91.37946579
■
```

The intersection points are: $x_1 = 2.796$ and $x_2 = 162.774$.

Thus, $A = \int_{2.796}^{162.772} [\ln(\ln x) - 0.01x]\,dx \approx 91.397$

66. $\int_5^{15} R(t)\,dt = \int_5^{15}\left(\dfrac{100t}{t^2 + 25} + 4\right)dt = 100\int_5^{15}\dfrac{t}{t^2 + 25}\,dt + \int_5^{15} 4\,dt$

Let $u = t^2 + 25$, then $du = 2t\,dt$

$$\int\dfrac{t}{t^2 + 25}\,dt = \dfrac{1}{2}\int\dfrac{2t}{t^2 + 25}\,dt = \dfrac{1}{2}\int\dfrac{1}{u}\,du = \dfrac{1}{2}\ln|u| = \dfrac{1}{2}\ln(t^2 + 25)$$

Thus,

$$\int_5^{15} R(t)\,dt = 50(\ln(t^2 + 25))\Big|_5^{15} + (4t)\Big|_5^{15}$$

$$= 50\{\ln(250) - \ln(50)\} + 4(15 - 5)$$

$$= 50\,\ln\left(\dfrac{250}{50}\right) + 40$$

$$= 50\,\ln(5) + 40 \approx 120$$

The total production from the end of the fifth year to the end of the fifteenth year is (approximately) 120 thousand barrels.

68. To find the useful life, set $R'(t) = C'(t)$ and solve for t:

$$5te^{-0.1t^2} = 2t$$

$$e^{-0.1t^2} = \dfrac{2}{5} = 0.4$$

$$-0.1t^2 = \ln(0.4)$$

$$t^2 = -\dfrac{\ln(0.4)}{0.1}$$

$$t \approx 3 \text{ years}$$

$$\int_0^3 [R'(t) - C'(t)]\,dt = \int_0^3 [5te^{-0.1t^2} - 2t]\,dt$$

$$= 5\int_0^3 te^{-0.1t^2}\,dt - 2\int_0^3 t\,dt$$

Let $u = -0.1t^2$, then $du = -0.2t\,dt$ and

$$\int te^{-0.1t^2}\,dt = \dfrac{1}{-0.2}\int e^{-0.1t^2}(-0.2t)\,dt$$

$$= -\dfrac{1}{0.2}\int e^u\,du = -\dfrac{1}{0.2}e^u$$

$$= -\dfrac{1}{0.2}e^{-0.1t^2}$$

Therefore,

$$\int_0^3 [R'(t) - C'(t)]\,dt = -\dfrac{5}{0.2}(e^{-0.1t^2})\Big|_0^3 + (-t^2)\Big|_0^3$$

$$= 25(1 - e^{-0.9}) - 9$$

$$= 16 - 25e^{-0.9} \approx 5.836$$

The total profit over the useful life of the game is approximately $5,836.

70. For 1962: $f(x) = \dfrac{3}{10}x + \dfrac{7}{10}x^2$

Index of Income Concentration $= 2\displaystyle\int_0^1 [x - f(x)]\,dx = 2\int_0^1 \left(x - \dfrac{3}{10}x - \dfrac{7}{10}x^2\right)dx$

$$= 2\int_0^1 \left(\dfrac{7}{10}x - \dfrac{7}{10}x^2\right)dx$$

$$= \dfrac{7}{5}\left(\dfrac{x^2}{2} - \dfrac{x^3}{3}\right)\Big|_0^1$$

$$= \dfrac{7}{5}\left(\dfrac{1}{2} - \dfrac{1}{3}\right) = \dfrac{7}{30} \approx 0.233$$

For 1972: $g(x) = \dfrac{1}{2}x + \dfrac{1}{2}x^2$

Index of Income Concentration $= 2\displaystyle\int_0^1 [x - g(x)]\,dx = 2\int_0^1 \left(x - \dfrac{1}{2}x - \dfrac{1}{2}x^2\right)dx$

$$= 2\int_0^1 \left(\dfrac{1}{2}x - \dfrac{1}{2}x^2\right)dx$$

$$= \int_0^1 (x - x^2)\,dx$$

$$= \left(\dfrac{x^2}{2} - \dfrac{x^3}{3}\right)\Big|_0^1$$

$$= \dfrac{1}{2} - \dfrac{1}{3} = \dfrac{1}{6} \approx 0.167$$

Interpretation: Income was more equally distributed in 1972.

72. For current Lorenz curve: $f(x) = x^{2.3}$

Index of Income Concentration $= 2\displaystyle\int_0^1 [x - f(x)]\,dx = 2\int_0^1 (x - x^{2.3})\,dx$

$$= 2\left(\dfrac{x^2}{2} - \dfrac{x^{3.3}}{3.3}\right)\Big|_0^1$$

$$= 2\left(\dfrac{1}{2} - \dfrac{1}{3.3}\right)$$

$$= \dfrac{2.6}{6.6} \approx 0.394$$

For projected Lorenz curve: $g(x) = 0.4x + 0.6x^2$

Index of Income Concentration $= 2\displaystyle\int_0^1 [x - g(x)]\,dx$

$$= 2\int_0^1 (x - 0.4x - 0.6x^2)\,dx$$

$$= 2\int_0^1 (0.6x - 0.6x^2)\,dx$$

$$= 1.2\left(\dfrac{x^2}{2} - \dfrac{x^3}{3}\right)\Big|_0^1$$

$$= 1.2\left(\dfrac{1}{2} - \dfrac{1}{3}\right) = 0.2$$

Interpretation: Yes, income will be more equally distributed after the changes in the tax laws.

74. (A)

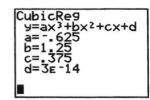

Lorenz curve:

$$y = -0.625x^3 + 1.25x^2 + 0.375x + 3 \times 10^{-14}.$$

(B) Index of income concentration:

$$2 \int_0^1 [x - f(x)]\, dx$$

$$\approx 0.104$$

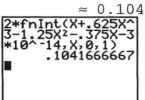

76. Area $= \int_{15}^{20} (12 + 0.006t^2)\, dt$

$= (12t + 0.002t^3) \Big|_{15}^{20}$

$= (240 + 16) - (180 + 6.75) = 69.25$

The total demand for wood from 1985 to 1990 is 69.25 billion cubic feet.

78. $V = \int_1^4 \dfrac{13}{t^{1/2}}\, dt = 13 \int_1^4 t^{-1/2}\, dt = 13 \left(\dfrac{t^{1/2}}{\frac{1}{2}} \right) \Big|_1^4$

$= 26(2 - 1) = 26$

Average number of words learned during the 2nd, 3rd, and 4th hours is 26.

EXERCISE 7-2

2. $\int_0^5 e^{0.08(5-t)}\, dt = \int_0^5 e^{0.4} e^{-0.08t}\, dt$

$= e^{0.4} \int_0^5 e^{-0.08t}\, dt$

$= e^{0.4} \left(\dfrac{e^{-0.08t}}{-0.08} \right) \Big|_0^5$

$= e^{0.4} \left[-\dfrac{e^{-0.4}}{0.08} + \dfrac{e^0}{0.08} \right]$

$= \dfrac{e^{0.4}}{0.08} (1 - e^{-0.4})$

$= \dfrac{e^{0.4} - 1}{0.08} \approx 6.15$

4. $\int_0^{20} 1{,}000 e^{0.03t} e^{0.15(20-t)}\, dt = \int_0^{20} 1{,}000 e^{0.03t} e^{3} e^{-0.15t}\, dt$

$$= 1{,}000 e^{3} \int_0^{20} e^{-0.12t}\, dt$$

$$= 1{,}000 e^{3} \left(-\frac{1}{0.12} e^{-0.12t} \right) \Big|_0^{20}$$

$$= -\frac{1{,}000 e^{3}}{0.12} (e^{-2.4} - 1)$$

$$= \frac{1{,}000}{0.12} (e^{3} - e^{0.6}) \approx 152{,}195.15$$

6. (A) and (B) are equal:

$$\int_0^{10} 2{,}000 e^{0.05t} e^{0.12(10-t)}\, dt = 2{,}000 \int_0^{10} e^{0.05t} e^{1.2} e^{-0.12t}\, dt$$

$$= 2{,}000 e^{1.2} \int_0^{10} e^{-0.07t}\, dt$$

So, (A) and (B) are the same.

$$(A) = (B) = 2{,}000 e^{1.2} \left(-\frac{e^{-0.07t}}{0.07} \right) \Big|_0^{10}$$

$$= \frac{2{,}000}{0.07} e^{1.2} (-e^{-0.7} + 1)$$

$$= \frac{2{,}000}{0.07} (e^{1.2} - e^{0.5}) \approx 47{,}754.16$$

(C) $2{,}000 e^{0.05} \int_0^{10} e^{0.12(10-t)}\, dt = 2{,}000 e^{0.05} \int_0^{10} e^{1.2} e^{-0.12t}\, dt$

$$= 2{,}000 e^{0.05} e^{1.2} \int_0^{10} e^{-0.12t}\, dt$$

$$= 2{,}000 e^{1.25} \left(-\frac{1}{0.12} e^{-0.12t} \right) \Big|_0^{10}$$

$$= \frac{2{,}000}{0.12} e^{1.25} (-e^{-1.2} + 1)$$

$$= \frac{2{,}000}{0.12} (e^{1.25} - e^{0.05}) \approx 40{,}651.20$$

8. $f(x) = \begin{cases} \dfrac{1}{(x+1)^2} & \text{if } x \geq 0 \\ 0 & \text{otherwise} \end{cases}$

(A) Probability $(0 \leq x \leq 3) = \displaystyle\int_0^3 \frac{1}{(x+1)^2}\, dx = \left(-\frac{1}{x+1} \right) \Big|_0^3$

$$= -\frac{1}{4} + 1 = \frac{3}{4} = 0.75$$

(B) Probability $(3 \leq x \leq 9) = \displaystyle\int_3^9 \frac{1}{(x+1)^2}\, dx = \left(-\frac{1}{x+1} \right) \Big|_3^9$

$$= -\frac{1}{10} + \frac{1}{4} = 0.15$$

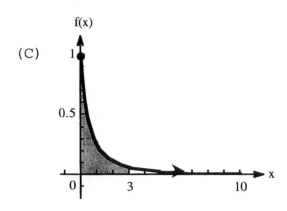

(C)

10. We want to find d such that
Probability $(0 \leq x \leq d) = 0.5$:

$$\int_0^d \frac{1}{(x + 1)^2} dx = 0.5$$

$$\left(-\frac{1}{x + 1}\right)\Big|_0^d = 0.5$$

$$-\frac{1}{d + 1} + 1 = 0.5$$

$$\frac{1}{d + 1} = 0.5 = \frac{1}{2} \quad \text{or} \quad d + 1 = 2 \quad \text{or} \quad d = 1 \text{ year}$$

12. $f(x) = \begin{cases} 0.15e^{-0.15x} & \text{if } x \geq 0 \\ 0 & \text{otherwise} \end{cases}$

(A) Probability $(0 \leq x \leq 4) = \int_0^4 0.15e^{-0.15x} dx$

$$= -e^{-0.15x}\Big|_0^4 = 1 - e^{-0.6} \approx 0.45$$

(B) Probability $(3 \leq x \leq 6 = \int_3^6 0.15e^{-0.15x} dx$

$$= -e^{-0.15x}\Big|_3^6$$

$$= -e^{-0.9} - e^{-0.45} \approx 0.23$$

14. Probability $(x > 4) = 1 - $ Probability $(0 \leq x \leq 4)$
$$= 1 - 0.45 \quad \text{(Problem 12)}$$
$$= 0.55$$

16. $f(t) = 3,000$

Total income $= \int_0^{10} 3,000 \, dt = 3,000(10 - 0) = \$30,000$

18. 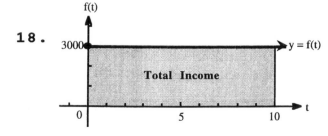 If $f(t)$ is the rate of flow of a continuous income stream, then the total income produced from 0 to 10 years is the area under the curve $y = f(t)$ from $t = 0$ to $t = 10$.

20. $f(t) = 600e^{0.06t}$

Total income $= \displaystyle\int_0^2 600e^{0.06t}\ dt = \dfrac{600}{0.06}e^{0.06t}\ \Big|_0^2$

$$= 10,000(e^{0.12} - 1) \approx \$1,275$$

22.

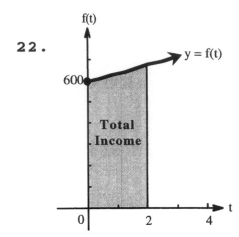

If $f(t)$ is the rate of flow of a continuous income stream, then the total income produced from 0 to 2 years is the area under the curve $y = f(t)$ from $t = 0$ to $t = 2$.

24. $f(t) = 2,000e^{0.06t}$

The amount in the account after 35 years is given by:

$$\int_0^{35} 2,000e^{0.06t}\ dt = \dfrac{2,000}{0.06}e^{0.06t}\ \Big|_0^{35} = \dfrac{100,000}{3}(e^{2.1} - 1) \approx \$238,872$$

Since $\$2,000 \times 35 = \$70,000$ was deposited into the account, the interest earned is:

$$\$238,872 - \$70,000 = \$168,872$$

26. $f(t) = 2,000e^{0.06t}$, $r = 0.0575$, $T = 6$.

$$FV = e^{0.0575(6)}\int_0^6 2,000e^{0.06t}e^{-0.0575t}\ dt$$

$$= 2,000e^{0.345}\int_0^6 e^{0.0025t}\ dt$$

$$= \dfrac{2,000}{0.0025}e^{0.345}(e^{0.0025t})\ \Big|_0^6$$

$$= 800,000e^{0.345}(e^{0.015} - 1)$$

$$= 800,000(e^{0.36} - e^{0.345}) \approx \$17,072$$

28. Total Income $= \displaystyle\int_0^6 2,000e^{0.06t}\ dt = \dfrac{2,000}{0.06}(e^{0.06t})\ \Big|_0^6$

$$= \dfrac{100,000}{3}(e^{0.36} - 1) \approx \$14,444$$

From Problem 26,

Interest earned $= \$17,072 - \$14,444 = \$2,628$.

30. Clothing store: $f(t) = 12,000$, $r = 0.1$, $T = 10$.

$$FV = e^{0.1(10)} \int_0^{10} 12,000e^{-0.1t}\, dt = 12,000e \int_0^{10} e^{-0.1t}\, dt$$

$$= \frac{12,000e}{-0.1}(e^{-0.1t})\Big|_0^{10} = -120,000e(e^{-1} - 1)$$

$$= 120,000(e - 1) \approx \$206,194$$

Computer store: $g(t) = 10,000e^{0.05t}$, $r = 0.1$, $T = 10$.

$$FV = e^{0.1(10)} \int_0^{10} 10,000e^{0.05t}e^{-0.1t}\, dt = 10,000e \int_0^{10} e^{-0.05t}\, dt$$

$$= \frac{10,000e}{-0.05}(e^{-0.05t})\Big|_0^{10} = -200,000e(e^{-0.5} - 1)$$

$$= 200,000(e - e^{0.5}) \approx \$213,912$$

The computer store is the better investment.

32. Bond: $P = \$10,000$, $r = 0.08$, $T = 5$.
$$FV = 10,000e^{0.08(5)} = 10,000e^{0.4} \approx \$14,918$$
Business: $f(t) = 3,000$, $r = 0.08$, $T = 5$.

$$FV = e^{0.08(5)} \int_0^5 3,000e^{-0.08t}\, dt = 3,000e^{0.4} \int_0^5 e^{-0.08t}\, dt$$

$$= \frac{3,000e^{0.4}}{-0.08}(e^{-0.08})\Big|_0^5 = -37,500e^{0.4}(e^{-0.4} - 1)$$

$$= 37,500(e^{0.4} - 1) \approx \$18,443$$

The business is the better investment.

34. $f(t) = 1,000e^{0.03t}$, $r = 0.0765$, $T = 12$.

$$FV = e^{0.0765(12)} \int_0^{12} 1,000e^{0.03t}e^{-0.0765t}\, dt$$

$$= 1,000e^{0.918} \int_0^{12} e^{-0.0465t}\, dt = \frac{1,000e^{0.918}}{-0.0465}(e^{-0.0465t})\Big|_0^{12}$$

$$= -\frac{1,000,000}{465}e^{0.918}(e^{-0.558} - 1)$$

$$= \frac{1,000,000}{465}(e^{0.918} - e^{0.36}) \approx \$23,031$$

The relationship between present value (PV) and future value (FV) at a continuously compounded interest rate r (expressed as a decimal) for t years is:

$$FV = PVe^{rt} \quad \text{or} \quad PV = FVe^{-rt}$$

Thus, we have:
$$PV = 23,031e^{-0.0765(12)} = 23,031e^{-0.918} \approx 9,197$$
Thus, the single deposit should be $9,197.

36. $f(t) = ke^{ct}$, rate r (expressed as a decimal), years T:

$$FV = e^{rT}\int_0^T ke^{ct}e^{-rt}\, dt = ke^{rT}\int_0^T e^{(c-r)t}\, dt, \quad c \neq r$$

$$= \frac{ke^{rT}}{(c-r)}\left(e^{(c-r)t}\right)\Big|_0^T$$

$$= \frac{ke^{rT}}{c-r}\left(e^{(c-r)T} - 1\right)$$

$$= \frac{k}{c-r}\left(e^{cT} - e^{rT}\right)$$

38. $D(x) = 200 - 0.02x$, $\bar{p} = 120$

First, find $\bar{x}$: $120 = 200 - 0.02\bar{x}$
$$\bar{x} = 4{,}000$$

$$CS = \int_0^{4,000}[200 - 0.02x - 120]\,dx = \int_0^{4,000}(80 - 0.02x)\,dx$$

$$= (80x - 0.01x^2)\Big|_0^{4,000} \approx \$160{,}000$$

40.

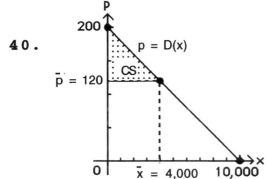

The shaded area is the consumers' surplus and represents the total savings to consumers who are willing to pay more than \$120 for a product but are still able to buy the product for \$120.

42. $p = S(x) = 15 + 0.1x + 0.003x^2$, $\bar{p} = 55$.

First find $\bar{x}$: $55 = 15 + 0.1\bar{x} + 0.003\bar{x}^2$

$$0.003\bar{x}^2 + 0.1\bar{x} - 40 = 0$$

$$\bar{x} = \frac{-0.1 + \sqrt{(0.1)^2 + 0.48}}{0.006}$$

$$= \frac{-0.1 + 0.7}{0.006} \approx 100$$

$$PS = \int_0^{100}[55 - (15 + 0.1x + 0.003x^2)]\,dx$$

$$= \int_0^{100}(40 - 0.1x - 0.003x^2)\,dx$$

$$= \left(40x - \frac{0.1x^2}{2} - \frac{0.003}{3}x^3\right)\Big|_0^{100} = \$2{,}500$$

44.

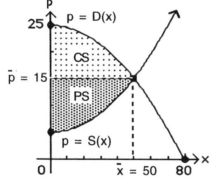

The area of the region *PS* is the producers' surplus and represents the total gain to producers who are willing to supply units at a lower price than \$55 but are still able to supply the product at \$55.

46. $p = D(x) = 25 - 0.004x^2$; $p = S(x) = 5 + 0.004x^2$

Equilibrium price: $D(x) = S(x)$

$$25 - 0.004x^2 = 5 + 0.004x^2$$
$$0.008x^2 = 20$$
$$x^2 = 2,500$$
$$x = 50$$

Thus, $\overline{x} = 50$ and $\overline{p} = 25 - 0.004(50)^2 = 15$.

$$CS = \int_0^{50} [(25 - 0.004x^2) - 15]\,dx = \int_0^{50} (10 - 0.004x^2)\,dx$$
$$= \left(10x - (0.004)\frac{x^3}{3} \right)\Big|_0^{50}$$
$$\approx \$333$$

$$PS = \int_0^{50} [15 - (5 + 0.004x^2)]\,dx = \int_0^{50} (10 - 0.004x^3)\,dx$$
$$= \left(10x - (0.004)\left(\frac{x^3}{3}\right) \right)\Big|_0^{50}$$
$$\approx \$333$$

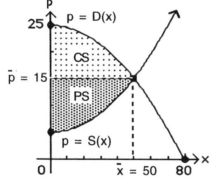

48. $D(x) = 185e^{-0.005x}$ and $S(x) = 25e^{0.005x}$

Equilibrium price: $D(x) = S(x)$

$$185e^{-0.005x} = 25e^{0.005x}$$
$$e^{0.01x} = \frac{185}{25} = 7.4$$
$$0.01x = \ln(7.4)$$
$$x = 100\ \ln(7.4) \approx 200$$

Thus, $\overline{p} = 25e^{0.005(200)} = 25e \approx 68$.

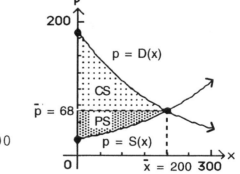

$$CS = \int_0^{200} [185e^{-0.005x} - 68]\,dx = \left(\frac{185e^{-0.005x}}{-0.005} - 68x\right)\Big|_0^{200}$$

$$= -37,000e^{-1} - 13,600 + 37,000 \approx \$9,788$$

$$PS = \int_0^{200} [68 - 25e^{0.005x}]\,dx = \left(68x - \frac{25e^{0.005x}}{0.005}\right)\Big|_0^{200}$$

$$= 13,600 - 5,000e + 5,000 \approx \$5,009$$

50. $D(x) = 190 - 0.2x$; $S(x) = 25e^{0.005x}$
Equilibrium price: $D(x) = S(x)$
$$190 - 0.2x = 25e^{0.005x}$$
Using a graphing utility, we find that
$$\overline{x} \approx 323$$
Thus, $\overline{p} = 190 - (0.2)(323) \approx 125$

$$CS = \int_0^{323} [190 - 0.2x - 125]\,dx = \int_0^{323} (65 - 0.2x)\,dx$$

$$= (65x - 0.1x^2)\Big|_0^{323}$$

$$\approx \$10,562$$

$$PS = \int_0^{323} [125 - 25e^{0.005x}]\,dx = \left(125 - \frac{25e^{0.005x}}{0.005}\right)\Big|_0^{323} \approx \$20,236$$

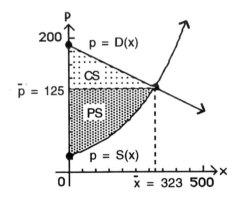

52. $D(x) = 185e^{-0.005x}$; $S(x) = 20 + 0.002x^2$
Equilibrium price: $D(x) = S(x)$
Using a graphing utility, we find that
$$\overline{x} \approx 172$$
Thus, $\overline{p} = 20 + 0.002(172)^2 \approx 79$

$$CS = \int_0^{172} [185e^{-0.005x} - 79]\,dx = \left(-\frac{185e^{-0.005x}}{0.005} - 79x\right)\Big|_0^{172}$$

$$\approx \$7,756$$

$$PS = \int_0^{172} [79 - (20 + 0.002x^2)]\, dx \; = \int_0^{172} (59 - 0.002x^2)\, dx$$

$$= \left(59x - \frac{0.002x^3}{3}\right)\Big|_0^{172}$$

$$\approx \$6,756$$

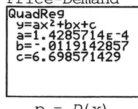

54. (A) Price-Demand

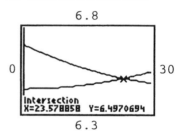

Price-Supply

Graph the price-demand and price-supply models and find their point of intersection.

Equilibrium quantity $\bar{x}$ = 23.579
Equilibrium price $\bar{p}$ = 6.50

(B) Let $D(x)$ be the quadratic regression model in part (A).

Consumers' surplus: $CS = \int_0^{23.579} [D(x) - 6.50]\, dx$

≈ 1.994 or \$1,994

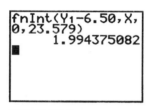

Let $S(x)$ be the quadratic regression model in part (A).

Consumers' surplus: $PS = \int_0^{23.579} [6.50 - S(x)]\, dx$

≈ 1.076 or \$1,076

EXERCISE 7-3

2. $\int xe^{4x}\, dx$

Let $u = x$ and $dv = e^{4x}\, dx$. Then $du = dx$ and $v = \dfrac{e^{4x}}{4}$.

$$\int xe^{4x}\, dx = \frac{xe^{4x}}{4} - \int \frac{e^{4x}}{4}\, dx = \frac{1}{4}xe^{4x} - \frac{1}{4}\int e^{4x}\, dx = \frac{1}{4}xe^{4x} - \frac{1}{16}e^{4x} + C$$

4. $\int x^3 \ln x \, dx$

Let $u = \ln x$ and $dv = x^3 \, dx$. Then $du = \dfrac{1}{x} dx$ and $v = \dfrac{x^4}{4}$.

$$\int x^3 \ln x \, dx = \frac{1}{4}x^4 \ln x - \int \frac{x^3}{4} dx$$

$$= \frac{1}{4}x^4 \ln x - \frac{1}{16}x^4 + C$$

6. $\int (5x - 7)(x - 1)^4 \, dx$

The better choice is $u = 5x - 7$, $dv = (x - 1)^4 \, dx$

The alternative is $u = (x - 1)^4$, $dv = (5x - 7) dx$, which will lead to an integral of the form

$$\int (x - 1)^3 (5x - 7)^2 \, dx.$$

Let $u = 5x - 7$ and $dv = (x - 1)^4 \, dx$. Then $du = 5 \, dx$ and $v = \dfrac{1}{5}(x - 1)^5$.

Substitute into the integration by parts formula:

$$\int (5x - 7)(x - 1)^4 dx = \frac{1}{5}(5x - 7)(x - 1)^5 - \int (x - 1)^5 \, dx$$

$$= \frac{1}{5}(5x - 7)(x - 1)^5 - \frac{1}{6}(x - 1)^6 + C$$

8. $\int (x - 1) e^{-x} \, dx$

Let $u = x - 1$ and $dv = e^{-x} \, dx$. Then $du = dx$ and $v = -e^{-x}$.

$$\int (x - 1) e^{-x} \, dx = -(x - 1) e^{-x} + \int e^{-x} \, dx$$

$$= -(x - 1) e^{-x} - e^{-x} + C$$

$$= -xe^{-x} + e^{-x} - e^{-x} + C = -xe^{-x} + C$$

10. $\int xe^{-x^2} dx$

Let $u = -x^2$, then $du = -2x \, dx$.

$$\int xe^{-x^2} dx = \int e^{-x^2} \frac{-2}{-2}x \, dx = -\frac{1}{2}\int e^u \, du$$

$$= -\frac{1}{2}e^u + C$$

$$= -\frac{1}{2}e^{-x^2} + C$$

12. $\int_0^1 (x + 1) e^x \, dx$

Let $u = x + 1$ and $dv = e^x \, dx$. Then $du = dx$ and $v = e^x$.

$$\int (x + 1) e^x \, dx = (x + 1) e^x - \int e^x \, dx = (x + 1) e^x - e^x + C$$

$$= xe^x + e^x - e^x + C$$

$$= xe^x + C$$

Thus, $\displaystyle\int_0^1 (x + 1) e^x \, dx = (xe^x)\Big|_0^1 = e - 0 = e \approx 2.7183$

14. $\int_{1}^{2} \ln\left(\dfrac{x}{2}\right) dx$

Let $u = \ln\left(\dfrac{x}{2}\right)$ and $dv = dx$. Then $du = \dfrac{1}{x/2} \cdot \dfrac{1}{2} dx = \dfrac{1}{x} dx$ and $v = x$.

$\int \ln\left(\dfrac{x}{2}\right) dx = x \ln\left(\dfrac{x}{2}\right) - \int dx = x \ln\left(\dfrac{x}{2}\right) - x + C$

Thus, $\int_{1}^{2} \ln\left(\dfrac{x}{2}\right) dx = \left(x \ln\left(\dfrac{x}{2}\right) - x\right)\Big|_{1}^{2}$

$= (2 \ln(1) - 2) - \left(\ln\left(\dfrac{1}{2}\right) - 1\right)$

$= -2 - \ln\left(\dfrac{1}{2}\right) + 1 = -1 + \ln 2 \approx -0.3069$

16. $\int \dfrac{x^2}{x^3 + 5} dx = \int (x^3 + 5)^{-1} x^2\, dx$

Let $u = x^3 + 5$, then $du = 3x^2\, dx$.

$\int \dfrac{x^2}{x^3 + 5} dx = \int (x^3 + 5)^{-1} x^2\, dx = \int (x^3 + 5)^{-1} \dfrac{3}{3} x^2\, dx$

$= \dfrac{1}{3} \int u^{-1}\, du$

$= \dfrac{1}{3} \ln|u| + C$

$= \dfrac{1}{3} \ln(x^3 + 5) + C \qquad (x > 0)$

18. $\int \dfrac{e^x}{e^x + 1} dx$

Let $u = e^x + 1$, then $du = e^x\, dx$.

$\int \dfrac{e^x}{e^x + 1} dx = \int (e^x + 1)^{-1} e^x\, dx = \int u^{-1}\, du$

$= \ln|u| + C$

$= \ln(e^x + 1) + C$

20. $\int \dfrac{\ln x}{\sqrt{x}} dx = \int (\ln x) x^{-1/2}\, dx$

Let $u = \ln x$ and $dv = x^{-1/2}\, dx$. Then $du = \dfrac{1}{x} dx$ and $v = 2x^{1/2}$.

$\int \dfrac{\ln x}{\sqrt{x}} dx = 2(\ln x) x^{1/2} - \int 2x^{-1/2}\, dx = 2x^{1/2} \ln x - 4x^{1/2} + C$

22.

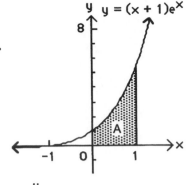

The integral represents the area between the curve $y = (x + 1)e^x$ and the x axis from $x = 0$ to $x = 1$.

24.

The integral represents the negative of the area between the curve $y = \ln\left(\dfrac{x}{2}\right)$ and the x axis from $x = 1$ to $x = 2$.

26. $\int x^3 e^x \, dx$

Let $u = x^3$ and $dv = e^x \, dx$. Then $du = 3x^2 \, dx$ and $v = e^x$.
$$\int x^3 e^x \, dx = x^3 e^x - \int 3x^2 e^x \, dx = x^3 e^x - 3\int x^2 e^x \, dx$$

$\int x^2 e^x \, dx$ can be computed by using integration-by-parts again.

Let $u = x^2$ and $dv = e^x \, dx$. Then $du = 2x \, dx$ and $v = e^x$.
$$\int x^2 e^x \, dx = x^2 e^x - 2\int x e^x \, dx$$

$\int x e^x \, dx$ can be computed by using integration-by parts again.

Let $u = x$ and $dv = e^x \, dx$. Then $du = dx$ and $v = e^x$.
$$\int x e^x \, dx = x e^x - \int e^x \, dx = x e^x - e^x + C_1$$

Thus,
$$\int x^3 e^x \, dx = x^3 e^x - 3[x^2 e^x - 2(x e^x - e^x + C_1)]$$
$$= x^3 e^x - 3x^2 e^x + 6x e^x - 6e^x + C$$
$$= (x^3 - 3x^2 + 6x - 6)e^x + C$$

28. $\int \ln(ax) \, dx, \quad a > 0$

Let $u = \ln(ax)$ and $dv = dx$. Then $du = \dfrac{1}{x} dx$ and $v = x$.
$$\int \ln(ax) \, dx = x \ln(ax) - \int dx = x \ln(ax) - x + C$$

30. $\int_1^2 x^3 e^{x^2}\, dx$

Let $t = x^2$, then $dt = 2x\, dx$.

$\int x^3 e^{x^2}\, dx = \int x^2 e^{x^2}\, \dfrac{2}{2} x\, dx = \dfrac{1}{2}\int t e^t\, dt$

To compute $\int t e^t\, dt$ we use integration-by-parts.

Let $u = t$ and $dv = e^t\, dt$. Then $du = dt$ and $v = e^t$.

$\int t e^t\, dt = t e^t - \int e^t\, dt = t e^t - e^t + C_1$.

Thus,

$\int x^3 e^{x^2}\, dx = \dfrac{1}{2}(t e^t - e^t + C_1)$

$\qquad\qquad = \dfrac{1}{2}(x^2 e^{x^2} - e^{x^2}) + C$

and

$\int_1^2 x^3 e^{x^2}\, dx = \left(\dfrac{1}{2}\left(x^2 e^{x^2} - e^{x^2}\right)\right)\Big|_1^2$

$\qquad\qquad = \dfrac{1}{2}(4e^4 - e^4) - \dfrac{1}{2}(e - e)$

$\qquad\qquad = \dfrac{3}{2}e^4 \approx 81.8972$

32. $\int_0^2 \ln(4 - x)\, dx$

Let $u = \ln(4 - x)$ and $dv = dx$. Then $du = -\dfrac{1}{4 - x}\, dx$ and $v = x$.

$\int \ln(4 - x)\, dx = x \ln(4 - x) + \int \dfrac{x}{4 - x}\, dx$

$\qquad\qquad = x \ln(4 - x) + \int \dfrac{(x - 4 + 4)}{4 - x}\, dx$

$\qquad\qquad = x \ln(4 - x) + \int \dfrac{-(4 - x)}{4 - x}\, dx + \int \dfrac{4}{4 - x}\, dx$

$\qquad\qquad = x \ln(4 - x) - \int dx + 4\int \dfrac{1}{4 - x}\, dx$

$\qquad\qquad = x \ln(4 - x) - x - 4 \ln|4 - x| + C$

Thus,

$\int_0^2 \ln(4 - x)\, dx = (x \ln(4 - x) - x - 4 \ln(4 - x))\Big|_0^2$

$\qquad\qquad = (2 \ln 2 - 2 - 4 \ln 2) - (-4 \ln 4)$

$\qquad\qquad = -2 - 2 \ln 2 + 4 \ln 4$

$\qquad\qquad = -2 - 2 \ln 2 + 8 \ln 2$

$\qquad\qquad = -2 + 6 \ln 2 \approx 2.1589$

34. $\int x e^{x+1}\, dx$

Let $u = x$ and $dv = e^{x+1}\, dx$. Then $du = dx$ and $v = e^{x+1}$.

$\int x e^{x+1}\, dx = x e^{x+1} - \int e^{x+1}\, dx = x e^{x+1} - e^{x+1} + C$

36. $\int x \ln(1 + x)\,dx$

Let $u = \ln(1 + x)$ and $dv = x\,dx$. Then $du = \dfrac{1}{1 + x}\,dx$ and $v = \dfrac{1}{2}x^2$.

$$\begin{aligned}
\int x \ln(1 + x)\,dx &= \frac{1}{2}x^2 \ln(1 + x) - \frac{1}{2}\int \frac{x^2}{1 + x}\,dx \\[2mm]
&= \frac{1}{2}x^2 \ln(1 + x) - \frac{1}{2}\int \frac{x^2 - 1 + 1}{1 + x}\,dx \\[2mm]
&= \frac{1}{2}x^2 \ln(1 + x) - \frac{1}{2}\int \frac{x^2 - 1}{1 + x} - \frac{1}{2}\int \frac{1}{1 + x}\,dx \\[2mm]
&= \frac{1}{2}x^2 \ln(1 + x) - \frac{1}{2}\int \frac{(x - 1)(x + 1)}{1 + x}\,dx - \frac{1}{2} \ln(1 + x) \\[2mm]
&= \frac{1}{2}x^2 \ln(1 + x) - \frac{1}{2}\int (x - 1)\,dx - \frac{1}{2}\ln(1 + x) \\[2mm]
&= \frac{1}{2}x^2 \ln(1 + x) - \frac{1}{2}\left(\frac{1}{2}(x - 1)^2\right) - \frac{1}{2}\ln(1 + x) + C \\[2mm]
&= \frac{1}{2}(x^2 - 1)\ln(1 + x) - \frac{1}{4}(x - 1)^2 + C
\end{aligned}$$

Note: The answer could also be given in the following equivalent form:
$$\int x \ln(1 + x)\,dx$$
$$= \frac{1}{2}(1 + x)^2 \ln(1 + x) - (1 + x)\ln(1 + x) + (1 + x) - \frac{1}{4}(1 + x)^2 + C$$

38. $\int \dfrac{\ln\left(1 + \sqrt{x}\right)}{\sqrt{x}}\,dx$

Let $t = \sqrt{x} = x^{1/2}$, then $dt = \dfrac{1}{2}x^{-1/2}\,dx$.

$$\int \frac{\ln\left(1 + \sqrt{x}\right)}{\sqrt{x}}\,dx = \int \ln(1 + \sqrt{x})\,\frac{2}{2}x^{-1/2}\,dx = 2\int \ln(1 + t)\,dt$$

To compute $\int \ln(1 + t)\,dt$ we use integration-by-parts.

Let $u = \ln(1 + t)$ and $dv = dt$. Then $du = \dfrac{1}{1 + t}\,dt$ and $v = t$.

$$\begin{aligned}
\int \ln(1 + t)\,dt &= t \ln(1 + t) - \int \frac{1}{1 + t}\,dt \\[2mm]
&= t \ln(1 + t) - \int \frac{t + 1 - 1}{1 + t}\,dt \\[2mm]
&= t \ln(1 + t) - \int \left(1 - \frac{1}{1 + t}\right)dt \\[2mm]
&= t \ln(1 + t) - t + \ln(1 + t) + C_1 \\[2mm]
&= \sqrt{x} \ln(1 + \sqrt{x}) - \sqrt{x} + \ln(1 + \sqrt{x}) + C_1 \\[2mm]
&= (1 + \sqrt{x})\ln(1 + \sqrt{x}) - \sqrt{x} + C_1
\end{aligned}$$

Thus, $\int \dfrac{\ln\left(1 + \sqrt{x}\right)}{\sqrt{x}}\,dx = 2(1 + \sqrt{x})\ln(1 + \sqrt{x}) - 2\sqrt{x} + C$

40. $\int x(\ln x)^2 \, dx$

Let $u = (\ln x)^2$ and $dv = x \, dx$. Then $du = 2\dfrac{\ln x}{x} dx$ and $v = \dfrac{1}{2}x^2$.

$$\int x(\ln x)^2 \, dx = \frac{1}{2}x^2(\ln x)^2 - \int x(\ln x) \, dx$$

To compute $\int x(\ln x) \, dx$ we use integration-by-parts.

Let $u = \ln x$ and $dv = x \, dx$. Then $du = \dfrac{1}{x} dx$ and $v = \dfrac{x^2}{2}$.

$$\int x(\ln x) \, dx = \frac{1}{2}x^2 \ln x - \frac{1}{2}\int x \, dx = \frac{1}{2}x^2 \ln x - \frac{1}{4}x^2 + C_1$$

Thus,

$$\int x(\ln x)^2 \, dx = \frac{1}{2}x^2(\ln x)^2 - \frac{1}{2}x^2 \ln x + \frac{1}{4}x^2 + C$$

$$= \frac{x^2}{2}(\ln x)^2 - \frac{x^2}{2}\ln x + \frac{x^2}{4} + C$$

42. $\int x(\ln x)^3 \, dx$

Let $u = (\ln x)^3$ and $dv = x \, dx$. Then $du = \dfrac{3(\ln x)^2}{x} dx$ and $v = \dfrac{1}{2}x^2 \, dx$.

$$\int x(\ln x)^3 \, dx = \frac{1}{2}x^2(\ln x)^3 - \frac{3}{2}\int x(\ln x)^2 \, dx$$

From Problem 40,

$$\int x(\ln x)^2 \, dx = \frac{x^2}{2}(\ln x)^2 - \frac{x^2}{2}\ln x + \frac{x^2}{4} + C,$$

and hence

$$\int x(\ln x)^3 \, dx = \frac{1}{2}x^2(\ln x)^3 - \frac{3}{4}x^2(\ln x)^2 + \frac{3}{4}x^2 \ln x - \frac{3}{8}x^2 + C_1.$$

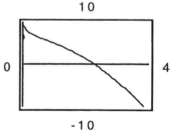

44. $y = 6 - x^2 - \ln x$, $1 \le x \le 4$

$y = 0$ at $x \approx 2.275$

$$A = \int_1^{2.275} (6 - x^2 - \ln x) \, dx + \int_{2.275}^4 [-(6 - x^2 - \ln x)] \, dx$$

$$= \int_1^{2.275} (6 - x^2 - \ln x) \, dx + \int_{2.275}^4 (-6 + x^2 + \ln x) \, dx$$

Now, $\int \ln x \, dx$ is found using integration-by-parts.

Let $u = \ln x$ and $dv = dx$. Then $du = \dfrac{1}{x} dx$ and $v = x$.

$$\int \ln x \, dx = x \ln x - \int dx = x \ln x - x + C$$

Thus,

$$A = \left(6x - \frac{x^3}{3} - x \ln x + x\right)\Bigg|_1^{2.275} + \left(-6x + \frac{x^3}{3} + x \ln x - x\right)\Bigg|_{2.275}^4$$

$$\approx (10.130 - 6.667) + (-1.121 + 10.130) = 12.47$$

46. $y = xe^x + x - 6, \quad 0 \le x \le 3$

$y = 0$ at $x \approx 1.293$

$$A = \int_0^{1.293} [-(xe^x + x - 6)]\, dx + \int_{1.293}^3 (xe^x + x - 6)\, dx$$

$$= \int_0^{1.293} (-xe^x - x + 6)\, dx + \int_{1.293}^3 (xe^x + x - 6)\, dx$$

Now, $\int xe^x\, dx$ is found using integration-by-parts.

Let $u = x$ and $dv = e^x\, dx$. Then, $du = dx$ and $v = e^x$.

$$\int xe^x\, dx = xe^x - \int e^x\, dx = xe^x - e^x + C$$

Thus,

$$A = \left(-xe^x + e^x - \frac{x^2}{2} + 6x\right)\Bigg|_0^{1.293} + \left(xe^x - e^x + \frac{x^2}{2} - 6x\right)\Bigg|_{1.293}^3$$

$$\approx (5.854 - 1) + (26.671 + 5.854) \approx 37.38$$

48. The total production over the first 12 months is given by the definite integral:

$$\int_0^{12} 10te^{-0.1t}\, dt = 10\int_0^{12} te^{-0.1t}\, dt$$

To calculate this integral we use integration-by-parts.

Let $u = t$ and $dv = e^{-0.1t}\, dt$. Then $du = dt$ and $v = \frac{1}{-0.1}e^{-0.1t} = -10e^{-0.1t}$

$$\int te^{-0.1t}\, dt = -10te^{-0.1t} + 10\int e^{-0.1t}\, dt = -10te^{-0.1t} + 10\left(\frac{e^{-0.1t}}{-0.1}\right) + C$$

$$= -10te^{-0.1t} - 100e^{-0.1t} + C$$

Thus,

$$\int_0^{12} 10te^{-0.1t}\, dt = 10(-10te^{-0.1t} - 100e^{-0.1t})\Big|_0^{12}$$

$$= 10[(-120e^{-1.2} - 100e^{-1.2}) - (-100)]$$

$$= 1{,}000 - 2{,}200e^{-1.2} \approx 337$$

To the nearest thousand, the total production is 337 thousand barrels.

50.

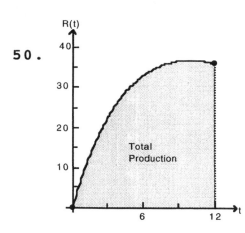

The total production for the first year of operation (in thousands of barrels) is the same as the area under the rate of production function, $R(t) = 10te^{-0.1t}$, from $t = 0$ to $t = 12$.

52. From Exercise 7-2, Future Value $= e^{rT} \int_0^T f(t)e^{-rt}\,dt$. Now $r = 0.10$, $T = 4$, $f(t) = 1,000 - 250t$. Thus,

$$FV = e^{(0.10)(4)} \int_0^4 (1,000 - 250t)e^{-0.10t}\,dt$$

$$= e^{0.4}\int_0^4 1,000e^{-0.10t}\,dt - 250e^{0.4}\int_0^4 te^{-0.10t}\,dt.$$

We calculate the second integral using integration-by-parts.

Let $u = t$, $dv = e^{-0.10t}\,dt$. Then $du = dt$ and $v = \dfrac{e^{-0.10t}}{-0.10}$.

$$\int te^{-0.10t}\,dt = -10te^{-0.10t} + 10\int e^{-0.10t}\,dt$$

$$= -10te^{-0.10t} - 100e^{-0.10t} + C$$

Thus, we have:

$$FV = 1,000e^{0.4}\left(\frac{e^{-0.10t}}{-0.10}\right)\bigg|_0^4 - 250e^{0.4}(-10te^{-0.10t} - 100e^{-0.10t})\bigg|_0^4$$

$$= 10,000e^{0.4}(1 - e^{-0.4}) - 250e^{0.4}[(-40e^{-0.4} - 100e^{-0.4}) - (-100)]$$

$$= 10,000(e^{0.4} - 1) - 250(-140 + 100e^{0.4}) \approx \$2,623$$

Total income $= \int_0^4 (1,000 - 250t)\,dt = (1,000t - 125t^2)\bigg|_0^4 = \$2,000$

Interest earned $\approx \$2,623 - \$2,000 = \$623$.

54. Index of Income Concentration $= 2\int_0^1 (x - x^2e^{x-1})\,dx$

$$= 2\int_0^1 x\,dx - 2\int_0^1 x^2e^{x-1}\,dx$$

We calculate the second integral using integration-by-parts.
Let $u = x^2$, $dv = e^{x-1}\,dx$. Then $du = 2x\,dx$, $v = e^{x-1}$.
$$\int x^2e^{x-1}\,dx = x^2e^{x-1} - 2\int xe^{x-1}\,dx$$

To compute $\int xe^{x-1}\,dx$ we use integration-by-parts again:

Let $u = x$ and $dv = e^{x-1}\,dx$. Then $du = dx$ and $v = e^{x-1}$.

$$\int xe^{x-1}\,dx = xe^{x-1} - \int e^{x-1}\,dx = xe^{x-1} - e^{x-1} + C$$

Therefore, $2\displaystyle\int_0^1 x\,dx - 2\int_0^1 x^2 e^{x-1}\,dx = 2\left(\dfrac{x^2}{2}\right)\Big|_0^1 - 2(x^2 e^{x-1} - 2xe^{x-1} + 2e^{x-1})\Big|_0^1$

$$= 1 - 2[(1 - 2 + 2) - (2e^{-1})]$$
$$= 1 - 2 + 4e^{-1} = 4e^{-1} - 1 \approx 0.472$$

56.

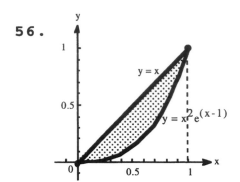

The area bounded by $y = x$ and the Lorenz curve $y = x^2 e^{(x-1)}$ divided by the area under the curve $y = x$ from $x = 0$ to $x = 1$ is the index of income concentration. It is a measure of the concentration of income—the closer to zero, the closer to all the income being equally distributed; the closer to one, the closer to all the income being concentrated in a few hands.

58. $S'(t) = 350 \ln(t + 1)$, $S(0) = 0$

$S(t) = \displaystyle\int 350 \ln(t + 1)\,dt = 350\int \ln(t + 1)\,dt$

Let $u = \ln(t + 1)$ and $dv = dt$. Then $du = \dfrac{1}{t + 1}\,dt$ and $v = t$.

$\displaystyle\int \ln(t + 1)\,dt = t \ln(t + 1) - \int \dfrac{t}{t + 1}\,dt$

$\qquad\qquad\qquad\ = t \ln(t + 1) - \displaystyle\int \dfrac{t + 1 - 1}{t + 1}\,dt$

$\qquad\qquad\qquad\ = t \ln(t + 1) - \displaystyle\int \left(1 - \dfrac{1}{t + 1}\right)dt$

$\qquad\qquad\qquad\ = t \ln(t + 1) - (t - \ln(t + 1)) + C$
$\qquad\qquad\qquad\ = t \ln(t + 1) - t + \ln(t + 1) + C$

Now,
$\quad S(t) = t \ln(t + 1) + \ln(t + 1) - t + C_1$

$\qquad\quad = 350((t + 1)\ln(t + 1) - t) + C$

Since $S(0) = 0$, we have $C = 0$ and hence
$\qquad S(t) = 350((t + 1)\ln(t + 1) - t).$

To find how long the company will continue to manufacture cartridges, solve $S(t) = 15,000$ for t.

The company will manufacture cartridges for 20 months.

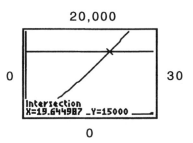

60. $p = S(x) = 5 \ln(x + 1)$; $\overline{p} = \$26$. To find $\overline{x}$, solve

$$5 \ln(\overline{x} + 1) = 26$$

$$\ln(\overline{x} + 1) = \frac{26}{5} = 5.2$$

$$\overline{x} + 1 = e^{5.2}$$

$$\overline{x} = e^{5.2} - 1 \approx 181 \quad \text{(to the nearest higher unit)}$$

$$PS = \int_0^{181} [\overline{p} - S(x)] dx = \int_0^{181} (26 - 5 \ln(x + 1)) dx$$

$$= \int_0^{181} 26 \, dx - 5 \int_0^{181} \ln(x + 1) dx$$

From Problem 58, $\int \ln(x + 1) dx = (x + 1) \ln(x + 1) - x + C$, and hence

$$PS = 26(x) \Big|_0^{181} - 5((x + 1) \ln(x + 1) - x) \Big|_0^{181}$$

$$= 4{,}706 - 5(182 \ln(182) - 181) \approx \$875$$

62.

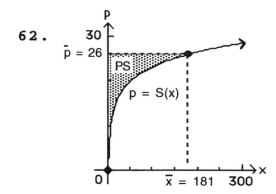

The area bounded by the price-supply equation, $p = 5 \ln(x + 1)$, and the price equation, $y = \overline{p} = 26$, from $x = 0$ to $x = \overline{x} = 181$, represents the producers' surplus. This is the amount gained by producers who are willing to sell for less.

64. $R(t) = te^{-0.2t}$

Total amount $= \int_0^{10} R(t) dt = \int_0^{10} te^{-0.2t} dt$

Let $u = t$ and $dv = e^{-0.2t} dt$. Then $du = dt$ and $v = \dfrac{e^{-0.2t}}{-0.2} = -5e^{-0.2t}$.

$$\int te^{-0.2t} dt = -5te^{-0.2t} + 5 \int e^{-0.2t} dt$$

$$= -5te^{-0.2t} + 5 \left(\frac{e^{-0.2t}}{-0.2} \right) + C$$

$$= -5te^{-0.2t} - 25e^{-0.2t} + C$$

Thus,

$$\int_0^{10} R(t) dt = (-5te^{-0.2t} - 25e^{-0.2t}) \Big|_0^{10}$$

$$= (-50e^{-2} - 25e^{-2}) - (-25)$$

$$= 25 - 75e^{-2} = 25(1 - 3e^{-2}) \approx 14.85$$

66. $N'(t) = (t + 10)e^{-0.1t}$, $0 \le t \le 15$; $N(0) = 0$

$$N(t) - N(0) = \int_0^t N'(x)\,dx = \int_0^t (x + 10)e^{-0.1x}\,dx$$

$$
\begin{aligned}
N(t) &= \int_0^t (x + 10)e^{-0.1x}\,dx = \int_0^t xe^{-0.1x}\,dx + 10\int_0^t e^{-0.1x}\,dx \\
&= \int_0^t xe^{-0.1x}\,dx + 10\left(\frac{e^{-0.1x}}{-0.1}\right)\Big|_0^t \\
&= \int_0^t xe^{-0.1x}\,dx + 10\left(\frac{e^{-0.1t}}{-0.1} + \frac{1}{0.1}\right) \\
&= \int_0^t xe^{-0.1x}\,dx + 100(1 - e^{-0.1t})
\end{aligned}
$$

To compute the last integral we use integration-by-parts. Let $u = x$ and $dv = e^{-0.1x}\,dx$. Then $du = dx$ and $v = \dfrac{e^{-0.1x}}{-0.1} = -10e^{-0.1x}$.

Thus,

$$
\begin{aligned}
\int xe^{-0.1x}\,dx &= -10xe^{-0.1x} + 10\int e^{-0.1x}\,dx \\
&= -10xe^{-0.1x} + 10\left(\frac{e^{-0.1x}}{-0.1}\right) + C \\
&= -10xe^{-0.1x} - 100e^{-0.1x} + C
\end{aligned}
$$

Therefore,

$$
\begin{aligned}
N(t) &= (-10xe^{-0.1x} - 100e^{-0.1x})\Big|_0^t + 100(1 - e^{-0.1t}) \\
&= (-10te^{-0.1t} - 100e^{-0.1t}) - (-100) + 100(1 - e^{-0.1t}) \\
N(t) &= -10te^{-0.1t} - 200e^{-0.1t} + 200
\end{aligned}
$$

To find how long it will take a student to achieve the 90 words per minute level, solve $N(t) = 90$:

It will take 10 weeks.

By the end of the course, a student should be able to type $N(15) = -10(15)e^{-1.5} - 200e^{-1.5} + 200$
≈ 122 words per minute.

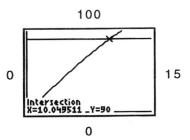

EXERCISE 7-4

2. Use Formula 10 with $a = b = 1$:
$$\int \frac{1}{x^2(1 + x)}\,dx = \frac{1}{x} + \ln\left|\frac{1 + x}{x}\right| + C$$

4. Use Formula 19 with $a = 5$, $b = 2$, $c = 2$, $d = 1$:
$$\int \frac{x}{(5 + 2x)^2(2 + x)}\,dx = -\frac{5}{2}\cdot\frac{1}{5 + 2x} - 2\ln\left|\frac{2 + x}{5 + 2x}\right| + C$$

6. Use Formula 27 with $a = 16$ and $b = 1$:

$$\int \frac{1}{x\sqrt{16 + x}}\,dx = \frac{1}{4}\ln\left|\frac{\sqrt{16 + x} - 4}{\sqrt{16 + x} + 4}\right| + C$$

8. Use Formula 31 with $a = 3$:

$$\int \frac{\sqrt{9 - x^2}}{x}\,dx = \sqrt{9 - x^2} - 3\ln\left|\frac{3 + \sqrt{9 - x^2}}{x}\right| + C$$

10. Use Formula 45 with $a = 4$:

$$\int \frac{1}{x^2\sqrt{x^6 - 16}}\,dx = \frac{\sqrt{x^2 - 16}}{16x} + C$$

12. Use Formula 51 with $n = 3$:

$$\int x^3 \ln x\,dx = \frac{1}{4}x^4 \ln x - \frac{1}{16}x^4 + C$$

14. Use Formula 48 with $a = 3$, $c = 5$, $d = 2$:

$$\int \frac{1}{5 + 2e^{3x}}\,dx = \frac{x}{5} - \frac{1}{15}\ln|5 + 2e^{3x}| + C$$

16. Use Formula 6 with $a = 6$, $b = 1$:

$$\int_2^6 \frac{x}{(6 + x)^2}\,dx = \left(\ln|6 + x| + \frac{6}{6 + x}\right)\Big|_2^6$$

$$= \left(\ln 12 + \frac{1}{2}\right) - \left(\ln 8 + \frac{3}{4}\right)$$

$$= \ln 12 - \ln 8 + \frac{1}{2} - \frac{3}{4}$$

$$= \ln\left(\frac{12}{8}\right) - \frac{1}{4} = \ln\left(\frac{3}{2}\right) - \frac{1}{4} \approx 0.1555$$

18. Use Formula 16 with $a = 3$, $b = 1$, $c = 1$, $d = 1$:

$$\int_0^7 \frac{x}{(3 + x)(1 + x)}\,dx = \frac{1}{2}(3\ln|3 + x| - \ln|1 + x|)\Big|_0^7$$

$$= \frac{1}{2}(3\ln 10 - \ln 8) - \frac{1}{2}(3\ln 3) \approx 0.7662$$

20. Use Formula 20 with $a = 4$:

$$\int_4^5 \sqrt{x^2 - 16}\,dx = \left(\frac{1}{2}\left(x\sqrt{x^2 - 16} - 16\ln\left|x + \sqrt{x^2 - 16}\right|\right)\right)\Big|_4^5$$

$$= \frac{1}{2}(15 - 16\ln 8) - \frac{1}{2}(-16\ln 4)$$

$$= \frac{15}{2} - 8\ln 2 \approx 1.9548$$

22. $\int x^2 \sqrt{9x^2 - 1} \, dx$

Let $u = 3x$, then $du = 3 \, dx$ and

$$\int x^2 \sqrt{9x^2 - 1} \, dx = \int \frac{9}{9} x^2 \sqrt{9x^2 - 1} \, \frac{3}{3} \, dx$$

$$= \frac{1}{27} \int u^2 \sqrt{u^2 - 1} \, du$$

Use Formula 41 with $a = 1$ for the integral on the right hand side:

$$\int u^2 \sqrt{u^2 - 1} \, du = \frac{1}{8} \left[u(2u^2 - 1)\sqrt{u^2 - 1} - \ln\left|u + \sqrt{u^2 - 1}\right| \right] + C$$

Therefore, by substituting $3x$ for u, we have:

$$\int x^2 \sqrt{9x^2 - 1} \, dx = \frac{1}{216} \left[3x(18x^2 - 1)\sqrt{9x^2 - 1} - \ln\left|3x + \sqrt{9x^2 - 1}\right| \right] + C$$

24. $\int x\sqrt{x^4 - 16} \, dx$

Let $u = x^2$, then $du = 2x \, dx$, and

$$\int x\sqrt{x^4 - 16} \, dx = \int \sqrt{x^4 - 16} \, \frac{2}{2} x \, dx$$

$$= \frac{1}{2} \int \sqrt{u^2 - 16} \, du$$

Using Formula 40 with $a = 4$, we have:

$$\int \sqrt{u^2 - 16} \, du = \frac{1}{2} \left(u\sqrt{u^2 - 16} - 16 \ln\left|u + \sqrt{u^2 - 16}\right| \right) + C$$

Therefore,

$$\int x\sqrt{x^4 - 16} \, dx = \frac{1}{4} \left(x^2\sqrt{x^4 - 16} - 16 \ln\left|x^2 + \sqrt{x^4 - 16}\right| \right) + C$$

26. $\int \dfrac{x^2}{\sqrt{x^6 + 4}} \, dx$

Let $u = x^3$, then $du = 3x^2 \, dx$, and

$$\int \frac{x^2}{\sqrt{x^6 + 4}} \, dx = \int \frac{1}{\sqrt{x^6 + 4}} \, \frac{3}{3} x^2 \, dx = \frac{1}{3} \int \frac{1}{\sqrt{u^2 + 4}} \, du$$

Using Formula 36 with $a = 2$, we have:

$$\int \frac{x^2}{\sqrt{x^6 + 4}} \, dx = \frac{1}{3} \ln\left|u + \sqrt{u^2 + 4}\right| + C$$

$$= \frac{1}{3} \ln\left|x^3 + \sqrt{x^6 + 4}\right| + C$$

28. $\int \dfrac{\sqrt{x^4 + 4}}{x}\,dx$

Let $u = x^2$, then $du = 2x\,dx$, and

$$\int \frac{\sqrt{x^4 + 4}}{x}\,dx = \int \frac{\sqrt{x^4 + 4}}{x^2}\,\frac{2}{2}x\,dx = \frac{1}{2}\int \frac{\sqrt{u^2 + 4}}{u}\,du$$

Using Formula 34 with $a = 2$, we have:

$$\int \frac{\sqrt{u^2 + 4}}{u}\,du = \sqrt{u^2 + 4} - 2\,\ln\left|\frac{2 + \sqrt{u^2 + 4}}{u}\right| + C$$

Thus,

$$\int \frac{\sqrt{x^4 + 4}}{x}\,dx = \frac{1}{2}\sqrt{x^4 + 4} - \ln\left|\frac{2 + \sqrt{x^4 + 4}}{x^2}\right| + C$$

30. $\int \dfrac{e^x}{(4 + e^x)^2(2 + e^x)}\,dx$

Let $u = e^x$, then $du = e^x\,dx$ and

$$\int \frac{e^x}{(4 + e^x)^2(2 + e^x)}\,dx = \int \frac{1}{(4 + u)^2(2 + u)}\,du$$

Now, using Formula 18 with $a = 4$, $b = 1$, $c = 2$, $d = 1$, we have (after substituting e^x for u):

$$\int \frac{e^x}{(4 + e^x)^2(2 + e^x)}\,dx = \frac{1}{2}\cdot\frac{1}{4 + e^x} + \frac{1}{4}\ln\left|\frac{2 + e^x}{4 + e^x}\right| + C$$

32. $\int \dfrac{1}{x\,\ln x\sqrt{4 + \ln x}}\,dx$

Let $u = \ln x$, then $du = \dfrac{1}{x}\,dx$ and

$$\int \frac{1}{x\,\ln x\sqrt{4 + \ln x}}\,dx = \int \frac{1}{\ln x\sqrt{4 + \ln x}}\cdot\frac{1}{x}\,dx$$
$$= \int \frac{1}{u\sqrt{4 + u}}\,du$$

Using Formula 27 with $a = 4$, $b = 1$, we have:

$$\int \frac{1}{u\sqrt{4 + u}}\,du = \frac{1}{2}\ln\left|\frac{\sqrt{4 + u} - 2}{\sqrt{4 + u} + 2}\right| + C$$

Therefore,

$$\int \frac{1}{x\,\ln x\sqrt{4 + \ln x}}\,dx = \frac{1}{2}\ln\left|\frac{\sqrt{4 + \ln x} - 2}{\sqrt{4 + \ln x} + 2}\right| + C$$

34. $\int x^2 e^{-4x}\, dx$

From Formula 47 with $n = 2$, $a = -4$, we have:

$$\int x^2 e^{-4x}\, dx = \frac{x^2 e^{-4x}}{-4} - \frac{2}{-4}\int x e^{-4x}\, dx$$

From Formula 47 with $n = 1$, $a = -4$, we have:

$$\int x e^{-4x}\, dx = \frac{x e^{-4x}}{-4} - \frac{1}{-4}\int e^{-4x}\, dx = -\frac{1}{4}x e^{-4x} - \frac{1}{16}e^{-4x} + C_1$$

Therefore,

$$\int x^2 e^{-4x}\, dx = -\frac{1}{4}x^2 e^{-4x} - \frac{1}{8}x e^{-4x} - \frac{1}{32}e^{-4x} + C$$

36. $\int x^3 e^{2x}\, dx$

From Formula 47 with $n = 3$, $a = 2$, we have:

$$\int x^3 e^{2x}\, dx = \frac{x^3 e^{2x}}{2} - \frac{3}{2}\int x^2 e^{2x}\, dx$$

From Formula 47 with $n = 2$, $a = 2$, we have:

$$\int x^2 e^{2x}\, dx = \frac{x^2 e^{2x}}{2} - \frac{2}{2}\int x e^{2x}\, dx$$

From Formula 47 with $n = 1$, $a = 2$, we have:

$$\int x e^{2x} = \frac{x e^{2x}}{2} - \frac{1}{2}\int e^{2x}\, dx = \frac{1}{2}x e^{2x} - \frac{1}{4}e^{2x} + C_1$$

Therefore,

$$\int x^2 e^{2x}\, dx = \frac{1}{2}x^2 e^{2x} - \frac{1}{2}x e^{2x} + \frac{1}{4}e^{2x} + C_2$$

and finally

$$\int x^3 e^{2x}\, dx = \frac{1}{2}x^3 e^{2x} - \frac{3}{4}x^2 e^{2x} + \frac{3}{4}x e^{2x} - \frac{3}{8}e^{2x} + C$$

38. $\int (\ln x)^4\, dx$

From Formula 52, with $n = 4$ we have:

$$\int (\ln x)^4\, dx = x(\ln x)^4 - 4\int (\ln x)^3\, dx$$

$$\int (\ln x)^3\, dx = x(\ln x)^3 - 3\int (\ln x)^2\, dx$$

$$\int (\ln x)^2\, dx = x(\ln x)^2 - 2\int (\ln x)\, dx$$

$$\int (\ln x)\, dx = x(\ln x) - \int dx = x \ln x - x + C$$

Therefore,

$$\int (\ln x)^2\, dx = x(\ln x)^2 - 2x(\ln x) + 2x + C_1$$

$$\int (\ln x)^3\, dx = x(\ln x)^3 - 3x(\ln x)^2 + 6x(\ln x) - 6x + C_2$$

and finally

$$\int (\ln x)^4\, dx = x(\ln x)^4 - 4x(\ln x)^3 + 12x(\ln x)^2 - 24x \ln x + 24x + C$$

40. $\int_3^5 x^2 \sqrt{x^2 - 9}\, dx$

From Formula 41 with $a = 3$, we have:

$$\int_3^5 x^2 \sqrt{x^2 - 9}\, dx = \frac{1}{8}\left[x(2x^2 - 9)\sqrt{x^2 - 9} - 81\ln\left|x + \sqrt{x^2 - 9}\right| \right]\Big|_3^5$$

$$= \frac{1}{8}\left[(820 - 81\ln 9) - (-81\ln 3) \right]$$

$$= \frac{1}{8}\left[820 - 81\ln 3 \right]$$

$$= \frac{205}{2} - \frac{81}{8}\ln 3 \approx 91.377$$

42. $\int_2^4 \frac{x}{(x^2 - 1)^2}\, dx$

Let $u = x^2 - 1$, then $du = 2x\, dx$, and

$$\int \frac{x}{(x^2 - 1)^2}\, dx = \int \frac{1}{(x^2 - 1)^2}\, \frac{2}{2} x\, dx = \int \frac{1}{u^2} \cdot \frac{1}{2}\, du$$

$$= \frac{1}{2}\int u^{-2}\, du$$

$$= -\frac{1}{2} u^{-1} + C$$

$$= -\frac{1}{2}(x^2 - 1)^{-1} + C$$

Thus,

$$\int_2^4 \frac{x}{(x^2 - 1)^2}\, dx = \left(-\frac{1}{2}(x^2 - 1)^{-1} \right)\Big|_2^4 = -\frac{1}{2}(15)^{-1} + \frac{1}{2}(3)^{-1}$$

$$= -\frac{1}{30} + \frac{1}{6} = \frac{4}{30} = \frac{2}{15}$$

44. $\int \frac{(\ln x)^2}{x}\, dx$

Let $u = \ln x$, then $du = \frac{1}{x}\, dx$, and

$$\int \frac{(\ln x)^2}{x}\, dx = \int (\ln x)^2\, \frac{1}{x}\, dx = \int u^2\, du$$

$$= \frac{1}{3} u^3 + C$$

$$= \frac{1}{3}(\ln x)^3 + C$$

46. $\int \dfrac{x^2}{\sqrt{x^2 - 1}} \, dx$

From Formula 44 with $a = 1$, we have:

$$\int \dfrac{x^2}{\sqrt{x^2 - 1}} \, dx = \dfrac{1}{2}\left(x\sqrt{x^2 - 1} + \ln\left| x + \sqrt{x^2 - 1} \right| \right) + C$$

48. $f(x) = \sqrt{1 + x^2}$, $g(x) = 5x - x^2$

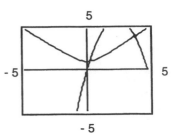

The graphs of f and g are shown at the right. The x-coordinates of the points of intersection are: $x_1 = 0.21$, $x_2 = 3.97$

$$A = \int_{0.21}^{3.97} \left[(5x - x^2) - \sqrt{1 + x^2} \right] dx$$

$$= \int_{0.21}^{3.97} (5x - x^2) \, dx - \int_{0.21}^{3.97} \sqrt{1 + x^2} \, dx$$

For the second integral we use Formula 32 with $a = 1$:

$$\int \sqrt{1 + x^2} \, dx = \dfrac{1}{2}\left(x\sqrt{x^2 + 1} + \ln\left| x + \sqrt{x^2 + 1} \right| \right) + C$$

Thus,

$$A = \left(\dfrac{5}{2}x^2 - \dfrac{1}{3}x^3 \right)\Big|_{0.21}^{3.97} - \dfrac{1}{2}\left(x\sqrt{x^2 + 1} + \ln\left| x + \sqrt{x^2 + 1} \right| \right)\Big|_{0.21}^{3.97}$$

$$\approx (18.545 - 0.107) - (9.170 - 0.212) = 9.48$$

50. $f(x) = \dfrac{x}{\sqrt{x + 4}}$, $g(x) = x - 2$

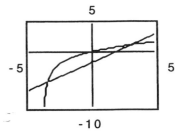

The graphs of f and g are shown at the right. The x-coordinates of the points of intersection are: $x_1 = -3.59$, $x_2 = 3.19$

$$A = \int_{-3.59}^{3.19} \left[\dfrac{x}{\sqrt{x + 4}} - (x - 2) \right] dx$$

$$= \int_{-3.59}^{3.19} \dfrac{x}{\sqrt{x + 4}} \, dx - \int_{-3.59}^{3.19} (x - 2) \, dx$$

For the first integral, we use Formula 25 with $a = 4$ and $b = 1$:

$$\int \dfrac{x}{\sqrt{x + 4}} x = \dfrac{2(x - 8)}{3}\sqrt{x + 4} + C, \text{ and therefore}$$

$$A = \left(\dfrac{2}{3}(x - 8)\sqrt{x + 4} \right)\Big|_{-3.59}^{3.19} - \dfrac{1}{2}(x - 2)^2 \Big|_{-3.59}^{3.19}$$

$$\approx (-8.598 + 4.947) + (-0.708 + 15.624) \approx 11.27$$

52. Find $\overline{x}$, the supply when the price $\overline{p} = 20$:

$$20 = \frac{10\overline{x}}{300 - \overline{x}}$$

$$6,000 - 20\overline{x} = 10\overline{x}$$

$$30\overline{x} = 6,000$$

$$\overline{x} = 200$$

Producers' surplus:

$$PS = \int_0^{\overline{x}} [\overline{p} - S(x)] \, dx = \int_0^{200} \left[20 - \frac{10x}{300 - x} \right] dx$$

$$= \int_0^{200} \left[\frac{6,000 - 20x - 10x}{300 - x} \right] dx$$

$$= \int_0^{200} \left(\frac{6,000}{300 - x} - \frac{30x}{300 - x} \right) dx$$

Use Formula 20 with $a = 6,000$, $b = -30$, $c = 300$, $d = -1$. Thus,

$$PS = \left[\frac{-30x}{-1} + \frac{-6,000 + 9,000}{1} \ln|300 - x| \right]_0^{200}$$

$$= (6,000 + 3,000 \ln 100) - (3,000 \ln 300)$$

$$= 6,000 + 3,000 \ln\left(\frac{100}{300}\right) = 6,000 + 3,000 \ln\left(\frac{1}{3}\right)$$

$$= 6,000 + 3,000 \ln 3 \approx 2,704$$

Thus, the producers' surplus is $2,704.

54.

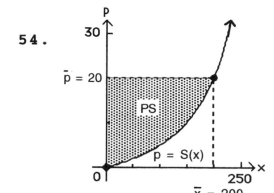

The shaded region represents the producers' surplus.

56. $C'(x) = \dfrac{65 + 20x}{1 + 0.4x}$, $C(0) = 11,000$

$$C(x) = \int \frac{65 + 20x}{1 + 0.4x} \, dx$$

Use Formula 20 with $a = 65$, $b = 20$, $c = 1$, $d = 0.4$:

$$C(x) = \frac{20x}{0.4} + \frac{26 - 20}{0.16} \ln|1 + 0.4x| + C_1$$

Since $C(0) = 11,000$, we have $C_1 = 11,000$ and therefore,

$$C(x) = 50x + 3.75 \ln(1 + 0.4x) + 11,000$$

To find the production level that produces a cost of $52,000 per week, we need to solve:

$$52,000 = 50x + 37.5 \ln(1 + 0.4x) + 11,000 \text{ for } x.$$

The production level is 816 CD players.

For a production level of 700 CD players per
week, the cost is:
$C(700) = 50(700) + 37.5 \ln(1 + 0.4(700)) + 11,000$
$\approx \$46,211$

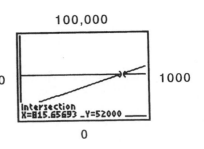

58. $FV = e^{rT} \int_0^T f(t) e^{-rt} \, dt$

Now, $r = 0.08$, $T = 5$, $f(t) = 200t$.

$FV = e^{(0.08)5} \int_0^5 200t e^{-0.08t} \, dt = 200 e^{0.4} \int_0^5 t e^{-0.08t} \, dt$

To evaluate the integral, use Formula 47 with $n = 1$ and $a = -0.08$:

$\int t e^{-0.08t} \, dt = \dfrac{t e^{-0.08t}}{-0.08} - \dfrac{1}{-0.08} \int e^{-0.08t} \, dt$

$= -12.5 t e^{-0.08t} + 12.5 \left(\dfrac{e^{-0.08t}}{-0.08} \right) + C$

$= -12.5 t e^{-0.08t} - (12.5)^2 e^{-0.08t} + C$

Thus,
$FV = (-2,500 t e^{0.4 - 0.08t} - 31,250 e^{0.4 - 0.08t}) \Big|_0^5$

$= (-12,500 e^0 - 31,250 e^0) - (-31,250 e^{0.4})$
$= 31,250 e^{0.4} - 43,750$

Total income $= \int_0^5 200t \, dt = 100 t^2 \Big|_0^5 = 2,500$

Thus, Interest Earned $= 31,250 e^{0.4} - 43,750 - 2,500$
$= 31,250 e^{0.4} - 46,250$
$\approx \$370$

60. Index of Income Concentration:
$2 \int_0^1 [x - f(x)] \, dx = 2 \int_0^1 \left[x - \dfrac{1}{2} x^2 \sqrt{1 + 3x} \right] dx$

$= 2 \int_0^1 x \, dx - \int_0^1 x^2 \sqrt{1 + 3x} \, dx$

For the second integral, use Formula 23 with $a = 1$ and $b = 3$:

$2 \int_0^1 [x - f(x)] \, dx = x^2 \Big|_0^1 - \left[\dfrac{2(135x^2 - 36x + 8)}{2,835} \sqrt{(1 + 3x)^3} \right]_0^1$

$= 1 - \left[\dfrac{1,712}{2,835} - \dfrac{16}{2,835} \right]$

$= 1 - \dfrac{1,696}{2,835} = \dfrac{1,139}{2,835} \approx 0.4018$

62.

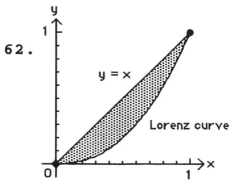

As the area bounded by the two curves gets larger, the Lorenz curve moves away from $y = x$ and the distribution of income approaches perfect inequality — one individual would have all of the wealth and the rest would have none.

64. $D(x) = \dfrac{50}{\sqrt{100 + 6x}}$

Average price $= \dfrac{1}{250 - 50} \displaystyle\int_{50}^{250} \dfrac{50}{\sqrt{100 + 6x}}\,dx$

$= \dfrac{1}{4} \displaystyle\int_{50}^{250} \dfrac{1}{\sqrt{100 + 6x}}\,dx$

For this integral use Formula 24 with $a = 100$ and $b = 6$. Then

Average price $= \bar{p} = \dfrac{1}{4}\left[\dfrac{2\sqrt{100 + 6x}}{6}\right]_{50}^{250}$

$= \dfrac{1}{12}\left(\sqrt{1,600} - \sqrt{400}\right)$

$= \dfrac{1}{12}(40 - 20) = \dfrac{20}{12} \approx \$1.67$

66.

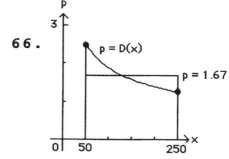

The area under the price-demand curve, $y = p(x)$, is the same as the area under the average price line, $y = 1.67$, from $x = 50$ to $x = 250$.

68. $R'(x) = \dfrac{x}{\sqrt{1 + 2x}}$, $R(0) = 0$

$R(x) = \displaystyle\int \dfrac{x}{\sqrt{1 + 2x}}\,dx = \dfrac{2(2x - 2)}{12}\sqrt{1 + 2x} + C$

(From Formula 25 with $a = 1$ and $b = 2$).

$R(0) = 0 = -\dfrac{1}{3} + C$ and hence $C = \dfrac{1}{3}$.

Thus, $R(x) = \dfrac{1}{3}(x - 1)\sqrt{1 + 2x} + \dfrac{1}{3}$

The number of calculators that must be sold to produce \$10,000 in revenue: 767
For $x = 1,000$,

$R(1,000) = \dfrac{1}{3}\, 999\sqrt{2,001} + \dfrac{1}{3} \approx \$14,896$

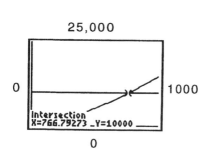

70. $C(t) = t\sqrt{24 - t}, \quad 0 \le t \le 24$

Average concentration $= \dfrac{1}{24 - 0} \displaystyle\int_0^{24} t\sqrt{24 - t}\, dt$

$$= \dfrac{1}{24}\left[\dfrac{2(-3t - 48)}{15}\sqrt{(24 - t)^3}\, \right]_0^{24}$$

(Formula 22 with $a = 24$, $b = -1$)

$$= \dfrac{1}{24}\left[(0) - \left(\dfrac{-96}{15}\sqrt{(24)^3}\, \right) \right]$$

$$= \dfrac{96\sqrt{24}}{15} = \dfrac{32\sqrt{24}}{5} = \dfrac{64\sqrt{6}}{5} \approx 31.35 \text{ ppm}$$

72. $f(t) = \dfrac{500}{2 + 3e^{-t}}, \quad [0, 10]$

Average $= \dfrac{1}{10 - 0}\displaystyle\int_0^{10} \dfrac{500}{2 + 3e^{-t}}\, dt$

$$= 50\displaystyle\int_0^{10} \dfrac{1}{2 + 3e^{-t}}\, dt$$

(Formula 48 with $a = -1$, $c = 2$, $d = 3$)

$$= 50\left[\dfrac{t}{2} + \dfrac{1}{2}\ln\left|2 + 3e^{-t}\right| \right]_0^{10}$$

$$= 50\left[\left(5 + \dfrac{1}{2}\ln(2 + 3e^{-10}) \right) - \left(\dfrac{1}{2}\ln 5 \right) \right]$$

$$= 250 + 25\ln(2 + 3e^{-10}) - 25\ln 5 \approx 227.094 \text{ or } 227{,}094 \text{ voters.}$$

74.

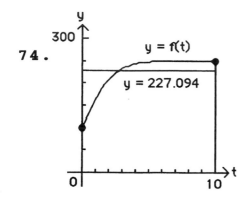

The area under voter equation, $y = f(t)$, is the same as the area under the line representing the average number of voters, $y = 227.094$, over the interval $[0, 10]$.

8 MULTIVARIABLE CALCULUS

2. $f(x, y) = 2x + 7y - 5$
$f(0, 10) = 2(0) + 7(10) - 5 = 65$

4. $f(x, y) = 2x + 7y - 5$
$f(5, 6) = 2(5) + 7(6) - 5 = 47$

6. $g(x, y) = \dfrac{88}{x^2 + 3y}$

$g(-2, 0) = \dfrac{88}{(-2)^2 + 3(0)} = \dfrac{88}{4} = 22$

8. $g(x, y) = \dfrac{88}{x^2 + 3y}$

$g(0, 0)$ is NOT DEFINED; the denominator is zero.

10. $f(x, y) = 2x + 7y - 2$ and $g(x, y) = \dfrac{88}{x^2 + 3y}$

$2f(10, -4) - 7g(10, -4) = 2[2(10) + 7(-4) - 5] - 7\left[\dfrac{88}{(10)^2 + 3(-4)}\right]$

$= 2(20 - 28 - 5) - 7\left(\dfrac{88}{100 - 12}\right)$

$= -26 - 7 = -33$

12. $f(x, y, z) = 2x - 3y^2 + 5z^3 - 1$
$f(0, 0, 2) = 2(0) - 3(0)^2 + 5(2)^3 - 1 = 39$

14. $f(x, y, z) = 2x - 3y^2 + 5z^3 - 1$
$f(-10, 4, -3) = 2(-10) - 3(4)^2 + 5(-3)^3 - 1 = -20 - 48 - 135 - 1$
$= -204$

16. $S(x, y) = 5x^2y^3$
$S(4, 2) = 5(4)^2(2)^3$
$= 640$
$(x = 4$ and $y = 2)$

18. $P(x, y) = -x^2 + 2xy - 2y^2 - 4x + 12y + 5$
$P(2, 2) = -(2)^2 + 2(2)(2) - 2(2)^2 - 4(2) + 12(2) + 5 = 17$
$(x = 2$ and $y = 2)$

20. $L(w, v) = (1.25 \times 10^{-5})wv^2$
$L(2,000, 50) = (1.25 \times 10^{-5})(2,000)(50)^2 = 62.5$
$(w = 2,000$ and $v = 50)$

22. $A(P, r, t, n) = P\left(1 + \dfrac{r}{n}\right)^{tn}$

$A(10, 0.04, 3, 2) = 10\left(1 + \dfrac{0.04}{2}\right)^{3(2)} = 10(1.02)^6 \approx 11.26$

$(P = 10,\ r = 0.04,\ t = 3$ and $n = 2)$

24. $F(r, t) = \int_0^T 4{,}000e^{r(T-t)} \, dt,$

$$F(0.07, 10) = \int_0^{10} 4{,}000e^{0.07(10-t)} \, dt$$

$$= 4{,}000e^{0.7} \int_0^{10} e^{-0.07t} \, dt$$

$$= 4{,}000e^{0.7} \left(\frac{e^{-0.07t}}{-0.07} \right) \Bigg|_0^{10}$$

$$= 4{,}000e^{0.7} \left(-\frac{e^{-0.7}}{0.07} + \frac{1}{0.07} \right)$$

$$= \frac{400{,}000}{7} (e^{0.7} - 1) \approx 57{,}928.73$$

26. $G(a, b, c) = a^3 + b^3 + c^3 - (ab + ac + bc) - 6$

$G(2, b, 1) = (2)^3 + b^3 + (1)^3 - (2b + 2 + b) - 6$

$\qquad\qquad = 8 + b^3 + 1 - 3b - 2 - 6$

$\qquad\qquad = b^3 - 3b + 1$

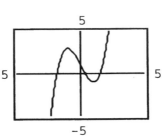

We use a graphing utility to solve $G(2, b, 1) = 0$.
The graph of $y = G(2, x, 1)$ is shown at the right.
The solutions of $G(2, x, 1) = 0$ are:
$x_1 = -1.879$, $x_2 = 0.347$, $x_3 = 1.532$.

28. $f(x, y) = x^2 + 2y^2$

$$\frac{f(x, y + k) - f(x, y)}{k} = \frac{(x^2 + 2(y + k)^2) - (x^2 + 2y^2)}{k}$$

$$= \frac{x^2 + 2y^2 + 4yk + 2k^2 - x^2 - 2y^2}{k}$$

$$= \frac{k(4y + 2k)}{k} = 4y + 2k$$

30. $f(x, y) = 2xy^2$

$$\frac{f(x, y + k) - f(x, y)}{k} = \frac{2x(y + k)^2 - 2xy^2}{k}$$

$$= \frac{2x(y^2 + 2ky + k^2) - 2xy^2}{k}$$

$$= \frac{2xy^2 + 4kxy + 2xk^2 - 2xy^2}{k}$$

$$= \frac{k(4xy + 2xk)}{k} = 4xy + 2xk$$

32. Coordinates of point $B = B(2, 0, 0)$.
Coordinates of point $H = H(0, 4, 3)$.

34. $f(x, y) = \sqrt{4 - y^2}$

    (A) In the plane $x = c$, c any constant, $z = \sqrt{4 - y^2}$ whose graph is the upper semicircle of radius 2 with center at the origin.

    (B) The line parallel to the x-axis and passing through the point $(0, 0, 2)$; the line parallel to the x-axis and passing through the point $(0, 2, 0)$: the empty set.

    (C) The upper half of a right circular cylinder of radius 2 whose axis is the x-axis.

36. $f(x, y) = 100 + 10x + 25y - x^2 - 5y^2$

    (A) Cross-sections corresponding to $y - 0$, $y - 1$, $y = 2$, and $y = 3$. Parabolas which open downward.

    (B) Cross-sections corresponding to $x = 0$, $x = 1$, $x = 2$, and $x = 3$: Parabolas which open downward.

    (C) A paraboloid which open downward.

38. $f(x, y) = 4 - \sqrt{x^2 + y^2}$

    (A) If the points (a, b) and (c, d) both lie on the same circle centered at the origin, then $a^2 + b^2 = r^2 = c^2 + d^2$, where r is the radius of the circle.

    (B) The cross-sections are:

        (i) $x = 0$, $f(0, y) = 4 - \sqrt{y^2}$; it is the union of two rays with vertex $(0, 0, 4)$.

        (ii) $y = 0$, $f(x, 0) = 4 - \sqrt{x^2}$; it is the union of two rays with vertex $(0, 0, 4)$.

        (iii) $x = y$, $f(x, x) = 4 - \sqrt{2x^2}$; it is the union of two rays with vertex $(0, 0, 4)$.

40. $S(x, y) = 5x^2y^3$
$S(3, 2) = 5(3)^2(2)^3 = \$360$ thousand
$S(2, 3) = 5(2)^2(3)^3 = \$540$ thousand

42. $R(x, y) = xp + yq = 230x - 9x^2 + xy + 130y + xy - 4y^2$
$\qquad\qquad\quad = 230x + 130y - 9x^2 + 2xy - 4y^2$

$P(x, y) = R(x, y) - C(x, y) = 150x + 100y - 9x^2 + 2xy - 4y^2 - 200$
$R(10, 15) = 230(10) + 130(15) - 9(10)^2 + 2(10)(15) - 4(15)^2 = \$2,750$
$P(10, 15) = 150(10) + 100(15) - 9(10)^2 + 2(10)(15) - 4(15)^2 - 200$
$\qquad\qquad = \$1,300$

44. $f(x, y) = 20x^{0.4}y^{0.6}$
$f(2,500, 3,400) = 20(2,500)^{0.4}(3,400)^{0.6} \approx 60,130$ units
Doubling the units of labor and capital doubles the productivity.

46. (A) $M(x, y, z) = xy + 2xz + 3yz$

$M(10, 12, 6) = (10)(12) + 2(10)(6) + 3(12)(6) = 546$

(B) For $x = y$, $M(x, x, z) = x^2 + 5xz$; also $x^2z = 720$.

Thus, $M(x, x, z) = x^2 + 5x\left(\dfrac{720}{x^2}\right) = x^2 + \dfrac{3,600}{x}$ and we need to

minimize this quantity with respect to x.

$\dfrac{d}{dx}M(x, x, z) = 2x - \dfrac{3,600}{x^2} = 0$ or $2x^3 - 3,600 = 0$

$$2x^3 = 3,600$$
$$x^3 = 1,800$$
$$x \approx 12.16$$

$\dfrac{d^2}{dx^2}M(x, x, z) = 2 + \dfrac{7,200}{x^3} > 0$ for $x > 0$, therefore

$x = 12.16$ is a minimum point.

Thus, the desired dimensions are 12.16 in × 12.16 in × 4.87 in

$$\left(z = \dfrac{720}{x^2} = \dfrac{720}{(12.16)^2} = 4.87\right)$$

48. $R(L, r) = k\dfrac{L}{r^4}$, k a constant

$R(8, 1) = k\dfrac{8}{1} = 8k$

$R(4, 0.2) = k\dfrac{4}{(0.2)^4} = 2,500k$

50. $L(w, v) = kwv^2$, k a constant

For $k = 0.000,013,3$ we have

$L = 0.000,013,3wv^2$

$L(2,000, 40) = k(2,000)(40)^2 = 3,200,000k \approx 42.56$ ft

$L(3,000, 60) = k(3,000)(60)^2 = 10,800,000k \approx 143.64$ ft

---

EXERCISE 8-2
___

2. $z = f(x, y) = 3 + 4x - 5y^2$

$\dfrac{\partial z}{\partial y} = -10y$

4. $z = f(x, y) = 3 + 4x - 5y^2$

$f_x(x, y) = 4$

$f_x(1, 2) = 4$

6. $z = f(x, y) = 8x + 6y^3 - 3xy^2$

$\dfrac{\partial z}{\partial x} = 8 - 3y^2$

8. $z = f(x, y) = 8x + 6y^3 - 3xy^2$

$\dfrac{\partial^2 z}{\partial x^2} = \dfrac{\partial}{\partial x}\left(\dfrac{\partial z}{\partial x}\right) = \dfrac{\partial}{\partial x}(8 - 3y^2)$ (See Problem 6 above)

$\qquad\qquad\qquad = 0$

10. $z = f(x, y) = 8x + 6y^3 - 3xy^2$

$f_y(x, y) = 18y^2 - 6xy$

$f_y(2, 3) = 18(3)^2 - 6(2)(3) = 162 - 36 = 126$

12. $C(x, y) = -7x^2 + 10xy + 4y^2 - 9x + 8y + 12$
$C_y(x, y) = 10x + 8y + 8$

14. $C(x, y) = -7x^2 + 10xy + 4y^2 - 9x + 8y + 12$
$C_y(x, y) = 10x + 8y + 8$
$C_y(2, 2) = 10(2) + 8(2) + 8 = 20 + 16 + 8 = 44$

16. $C(x, y) = -7x^2 + 10xy + 4y^2 - 9x + 8y + 12$

$C_{yx}(x, y) = \dfrac{\partial}{\partial x}(C_y(x, y)) = \dfrac{\partial}{\partial x}(10x + 8y + 8)$

$\qquad\qquad\qquad = 10$

18. $C(x, y) = -7x^2 + 10xy + 4y^2 - 9x + 8y + 12$

$C_{yy}(x, y) = \dfrac{\partial}{\partial y}(C_y(x, y)) = \dfrac{\partial}{\partial y}(10x + 8y + 8)$

$\qquad\qquad\qquad = 8$

20. $S(x, y) = 2y^3 e^x + 5x^4 \ln y$

$S_y(x, y) = 6y^2 e^x + 5x^4\left(\dfrac{1}{y}\right) = 6y^2 e^x + 5x^4 y^{-1}$

22. $S(x, y) = 2y^3 e^x + 5x^4 \ln y$
$S_x(x, y) = 2y^3 e^x + 20x^3 \ln y$
$S_x(2, 1) = 2(1)^3 e^2 + 20(2)^3 \ln 1 = 2e^2$

24. $S(x, y) = 2y^3 e^x + 5x^4 \ln y$

$S_{yx}(x, y) = \dfrac{\partial}{\partial x}(S_y(x, y)) = \dfrac{\partial}{\partial x}(6y^2 e^x + 5x^4 y^{-1})$ (see Problem 20 above)

$\qquad\qquad\qquad = 6y^2 e^x + 20x^3 y^{-1}$

26. $z = f(x, y) = e^{4x^2+5y}$

$\dfrac{\partial z}{\partial y} = e^{4x^2+5y}(5) = 5e^{4x^2+5y}$

28. $z = f(x, y) = e^{4x^2+5y}$

$\dfrac{\partial z}{\partial y} = 5e^{4x^2+5y}$ (From Problem 26)

$\dfrac{\partial^2 z}{\partial y \partial x} = \dfrac{\partial}{\partial x}(5e^{4x^2+5y}) = 5e^{4x^2+5y}(8x)$

$\qquad\qquad\qquad = 40xe^{4x^2+5y}$

30. $z = f(x, y) = e^{4x^2+5y}$

$f_{yx}(x, y) = 40xe^{4x^2+5y}$ (From Problem 28)

$f_{yx}(0, 1) = 40(0)e^{4(0)^2+5(1)} = 0$

32. $z = f(x, y) = e^{4x^2+5y}$

$f_y(x, y) = 5e^{4x^2+5y}$ (From Problem 26)

$f_{yy}(x, y) = 5e^{4x^2+5y}(5) = 25e^{4x^2+5y}$

$f_{yy}(1, 0) = 25e^{4(1)^2+5(0)} = 25e^4$

34. $f(x, y) = \sqrt{2x - y^2} = (2x - y^2)^{1/2}$

$f_x(x, y) = \dfrac{1}{2}(2x - y^2)^{-1/2}(2) = (2x - y^2)^{-1/2}$

$f_y(x, y) = \dfrac{1}{2}(2x - y^2)^{-1/2}(-2y) = -y(2x - y^2)^{-1/2}$

36. $f(x, y) = (3 + 2xy^2)^3$

$f_x(x, y) = 3(3 + 2xy^2)^2(2y^2) = 6y^2(3 + 2xy^2)^2$

$f_y(x, y) = 3(3 + 2xy^2)^2(4xy) = 12xy(3 + 2xy^2)^2$

38. $f(x, y) = \ln(2x - 3y)$

$f_x(x, y) = \dfrac{1}{2x - 3y}(2) = \dfrac{2}{2x - 3y}$

$f_y(x, y) = \dfrac{1}{2x - 3y}(-3) = \dfrac{-3}{2x - 3y}$

40. $f(x, y) = x^3 e^{x^2 y}$

$f_x(x, y) = 3x^2 e^{x^2 y} + x^3 e^{x^2 y}(2xy)$

$\qquad\qquad = 3x^2 e^{x^2 y} + 2x^4 y e^{x^2 y}$

$\qquad\qquad = (3 + 2x^2)x^2 e^{x^2 y}$

$f_y(x, y) = x^3 e^{x^2 y}(x^2) = x^5 e^{x^2 y}$

42. $f(x, y) = \dfrac{2x^2y}{x^2 + y^2}$

$\qquad f_x(x, y) = \dfrac{4xy(x^2 + y^2) - 2x(2x^2y)}{(x^2 + y^2)^2}$

$\qquad\qquad = \dfrac{4x^3y + 4xy^3 - 4x^3y}{(x^2 + y^2)^2} = \dfrac{4xy^3}{(x^2 + y^2)^2}$

$\qquad f_y(x, y) = \dfrac{2x^2(x^2 + y^2) - 2y(2x^2y)}{(x^2 + y^2)^2}$

$\qquad\qquad = \dfrac{2x^4 + 2x^2y^2 - 4x^2y^2}{(x^2 + y^2)^2} = \dfrac{2x^4 - 2x^2y^2}{(x^2 + y^2)^2}$

44. (A) $f(x, y) = 3x + 2y$, $\dfrac{\partial f}{\partial x} = 3$, $\dfrac{\partial f}{\partial y} = 2$

(B) Infinitely many, since adding a constant to f does not change the partial derivatives.

46. $f(x, y) = x^3y^3 + x + y^2$

$\qquad f_x(x, y) = 3x^2y^3 + 1 \quad ; \quad f_y(x, y) = 3x^3y^2 + 2y$

$\qquad f_{xx}(x, y) = 6xy^3$

$\qquad f_{xy}(x, y) = 9x^2y^2 = f_{yx}(x, y)$

$\qquad f_{yy}(x, y) = 6x^3y + 2$

48. $f(x, y) = \dfrac{x^2}{y} - \dfrac{y^2}{x}$

$\qquad f_x(x, y) = \dfrac{2x}{y} + \dfrac{y^2}{x^2} \quad ; \quad f_y(x, y) = -\dfrac{x^2}{y^2} - \dfrac{2y}{x}$

$\qquad f_{xx}(x, y) = \dfrac{2}{y} - \dfrac{2y^2}{x^3}$

$\qquad f_{xy}(x, y) = -\dfrac{2x}{y^2} + \dfrac{2y}{x^2} = f_{yx}(x, y)$

$\qquad f_{yy}(x, y) = \dfrac{2x^2}{y^3} - \dfrac{2}{x}$

50. $f(x, y) = x \ln(xy) = x(\ln x + \ln y) = x \ln x + x \ln y$

$\qquad f_x(x, y) = \ln x + 1 + \ln y \quad ; \quad f_y(x, y) = \dfrac{x}{y}$

$\qquad f_{xx}(x, y) = \dfrac{1}{x}$

$\qquad f_{xy}(x, y) = \dfrac{1}{y} = f_{yx}(x, y)$

$\qquad f_{yy}(x, y) = -\dfrac{x}{y^2}$

52. $C(x, y) = 2x^2 + 2xy + 3y^2 - 16x - 18y + 54$
$C_x(x, y) = 4x + 2y - 16$
$C_y(x, y) = 2x + 6y - 18$

$C_x(x, y) = 0$ and $C_y(x, y) = 0$ when

$$4x + 2y - 16 = 0 \quad \text{or} \quad 2x + y = 8 \quad (1)$$
$$2x + 6y - 18 = 0 \quad \quad\quad\quad x + 3y = 9 \quad (2)$$

Multiply (2) by -2 and add to (1): $-5y = -10$
$$y = 2$$

Substitute $y = 2$ into (2): $x = 9 - 6 = 3$
Thus, $C_x(x, y) = 0$ and $C_y(x, y) = 0$ when $x = 3$ and $y = 2$.

54. $G(x, y) = x^2 \ln y - 3x - 2y + 1$
$G_x(x, y) = 2x \ln y - 3$

$G_y(x, y) = \dfrac{x^2}{y} - 2$

$G_x(x, y) = 0$ and $G_y(x, y) = 0$ when:
$$2x \ln y - 3 = 0 \quad \text{or} \quad 2x \ln y = 3 \quad (1)$$
$$\dfrac{x^2}{y} - 2 = 0 \quad\quad\quad\quad \dfrac{x^2}{y} = 2 \quad (2)$$

From (2), $y = \dfrac{x^2}{2}$ and substituting for y into (1),

$$2x \ln\left(\dfrac{x^2}{2}\right) = 3$$

$$x \ln\left(\dfrac{x^2}{2}\right) = 1.5$$

Using a graphing utility, we find the x coordinate of the point of intersection of $y_1 = x \ln\left(\dfrac{x^2}{2}\right)$ and $y = 1.5$ is $x \approx 2.042$. Substituting this value into (2) we get $y \approx 2.085$.

56. $f(x, y) = 5 - 2x + 4y - 3x^2 - y^2$

(A) $f(2, y) = 5 - 4 + 4y - 12 - y^2 = -11 + 4y - y^2$
$\dfrac{d}{dy}[f(2, y)] = 4 - 2y$; critical value(s): $4 - 2y = 0$
$$y = 2$$

$\dfrac{d^2}{dy}[f(2, y)] = -2 < 0$

Therefore, $f(2, 2) = -11 + 4(2) - (2)^2 = -7$ is the maximum value of $f(2, y)$.

(B) -7 is the maximum value of $f(x, y)$ on the curve $f(2, y)$; $f(x, y)$ may have larger values on other curves $f(h, y)$, h constant, or $f(x, k)$, k constant. For example, $f(0, 0) = 5$ is greater than -7.

58. $f(x, y) = e^x + 2e^y + 3xy^2 + 1$

(A) Let $x = 1$ and find the minimum value of $f(1, y) = e + 2e^y + 3y^2 + 1$ $= 2e^y + 3y^2 + (1 + e)$. Using a graphing utility we find that the minimum value of $f(1, y)$ is 5.463 at $y = d \approx -0.258$.

(B) $f_x(x, y) = e^x + 3y^2$; $f_y(x, y) = 2e^y + 6xy$

$f_x(1, -0.258) = e + 3(-0.258)^2 = 2.918$

$f_y(1, -0.258) = 2e^{-0.258} + 6(1)(-0.258) \approx 0$

60. $f(x, y) = x^3 - 3xy^2$

$f_x(x, y) = 3x^2 - 3y^2$; $f_y(x, y) = -6xy$

$f_{xx}(x, y) = 6x$ $f_{yy}(x, y) = -6x$

$f_{xx}(x, y) + f_{yy}(x, y) = 6x - 6x = 0$

62. $f(x, y) = 2xy^2$

(A) $\lim\limits_{h \to 0} \dfrac{f(x + h, y) - f(x, y)}{h} = \lim\limits_{h \to 0} \dfrac{2(x + h)y^2 - 2xy^2}{h}$

$= \lim\limits_{h \to 0} \dfrac{2xy^2 + 2hy^2 - 2xy^2}{h}$

$= \lim\limits_{h \to 0} \dfrac{2hy^2}{h} = \lim\limits_{h \to 0} (2y^2) = 2y^2$

(B) $\lim\limits_{k \to 0} \dfrac{f(x, y + k) - f(x, y)}{k} = \lim\limits_{k \to 0} \dfrac{2x(y + k)^2 - 2xy^2}{k}$

$= \lim\limits_{k \to 0} \dfrac{2x(y^2 + 2ky + k^2) - 2xy^2}{k}$

$= \lim\limits_{k \to 0} \dfrac{2xy^2 + 4kxy + 2xk^2 - 2xy^2}{k}$

$= \lim\limits_{k \to 0} (4xy + 2xk)$

$= 4xy$

64. $S(x, y) = 10x^{0.4}y^{0.8}$

$S_x(x, y) = 10(0.4)x^{-0.6}y^{0.8}$

$= 4x^{-0.6}y^{0.8}$

$S_x(3,000, 2,000) = 4(3,000)^{-0.6}(2,000)^{0.8} = 14.34$

Sales will increase approximately \$14.34 per \$1 increase in newspaper advertising at the (3,000, 2,000) expenditure level.

$S_y(x, y) = 10x^{0.4}(0.8)y^{-0.2} = 8x^{0.4}y^{-0.2}$

$S_y(3,000, 2,000) = 8(3,000)^{0.4}(2,000)^{-0.2} = 43.03$

Sales will increase approximately \$43.03 per \$1 increase in television advertising at the (3,000, 2,000).

66. $R(x, y) = xp + yq$
$$= x(230 - 9x + y) + y(130 + x - 4y)$$
$$= 230x + 130y - 9x^2 + 2xy - 4y^2$$
$R_x(x, y) = 230 - 18x + 2y$
$R_x(10, 5) = 230 - 18(10) + 2(5) = 60$

Revenue will increase approximately \$60 per unit increase in production of ten-speed bicycles at the (10, 5) production level.

$P(x, y) = R(x, y) - C(x, y)$
$$= 230x + 130y - 9x^2 + 2xy - 4y^2 - (200 + 80x + 30y)$$
$$= 150x + 100y - 9x^2 + 2xy - 4y^2 - 200$$

$P_x(x, y) = 150 - 18x + 2y$
$P_x(10, 5) = 150 - 18(5) + 2(5) = -20$

Profit will decrease approximately \$20 per unit increase in production of ten-speed bicycles at the (10, 5) production level.

68. $f(x, y) = 50\sqrt{xy} = 50x^{0.5}y^{0.5}$

(A) $f_x(x, y) = 50(0.5)x^{-0.5}y^{0.5} = 25x^{-0.5}y^{0.5}$

$\quad\ f_y(x, y) = 50(0.5)x^{0.5}y^{-0.5} = 25x^{0.5}y^{-0.5}$

(B) Marginal productivity of labor $= f_x(250, 125)$
$$= 25(250)^{-0.5}(125)^{0.5} \approx 17.68$$

Marginal productivity of capital $= f_y(250, 125)$
$$= 25(250)^{0.5}(125)^{-0.5} \approx 35.36$$

(C) The management should encourage the increased use of capital.

70. $x = f(p, q) = 200 - 5p + 4q$ (Brand A coffee)
$y = g(p, q) = 300 + 2p - 4q$ (Brand B coffee)
$f_q(p, q) = 4 > 0$
$g_p(p, q) = 2 > 0$
Thus, the products are competitive.

72. $x = f(p, q) = 500 - 0.5p - q^2$ (tennis rackets)
$y = g(p, q) = 10,000 - 8p - 100q^2$ (tennis balls)
$f_q(p, q) = -2q < 0$
$g_p(p, q) = -8 < 0$
Thus, the products are complementary.

74. $R(L, r) = k\dfrac{L}{r^4}$, k constant

$R_L(L, r) = \dfrac{k}{r^4}$; $R_r(L, r) = \dfrac{-4kL}{r^5}$

$R_L(4, 0.2) = \dfrac{k}{(0.2)^4}$; $R_r(4, 0.2) = \dfrac{-4k(4)}{(0.2)^5}$

$\qquad\qquad = 625k$ $\qquad\qquad\qquad = -50,000k$

$R_L(4, 0.2) = 625k$ is the approximate change in resistance per unit increase in length (radius is held constant) when $L = 4$ and $r = 0.2$.

$R_r(4, 0.2) = -50,000k$ is the approximate change in resistance per unit increase in radius (length is held constant) when $L = 4$ and $r = 0.2$.

76. $L(w, v) = kwv^2$, $k = 0.0000133$

$L_w(w, v) = kv^2$; $L_v(w, v) = 2kwv$

$L_w(2,500, 60) = 3,600k$; $L_v(2,500, 60) = 300,000k$

$\qquad\qquad \approx 0.048$ $\qquad\qquad\qquad \approx 3.99$

$L_w(2,500, 60) \approx 0.048$ is increase in length of skidmark for one pound increase in weight (speed held fixed) when $w = 2,500$ lb and $v = 6$ mph.

$L_v(2,500, 60) \approx 39$ is increase in length of skidmark for 1 mph increase in speed (weight held fixed) when $w = 2,500$ lb and $v = 60$ mph.

EXERCISE 8-3

2. $f(x, y) = 10 - 2x - 3y + x^2$

$f_x(x, y) = -2 + 2x$

$f_y(x, y) = -3 \neq 0$

The function $f_y(x, y)$ is nonzero for all (x, y).

4. $f(x, y) = x^3 - y^2 + 7x + 3y + 1$

$f_x(x, y) = 3x^2 + 7 \neq 0$

$f_y(x, y) = -2y + 3$

The function $f_x(x, y)$ is nonzero for all (x, y).

6. $f(x, y) = 3 - x^2 - y^2 + 6y$

$f_x(x, y) = -2x = 0$

$\qquad\qquad x = 0$

$f_y(x, y) = -2y + 6 = 0$

$\qquad\qquad y = 3$

Thus, $(0, 3)$ is a critical point.

$f_{xx} = -2$, $f_{xy} = 0$, $f_{yy} = -2$,

$f_{xx}(0, 3) \cdot f_{yy}(0, 3) - [f_{xy}(0, 3)]^2 = (-2)(-2) - 0^2 = 4 > 0$

and $\qquad\qquad\qquad\qquad f_{xx}(0, 3) = -2 < 0$.

Thus, $f(0, 3) = 3 - 0 - 9 + 18 = 12$ is a local maximum (by Theorem 2).

8. $f(x, y) = x^2 + y^2 - 4x + 6y + 23$
$f_x(x, y) = 2x - 4 = 0$

$$x = 2$$

$f_y(x, y) = 2y + 6 = 0$

$$y = -3$$

Thus, $(2, -3)$ is a critical point.

$f_{xx} = 2, \ f_{xy} = 0, \ f_{yy} = 2$

$f_{xx}(2, -3) \cdot f_{yy}(2, -3) - [f_{xy}(2, -3)]^2 = (2)(2) - 0^2 = 4 > 0$
and $\quad\quad\quad f_{xx}(2, -3) = 2 > 0$

Thus, $f(2, -3) = 2^2 + (-3)^2 - 4(2) + 6(-3) + 23 = 10$ is a local minimum (by Theorem 2).

10. $f(x, y) = x^2 - y^2 + 2x + 6y - 4$
$f_x(x, y) = 2x + 2 = 0$

$$x = -1$$

$f_y(x, y) = -2y + 6 = 0$

$$y = 3$$

Thus, $(-1, 3)$ is a critical point.
$f_{xx} = 2, \ f_{xy} = 0, \ f_{yy} = -2$

$f_{xx}(-1, 3) \cdot f_{yy}(-1, 3) - [f_{xy}(-1, 3)]^2 = (2)(-2) - 0^2 = -4 < 0$

Thus, f has a saddle point at $(-1, 3)$ (by Theorem 2).

12. $f(x, y) = -x^2 + xy - 2y^2 + x + 10y - 5$
$f_x(x, y) = -2x + y + 1 = 0 \quad\quad (1)$
$f_y(x, y) = x - 4y + 10 = 0 \quad\quad (2)$
Solving (1) and (2) for x and y, we obtain $x = 2$ and $y = 3$.
Thus, $(2, 3)$ is a critical point.
$f_{xx} = -2, \ f_{xy} = 1, \ f_{yy} = -4$

$f_{xx}(2, 3) \cdot f_{yy}(2, 3) - [f_{xy}(2, 3)]^2 = (-2)(-4) - 1^2 = 7 > 0$
and $\quad f_{xx}(2, 3) = -2 < 0.$

Thus, $f(2, 3) = 11$ is a local maximum (by Theorem 2).

14. $f(x, y) = 2x^2 - xy + y^2 - x - 5y + 8$
$f_x(x, y) = 4x - y - 1 = 0 \quad\quad (1)$
$f_y(x, y) = -x + 2y - 5 = 0 \quad\quad (2)$
Solving (1) and (2) for x and y, we obtain $x = 1$ and $y = 3$.
Thus, $(1, 3)$ is a critical point.
$f_{xx} = 4, \ f_{xy} = -1, \ f_{yy} = 2$

$f_{xx}(1, 3) \cdot f_{yy}(1, 3) - [f_{xy}(1, 3)]^2 = (4)(2) - (-1)^2 = 7 > 0$
and $\quad f_{xx}(1, 3) = 4 > 0.$

Thus, $f(1, 3)$ is a local minimum (by Theorem 2).

16. $f(x, y) = x^2y - xy^2$

$f_x(x, y) = 2xy - y^2 = 0$ (1)

$f_y(x, y) = x^2 - 2xy = 0$ (2)

The only solution of (1) and (2) is $(0, 0)$ (i.e. the only critical point).

$f_{xx}(x, y) = 2y$, $f_{xy}(x, y) = 2x - 2y$, $f_{yy}(x, y) = -2x$. Thus, $f_{xx}(0, 0) = f_{xy}(0, 0) = f_{yy}(0, 0) = 0$ and hence the test fails.

18. $f(x, y) = 2y^3 - 6xy - x^2$

$f_x(x, y) = -6y - 2x = 0$ (1)

$f_y(x, y) - 6y^2 - 6x = 0$ (2)

Solving (1) and (2), we obtain $(0, 0)$ and $(9, -3)$ and hence there are two critical points.

$f_{xx} = -2$, $f_{xy} = -6$, $f_{yy} = 12y$

For $(0, 0)$:

$f_{xx}(0, 0) \cdot f_{yy}(0, 0) - [f_{xy}(0, 0)] = (-2)(0) - (-6)^2 = -34 < 0$

and hence f has a saddle point at $(0, 0)$.

For $(9, -3)$:

$f_{xx}(9, -3) \cdot f_{yy}(9, -3) - [f_{xy}(9, -3)]^2 = (-2)(-36) - (-6)^2 = 36 > 0$

and $f_{xx}(9, -3) = -2 < 0$.

Thus, $f(9, -3)$ is a local maximum.

20. $f(x, y) = 16xy - x^4 - 2y^2$

$f_x(x, y) = 16y - 4x^3$ (1)

$f_y(x, y) = 16x - 4y$ (2)

Solving (1) and (2), we obtain $(0, 0)$, $(-4, -16)$, $(4, 16)$ as critical points.

Now,

$f_{xx} = -12x^2$, $f_{xy} = 16$, $f_{yy} = -4$

For the critical point $(0, 0)$:

$f_{xx}(0, 0) \cdot f_{yy}(0, 0) - [f_{xy}(0, 0)]^2 = (0)(-4) - (16)^2 = -256 < 0$.

Thus, f has a saddle point at $(0, 0)$.

For the critical point $(-4, -16)$:

$f_{xx}(-4, -16) \cdot f_{yy}(-4, -16) - [f_{xy}(-4, -16)]^2 = (-192)(-4) - (16)^2$

$$= 512 > 0$$

and $f_{xx}(-4, -16) = -192 < 0$.

Thus, $f(-4, -16) = 256$ is a local maximum.

For the critical point $(4, 16)$:

$f_{xx}(4, 16) \cdot f_{yy}(4, 16) - [f_{xy}(4, 16)]^2 = (-192)(-4) - (16)^2 = 512 > 0$

and $f_{xx}(4, 16) = -192 < 0$.

Thus, $f(4, 16) = 256$ is a local maximum.

22. $f(x, y) = 2x^2 - 2x^2y + 6y^3$
$f_x(x, y) = 4x - 4xy$ (1)

$f_y(x, y) = -2x^2 + 18y^2$ (2)

Solving (1) and (2), we obtain $(0, 0)$, $(-3, 1)$, $(3, 1)$.

Now,
$f_{xx} = 4 - 4y$, $f_{xy} = -4x$, $f_{yy} = 36y$

For the critical point $(0, 0)$:
$f_{xx}(0, 0) \cdot f_{yy}(0, 0) - [f_{xy}(0, 0)]^2 = (4)(0) - [0]^2 = 0$
Thus, the test fails.

For the critical point $(-3, 1)$:
$f_{xx}(-3, 1) \cdot f_{yy}(-3, 1) - [f_{xy}(-3, 1)]^2 = (0)(36) - (12)^2 < 0$
Thus, $f(x, y)$ has a saddle point at $(-3, 1)$.

For the critical point $(3, 1)$:
$f_{xx}(3, 1) \cdot f_{yy}(3, 1) - [f_{xy}(3, 1)]^2 = (0)(36) - (-12)^2 < 0$,
and hence f has a saddle point at $(3, 1)$ as well.

24. $f(x, y) = x \ln y + x^2 - 4x - 5y + 3$
$f_x(x, y) = \ln y + 2x - 4 = 0$ (1)

$f_y(x, y) = \dfrac{x}{y} - 5 = 0$ (2)

From (2), $x = 5y$. Substituting this into (1), we have
     $\ln y + 10y - 4 = 0$

Using a graphing utility, we find that $y = 0.475$ and $x = 2.373$.

Now, $f_{xx} = 2$, $f_{xy} = \dfrac{1}{y}$, $f_{yy} = -\dfrac{x}{y^2}$

$f_{xx}(2.373, 0.475) \cdot f_{yy}(2.373, 0.475) - [f_{xy}(2.373, 0.475)]^2$

$= (2) - \left(-\dfrac{2.373}{(0.475)^2}\right) - \left[\dfrac{1}{0.475}\right]^2 = -\dfrac{5.746}{(0.475)^2} < 0$

and hence $f(x, y)$ has a saddle point at $(2.373, 0.475)$.

26. (A) $f(x, y) = x + y$
     $f_x(x, y) = 1 \ne 0$
     $f_y(x, y) = 1 \ne 0$

Thus, f has no local extrema.

$g(x, y) = x^2 + y^2$
$g_x(x, y) = 2x = 0$ (1)
$g_y(x, y) = 2y = 0$ (2)

The only solution of (1) and (2) is $(0, 0)$.

$f_{xx} = 2$, $f_{xy} = 0$, $f_{yy} = 2$

$f_{xx}(0, 0) \cdot f_{yy}(0, 0) - [f_{xy}(0, 0)]^2 = (2)(2) - (0)^2 = 4 > 0$,
and $f_{xx}(0, 0) = 2 > 0$.

Thus, $f(0, 0) = 0$ is a local minimum.

$h(x, y) = x^3 + y^3$
$h_x(x, y) = 3x^2 = 0$ (3)
$h_y(x, y) = 3y^2 = 0$ (4)

The only solution of (3) and (4) is $(0, 0)$.
$h_{xx} = 6x$, $h_{xy} = 0$, $h_{yy} = 6y$

$h_{xx}(0, 0) \cdot h_{yy}(0, 0) - [h_{xy}(0, 0)]^2 = (0)(0) - (0)^2 = 0$
Thus, test fails. h has no local extrema.

(B) $k(x, y) = x^n + y^n$
$k_x(x, y) = nx^{n-1} = 0$ (5)
$k_y(x, y) = ny^{n-1} = 0$ (6)
The only solution of (5) and (6) is $(0, 0)$.

$k_{xx}(x, y) = n(n - 1)x^{n-2}$
$k_{xy}(x, y) = 0$
$k_{yy}(x, y) = n(n - 1)y^{n-2}$

$k_{xx}(0, 0) \cdot k_{yy}(0, 0) - [k_{xy}(0, 0)]^2 = 0$ and the second derivative test
fails. But it is clear that for n even, $k(0, 0) = 0$, is a local
minimum for n odd k has no local extrema.

28. (A) $g(x, y) = e^{xy^2} + x^2 y^3 + 2$
$g_x(x, y) = y^2 e^{xy^2} + 2xy^3 = 0$ (1)
$g_y(x, y) = 2xye^{xy^2} + 3x^2 y^2 = 0$ (2)

It is clear that $(0, 0)$ is a critical point of f and
$f_{xx} = y^4 e^{xy^2} + 2y^3$, $f_{xy} = 2ye^{xy^2} + 2xy^3 e^{xy^2} + 6xy^2$,
$f_{yy} = 2xe^{xy^2} + 4x^2 y^2 e^{xy^2} + 6x^2 y$

$f_{xx}(0, 0) \cdot f_{yy}(0, 0) - [f_{xy}(0, 0)]^2 = (0)(0) - (0)^2 = 0$
So, the second derivative test fails.

(B) Cross-sections of f by the planes $y = 0$,
$x = 0$, $y = x$ and $y = -x$ are shown at the
right.

The cross-sections indicate that f has a
saddle point at $(0, 0)$.

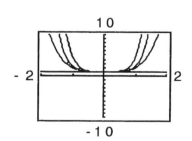

30. $C(x, y) = 2x^2 + 2xy + 3y^2 - 16x - 18y + 54$

$C_x(x, y) = 4x + 2y - 16 = 0$ (1)

$C_y(x, y) = 2x + 6y - 18 = 0$ (2)

Solving (1) and (2) for x and y, we obtain $x = 3$ and $y = 2$. Thus, (3, 2) is a critical point of $C(x, y)$.

$C_{xx} = 4$, $C_{xy} = 2$, $C_{yy} = 6$

$C_{xx}(3, 2) \cdot C_{yy}(3, 2) - [C_{xy}(3, 2)]^2 = (4)(6) - (2)^2 = 20 > 0$

and $C_{xx}(3, 2) = 4 > 0$.

Thus, $C(3, 2) = 12$ million dollars is a minimum cost; i.e. \$3,000,000 on labor and \$2,000,000 on automated equipment will result in minimum cost.

32. $x = 75 - 40p + 25q$ (Brand A)

$y = 80 + 20p - 30q$ (Brand B)

(A)

p	q	x	y
4	5	40	10
4	x	15	40

(B) The profit function P is given by:

$P(x, y) = R(x, y) - C(x, y) = px + qy - (2x + 3y)$
$$= (p - 2)x + (q - 3)y$$

In terms of p and q, P can be written as:

$P = (p - 2)(75 - 40p + 25q) + (q - 3)(80 + 20p - 30q)$

$\quad = 75p - 40p^2 + 25pq - 150 + 80p - 50q + 80q + 20pq$

$\qquad\qquad\qquad\qquad - 30q^2 - 240 - 60p + 90q$

$\quad = 95p - 40p^2 + 45pq + 120q - 30q^2 - 390$

Now, calculating P_p and P_q and setting these equal to 0, we have:

$P_p = 95 - 80p + 45q = 0$ (1)

$P_q = 45p + 120 + 60q = 0$ (2)

Solving (1) and (2), we obtain $p = 4$ and $q = 5$. Thus, (4, 5) is a critical point of P.

$P_{pp} = -80$, $P_{pq} = 45$, $P_{qq} = -60$

$P_{pp}(4, 5) \cdot P_{qq}(4, 5) - [P_{pq}(4, 5)]^2 = (-80)(-60) - (45)^2 = 2,775 > 0$

and $P_{pp}(4, 5) = -80 < 0$.

Thus, P has a maximum at (4, 5); the daily maximum profit is $P(4, 5) = 100$. Therefore, for $p = \$4$, $q = \$5$, the maximum daily profit is \$100.

34. The square of the distance from P to A is: $x^2 + y^2$.
The square of the distance from P to B is:
$(x - 6)^2 + (y - 9)^2 = x^2 - 12x + y^2 - 18y + 117$
The square of the distance from P to C is:
$(x - 9)^2 + (y - 0)^2 = x^2 - 18x + y^2 + 81$
Thus, we have: $P(x, y) = 3x^2 - 30x + 3y^2 - 18y + 198$

$$P_x = 6x - 30 = 0 \qquad\qquad P_y = 6y - 18 = 0$$
$$x = 5 \qquad\qquad y = 3$$

Therefore, $(5, 3)$ is a critical point.

$P_{xx} = 6$ and $P_{xx}(5, 3) = 6 > 0$
$P_{xy} = 0$ and $P_{xy}(5, 3) = 0$
$P_{yy} = 6$ and $P_{yy}(5, 3) = 6 > 0$
$P_{xx} \cdot P_{yy} - [P_{xy}]^2 = 6 \cdot 6 - (0)^2 = 36 > 0$

Therefore, P has a minimum at the point $(5, 3)$.

36. Let x = length, y = width, and z = height. Then $V = xyz = 72$ or $z = \dfrac{72}{xy}$. The surface area of the box is:

$$S = xy + 3xz + 3yz \quad \text{or} \quad S(x, y) = xy + \frac{216}{y} + \frac{216}{x}, \quad x > 0, \ y > 0$$

$$S_x = y - \frac{216}{x^2} = 0 \quad \text{or} \quad y = \frac{216}{x^2} \quad (1)$$

$$S_y = x - \frac{216}{y^2} = 0 \quad \text{or} \quad x = \frac{216}{y^2} \quad (2)$$

Using (2) in (1) we have:

$$y = \frac{216}{\left(\frac{216}{y^2}\right)^2} = \frac{y^4}{216}$$

$$y^4 - 216y = 0$$
$$y(y^3 - 216) = 0$$
$$y = 0, \quad y = 6$$

Since $y > 0$, $y = 0$ does not yield a critical point, so only $y = 6$ is acceptable. Setting $y = 6$ in (2) we find $x = 6$. Therefore, the critical point is $(6, 6)$. Now we have:

$S_{xx} = \dfrac{432}{x^3}$ and $S_{xx}(6, 6) = 2$

$S_{xy} = 1$ and $S_{xy}(6, 6) = 1$

$S_{yy} = \dfrac{432}{y^3}$ and $S_{yy}(6, 6) = 2$

$S_{xx}(6, 6) \cdot S_{yy}(6, 6) - [S_{xy}(6, 6)]^2 = (2)(2) - (1)^2 = 3 > 0$,
and $S_{xx}(6, 6) = 2 > 0$.

Thus, the dimensions that will require the least amount of material are:

length $x = 6$ inches; width $y = 6$ inches; height $z = \dfrac{72}{(6)(6)} = 2$ inches.

38. Let x = length of the box, y = width, and z = height.
Then $4(x + y + z) = 144$ or
$$x + y + z = 36 \qquad (1)$$
Volume = $V = xyz$ and from (1) $z = 36 - x - y$.
Thus, we have:
$$V(x, y, z) = xy(36 - x - y) = 36xy - x^2y - xy^2, \quad x > 0, \ y > 0$$
$$V_x = 36y - 2xy - y^2 = y(36 - 2x - y) = 0$$
$$\qquad\qquad\qquad 36 - 2x - y = 0 \qquad \text{(Since } y > 0\text{)}$$
$$V_y = 36x - x^2 - 2xy = x(36 - x - 2y) = 0$$
$$\qquad\qquad\qquad 36 - x - 2y = 0 \qquad \text{(Since } x > 0\text{)}$$
Therefore,
$$36 - 2x - y = 0 \qquad (2)$$
$$36 - x - 2y = 0 \qquad (3)$$
Solving (2) and (3) for x and y, we obtain $x = 12$ and $y = 12$. Thus, (12, 12) is the critical point.
$$V_{xx} = -2y \qquad\qquad \text{and} \quad V_{xx}(12, 12) = -24 < 0$$
$$V_{xy} = 36 - 2x - 2y \quad \text{and} \quad V_{xy}(12, 12) = -12$$
$$V_{yy} = -2x \qquad\qquad \text{and} \quad V_{yy}(12, 12) = -24$$
$$V_{xx}(12, 12) \cdot V_{yy}(12, 12) - [V_{xy}(12, 12)]^2 = (-24)(-24) - [-12]^2$$
$$= 432 > 0$$
Thus, the maximum volume of the box is obtained when $x = 12$, $y = 12$, and $z = 36 - x - y = 12$ inches. The box has dimensions:
length $x = 12$ inches; width $y = 12$ inches; height $z = 12$ inches.

EXERCISE 8-4

2. <u>Step 1.</u> Maximize $f(x, y) = 6xy$
Subject to: $g(x, y) = y - x - 6 = 0$

<u>Step 2.</u> $F(x, y, \lambda) = f(x, y) + \lambda g(x, y)$
$$= 6xy + \lambda(y - x - 6)$$

<u>Step 3.</u> $F_x = 6y - \lambda = 0 \qquad (1)$

$F_y = 6x + \lambda = 0 \qquad (2)$

$F_\lambda = y - x - 6 = 0 \qquad (3)$

From (1) and (2), we obtain:
$$x = -\frac{\lambda}{6}, \ y = \frac{\lambda}{6}$$
Substituting these into (3), we have:
$$\frac{\lambda}{6} + \frac{\lambda}{6} - 6 = 0$$
$$\lambda = 18.$$
Thus, the critical point is (-3, 3, 18).

<u>Step 4.</u> Since (-3, 3, 18) is the only critical point for F, we conclude that min $f(x, y) = f(-3, 3) = 6(-3) \cdot 3 = -54$.

4. <u>Step 1.</u>   Minimize $f(x, y) = 25 - x^2 - y^2$
Subject to: $g(x, y) = 2x + y - 10 = 0$

<u>Step 2.</u> $F(x, y, \lambda) = f(x, y) + \lambda g(x, y)$
$$= 25 - x^2 - y^2 + \lambda(2x + y - 10)$$

<u>Step 3.</u> $F_x = -2x + 2\lambda = 0$ (1)

$F_y = -2y + \lambda = 0$ (2)

$F_\lambda = 2x + y - 10 = 0$ (3)

From (1) and (2), we obtain:

$x = \lambda, \quad y = \dfrac{\lambda}{2}$

Substituting these into (3), we have:
$$2\lambda + \frac{\lambda}{2} - 10 = 0$$
$$5\lambda = 20$$
$$\lambda = 4$$

Thus, the critical point is $(4, 2, 4)$.

<u>Step 4.</u>   Since $(4, 2, 4)$ is the only critical point for F, we conclude that max $f(x, y) = f(4, 2) = 25 - 16 - 4 = 5$.

6. <u>Step 1.</u>   Maximize $f(x, y) = 6x + 5y + 24$ subject to $3x + 2y - 4 = 0$.

<u>Step 2.</u> $F(x, y, \lambda) = 6x + 5y + 24 + \lambda(3x + 2y - 4)$

<u>Step 3.</u> $F_x = 6 + 3\lambda = 0$ (1)

$F_y = 5 + 2\lambda = 0$ (2)

$F_\lambda = 3x + 2y - 4 = 0$ (3)

From (1), $\lambda = -2$, from (2), $\lambda = -2.5$. Thus, the system (1), (2), (3) does not have a solution.

8. <u>Step 1.</u>   Maximize and minimize $f(x, y) = x^2 - y^2$
Subject to: $g(x, y) = x^2 + y^2 - 25 = 0$

<u>Step 2.</u> $F(x, y, \lambda) = f(x, y) + \lambda g(x, y)$
$$= x^2 - y^2 + \lambda(x^2 + y^2 - 25)$$

<u>Step 3.</u> $F_x = 2x + 2\lambda x = 0$ (1)

$F_y = -2y + 2\lambda y = 0$ (2)

$F_\lambda = x^2 + y^2 - 25 = 0$ (3)

From (1), (2), and (3), we obtain the critical points
$(5, 0, -1), (-5, 0, 1), (0, 5, 1)$ and $(0, -5, -1)$.

Step 4. $f(5, 0) = 25$
$f(-5, 0) = 25$
$f(0, 5) = -25$
$f(0, -5) = -25$
Thus, max $f(x, y) = f(5, 0) = f(-5, 0) = 25$;
min $f(x, y) = f(0, 5) = f(0, -5) = -25$.

10. Let x and y be the required numbers.
Step 1. Maximize $f(x, y) = xy$
Subject to: $x - y = 10$ or $g(x, y) = x - y - 10 = 0$

Step 2. $F(x, y, \lambda) = xy + \lambda(x - y - 10)$

Step 3. $F_x = y + \lambda = 0$ \hspace{2cm} (1)

$F_y = x - \lambda = 0$ \hspace{2cm} (2)

$F_\lambda = x - y - 10 = 0$ \hspace{1.3cm} (3)

From (1) and (2), we obtain:
$x = \lambda, \ y = -\lambda$
Substituting these into (3), we have:
$\lambda = 5$
The critical point is $(5, -5, 5)$.

Step 4. Since $(5, -5, 5)$ is the only critical point for F, we conclude
that min $f(x, y) = f(5, -5) = -25$. Thus, the minimum
product is -25 when one number is 5 and the other is -5.

12. Step 1. Maximize $f(x, y, z) = xyz$
Subject to: $g(x, y, z) = 2x + y + 2z - 120 = 0$

Step 2. $F(x, y, z, \lambda) = xyz + \lambda(2x + y + 2z - 120)$

Step 3. $F_x = yz + 2\lambda = 0$ \hspace{2cm} (1)

$F_y = xz + \lambda = 0$ \hspace{2cm} (2)

$F_z = xy + 2\lambda = 0$ \hspace{2cm} (3)

$F_\lambda = 2x + y + 2z - 120 = 0$ \hspace{0.5cm} (4)

From (1) and (3), $x = z$; from (1) and (2), $y = 2x$.
Substituting for y and z in terms of x into (4), we have:
$2x + 2x + 2x - 120 = 0$ \ or \ $x = 20$
Thus, the critical point of F is $(20, 40, 20)$, which is the
only critical point.
Thus, max $f(x, y, z) = f(20, 40, 20) = 16,000$.

14. Step 1. Maximize and minimize $f(x, y, z) = 2x + 4y + 4z$
Subject to: $g(x, y, z) = x^2 + y^2 + z^2 - 9 = 0$

Step 2. $F(x, y, z, \lambda) = 2x + 4y + 4z + \lambda(x^2 + y^2 + z^2 - 9)$

<u>Step 3</u>. $F_x = 2 + 2\lambda x = 0$ (1)

$F_y = 4 + 2\lambda y = 0$ (2)

$F_z = 4 + 2\lambda z = 0$ (3)

$F_\lambda = x^2 + y^2 + z^2 - 9 = 0$ (4)

From (1), (2), and (3), we obtain:

$x = -\dfrac{1}{\lambda}$, $y = -\dfrac{2}{\lambda}$, $z = -\dfrac{2}{\lambda}$

Substituting these into (4), we have:

$$\dfrac{1}{\lambda^2} + \dfrac{4}{\lambda^2} + \dfrac{4}{\lambda^2} - 9 = 0$$

$$\dfrac{9}{\lambda^2} = 9$$

$$\lambda^2 = 1$$

$$\lambda = \pm 1$$

Thus, the critical points are $(-1, -2, -2, 1)$ and $(1, 2, 2, -1)$.

<u>Step 4</u>. $f(-1, -2, -2) = -2 - 8 - 8 = -18$

$f(1, 2, 2) = 2 + 8 + 8 = 18$

Thus, max $f(x, y, z) = f(1, 2, 2) = 18$;

min $f(x, y, z) = f(-1, -2, -2) = -18$.

16. <u>Step 1</u>. Maximize $f(x, y) = x + e^y$

Subject to: $x^2 + y^2 = 1$ or $g(x, y) = x^2 + y^2 - 1 = 0$

<u>Step 2</u>. $F(x, y, \lambda) = x + e^y + \lambda(x^2 + y^2 - 1)$

<u>Step 3</u>. $F_x = 1 + 2\lambda x = 0$ (1)

$F_y = e^y + 2\lambda y = 0$ (2)

$F_\lambda = x^2 + y^2 - 1 = 0$ (3)

From (1), $x = -\dfrac{1}{2\lambda}$ and from (3) $x^2 = 1 - y^2$. Combining these

two we have $(2\lambda)^2 = \dfrac{1}{1 - y^2}$. Substituting this for $(2\lambda)^2$ in (2),

we have:

$$e^y = -2\lambda y$$

$$e^{2y} = (2\lambda)^2 y^2 = \dfrac{y^2}{1 - y^2}$$

or

$$e^{-2y} = \dfrac{1 - y^2}{y^2} = \dfrac{1}{y^2} - 1$$

or

$$y^2(1 + e^{-2y}) = 1$$

Using a graphing utility to solve this equation, we get
$y_1 = -0.513$ and $y_2 = 0.930$. Then $x_1 = \pm\sqrt{1 - (-0.513)^2}$ and
$x_2 = \pm\sqrt{1 - (0.930)^2}$. In view of (1) and (2), x and y should have
the same sign. Thus, $x_1 = -\sqrt{1 + (-0.513)^2} = -0.858$ and
$x_2 = \sqrt{1 - (0.930)^2} = 0.367$.

Step 4. $f(0.367, 0.930) = 2.902$
$f(-0.858, -0.531) = -0.260$;
Thus, max $f(x, y) = f(0.367, 0.930) = 2.902$
         min $f(x, y) = f(-0.858, -0.531) = -0.260$

18. Step 1.   Minimize $f(x, y) = x^3 + 2y^3$
            Subject to $g(x, y) = 6x - 2y - 1 = 0$

Step 2. $F(x, y, \lambda) = x^3 + 2y^3 + \lambda(6x - 2y - 1)$

Step 3. $F_x = 3x^2 + 6\lambda = 0$ (1)

            $F_y = 6y^2 - 2\lambda = 0$ (2)
            $F_\lambda = 6x - 2y - 1 = 0$ (3)

From (1), $\lambda = -\dfrac{1}{2}x^2$, which implies λ is negative.

From (2), $\lambda = 3y^2$ which implies λ is positive.
Thus, (1) and (2) have no simultaneous solution.

20. The constraint $g(x, y) = 4x - y + 3 = 0$ implies $y = 4x + 3$. Substituting
for y in the function f, the problem reduces to minimizing the function
$f(x, 4x + 3)$, a function of just one independent variable.

22. Minimize $f(x, y) = x^2 + 2y^2$
Subject to: $g(x, y) = ye^{x^2} - 1 = 0$
(A) $ye^{x^2} - 1 = 0$; $ye^{x^2} = 1$ or $y = e^{-x^2}$
     Substituting $y = e^{-x^2}$ into $f(x, y)$, we get
       $h(x) = f(x, e^{-x^2}) = x^2 + 2e^{-2x^2}$

   Now, $h'(x) = 2x - 8xe^{-2x^2} = 2x(1 - 4e^{-2x^2})$
                     $= 2x(1 - 2e^{-x^2})(1 + 2e^{-x^2})$

   Critical values: $x = 0$, $1 - 2e^{-x^2} = 0$
                 $x = 0$, $x = \pm\sqrt{\ln 2} = \pm 0.833$

       From the constraint equation, $y = \dfrac{1}{2}$ when $x = \pm 0.833$.

       Min $f(x, y) = f(0.833, 0.5) = f(-0.833, 0.5) = 1.193$.

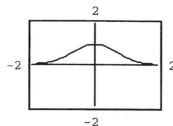

(B) $F(x, y, \lambda) = x^2 + 2y^2 + \lambda(ye^{x^2} - 1)$

$F_x = 2x + 2\lambda xye^{x^2} = 0$ (1)

$F_y = 4y + \lambda e^{x^2} = 0$ (2)

$F_\lambda = ye^{x^2} - 1 = 0$ (3)

From (3), $y = e^{-x^2}$ and from (2),
$\lambda = -4ye^{-x^2} = -4e^{-x^2}e^{-x^2} = -4e^{-2x^2}$.

Substituting these values into (1), we have:
$$2x + 2(-4e^{-2x^2})x(e^{-x^2})e^{x^2} = 0$$
$$2x - 8xe^{-2x^2} = 0$$
$$2x(1 - 4e^{-2x^2}) = 2x(1 - 2e^{-x^2})(1 + 2e^{-x^2}) = 0$$
$$x = 0, \quad x = \pm\sqrt{\ln 2}$$

Now, $y = 1$ when $x = 0$, and $y = \dfrac{1}{2}$ when $x = \pm\sqrt{\ln 2} = \pm 0.833$.

$$f(0, 1) = 0^2 + 2(1)^2 = 2$$
$$f(0.833, 0.5) = f(-0.833, 0.5) = 1.193$$

Thus, Min $f(x, y) = 1.193$.

24. <u>Step 1</u>.   Maximize production function $N(x, y) = 4xy - 8x$
               Subject to: $g(x, y) = x + y - 60 = 0$

<u>Step 2</u>. $F(x, y, \lambda) = 4xy - 8x + \lambda(x + y - 60)$

<u>Step 3</u>. $F_x = 4y - 8 + \lambda = 0$ (1)

              $F_y = 4x + \lambda = 0$ (2)
              $F_\lambda = x + y - 60 = 0$ (3)

              From (1) and (2), we obtain
              $x = -\dfrac{\lambda}{4}, \quad y = 2 - \dfrac{\lambda}{4}$

              Substituting these into (3), we have:
              $-\dfrac{\lambda}{4} + 2 - \dfrac{\lambda}{4} - 60 = 0$

$$\frac{\lambda}{2} = -58 \quad \text{and} \quad \lambda = -116$$

              The critical point is $(29, 31, -116)$.

<u>Step 4</u>.   Since $(29, 31, -116)$ is the only critical point for F, we
              conclude that:
              Max $N(x, y) = N(29, 31) = 4(29)(31) - 8(29) = 3,364$
              Thus, \$29,000 on labor and \$31,000 on materials will yield a
              maximum of 3,364 units of production per month.

26. (A) <u>Step 1</u>. Maximize the production function $N(x, y) = 10x^{0.6}y^{0.4}$
Subject to the constraint: $C(x, y) = 30x + 60y = 300,000$
i.e., $g(x, y) = 30x + 60y - 300,000 = 0$

<u>Step 2</u>. $F(x, y, \lambda) = 10x^{0.6}y^{0.4} + \lambda(30x + 60y - 300,000)$

<u>Step 3</u>. $F_x = 6x^{-0.4}y^{0.4} + 30\lambda = 0$ (1)

$F_y = 4x^{0.6}y^{-0.6} + 60\lambda = 0$ (2)

$F_\lambda = 30x + 60y - 300,000 = 0$ (3)

From (1), $\lambda = -\dfrac{y^{0.4}}{5x^{0.4}}$.   From (2), $\lambda = -\dfrac{x^{0.6}}{15y^{0.6}}$.

Thus, we obtain

$$-\frac{y^{0.4}}{5x^{0.4}} = -\frac{x^{0.6}}{15y^{0.6}} \quad \text{or} \quad x = 3y$$

Substituting into (3), we have:
$30(3y) + 60y - 300,000 = 0$
$$y = 2,000$$

Therefore, $x = 6,000$, $\lambda \approx -0.1289$, and the critical point is $(6,000, 2,000, -0.1289)$. Thus, we conclude that: Max $N(x, y) = N(6,000, 2,000) \approx 38,664$ units, and production is maximized with 6,000 labor units and 2,000 capital units are used.

(B) The marginal productivity of money is $-\lambda = 0.1289$. The increase in production if an additional \$80,000 is budgeted for production is: $0.1289(80,000) \approx 10,312$ units.

28. Let x = length, y = width, and z = height.

<u>Step 1</u>. Maximize volume $V = xyz$
Subject to: $g(x, y, z) = x + 2y + 2z - 120 = 0$

<u>Step 2</u>. $F(x, y, z, \lambda) = xyz + \lambda(x + 2y + 2z - 120)$

<u>Step 3</u>. $F_x = yz + \lambda = 0$ (1)

$F_y = xz + 2\lambda = 0$ (2)

$F_z = xy + 2\lambda = 0$ (3)

$F_\lambda = x + 2y + 2z - 120 = 0$ (4)

Solving this system of equations, (1)-(4), simultaneously, yields:
$x = 40$, $y = 20$, $z = 20$, $\lambda = -400$.
Thus, the critical point is $(40, 20, 20, -400)$.

Step 4. Since $(40, 20, 20, -400)$ is the only critical point for F:
max $V(x, y, z) = V(40, 20, 20) = 16,000$ cubic inches.
Thus, the dimensions that will maximize the volume of the
package are: length $x = 40$ inches; width $y = 20$ inches;
height $z = 20$ inches.

30. Step 1. Minimize $C(x, y) = x + 2y$
Subject to: $g(x, y) = 200xy - 25,600 = 0$

Step 2. $F(x, y, \lambda) = x + 2y + \lambda(200xy - 25,600)$

Step 3. $F_x = 1 + 200\lambda y = 0$ (1)

$F_y = 2 + 200\lambda x = 0$ (2)

$F_\lambda = 200xy - 25,600 = 0$ (3)

From (1) and (2), we have:

$$x = -\frac{1}{100\lambda} \quad \text{and} \quad y = -\frac{1}{200\lambda}$$

Substituting these into (3), we obtain:

$$200\left(\frac{1}{20,000\lambda^2}\right) - 25,600 = 0$$

$$\lambda^2 = \frac{1}{2,560,000}$$

or $$\lambda = \pm\frac{1}{1,600}$$

Since $x \geq 0$, $y \geq 0$, we have to take $\lambda = -\dfrac{1}{1,600}$.

Thus, $x = 16$, $y = 8$, and $\left(16, 8, -\dfrac{1}{1,600}\right)$ is the only critical

point for F.

Step 4. Since $\left(16, 8, -\dfrac{1}{1,600}\right)$ is the only critical point for F,

min $C(x, y) = C(16, 8) = 32$.
Therefore, $x = 16$ kg of type M food and $y = 8$ kg of type N food
will minimize the weekly cost at \$32.

EXERCISE 8-5

2.

	x_k	y_k	$x_k y_k$	x_k^2
	1	-2	-2	1
	2	-1	-2	4
	3	3	9	9
	4	5	20	16
Totals	10	5	25	30

Thus, $\displaystyle\sum_{k=1}^{4} x_k = 10$, $\displaystyle\sum_{k=1}^{4} y_k = 5$, $\displaystyle\sum_{k=1}^{4} x_k y_k = 25$, $\displaystyle\sum_{k=1}^{4} x_k^2 = 30$.

Substituting these values into formulas for slope and y intercept respectively, we have:

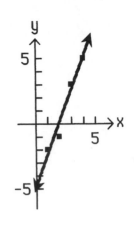

$$m = \frac{n\left(\sum\limits_{k=1}^{n} x_k y_k\right) - \left(\sum\limits_{k=1}^{n} x_k\right)\left(\sum\limits_{k=1}^{n} y_k\right)}{n\left(\sum\limits_{k=1}^{n} x_k^2\right) - \left(\sum\limits_{k=1}^{n} x_k\right)^2} = \frac{4(25) - (10)\,(5)}{4(30) - (10)^2} = 2.5$$

$$d = \frac{\sum\limits_{k=1}^{n} y_k - m\left(\sum\limits_{k=1}^{n} x_k\right)}{n} = \frac{5 - 2.5(10)}{4} = -5$$

Thus, the least squares line is $y = mx + d = 2.5x - 5$.

4.

x_k	y_k	$x_k y_k$	x_k^2
1	20	20	1
2	14	28	4
3	11	33	9
4	3	12	16
Totals 10	48	93	30

Thus, $\sum\limits_{k=1}^{4} x_k = 10$, $\sum\limits_{k=1}^{4} y_k = 48$, $\sum\limits_{k=1}^{4} x_k y_k = 93$, $\sum\limits_{k=1}^{4} x_k^2 = 30$.

Substituting these values in the system:

$$\left(\sum\limits_{k=1}^{n} x_k\right)m + nd = \sum\limits_{k=1}^{n} y_k$$

$$\left(\sum\limits_{k=1}^{n} x_k^2\right)m + \left(\sum\limits_{k=1}^{n} x_k\right)d = \sum\limits_{k=1}^{n} x_k y_k$$

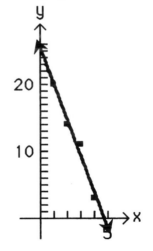

we have:

$$10m + 4d = 48$$
$$30m + 10d = 93$$

The solution of this system is $m = -5.4$ and $d = 25.5$. Thus, the least squares line is $y = mx + d = -5.4x + 25.5$.

6.

x_k	y_k	$x_k y_k$	x_k^2
1	2	2	1
2	3	6	4
3	3	9	9
4	2	8	16
Totals 10	10	25	30

Thus, $\sum\limits_{k=1}^{4} x_k = 10$, $\sum\limits_{k=1}^{4} y_k = 10$, $\sum\limits_{k=1}^{4} x_k y_k = 25$, $\sum\limits_{k=1}^{4} x_k^2 = 30$.

Substituting these values into formulas for m and d respectively (see Problem 2), we have:

$$m = \frac{4(25) - (10)(10)}{4(30) - (10)^2} = \frac{0}{20} = 0,$$

$$d = \frac{10 - 0(10)}{4} = \frac{10}{4} = 2.5$$

Thus, the least squares line is $y = mx + d = 2.5$.

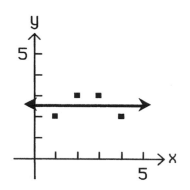

8.

x_k	y_k	$x_k y_k$	x_k^2
1	0	0	1
3	1	3	9
3	6	18	9
3	4	12	9
Totals 10	11	33	28

Thus, $\sum\limits_{k=1}^{4} x_k = 10$, $\sum\limits_{k=1}^{4} y_k = 11$, $\sum\limits_{k=1}^{4} x_k y_k = 33$, $\sum\limits_{k=1}^{4} x_k^2 = 28$.

Substituting these values into formulas for m and d respectively (see Problem 2), we have:

$$m = \frac{4(33) - (10)(11)}{4(28) - (10)^2} = 1.83, \quad d = \frac{11 - 1.83(10)}{4} = -1.83$$

Thus, the least squares line is $y = 1.83x - 1.83$.
When $x = 3$, $y = 1.83(3) - 1.83 = 3.66$.

10.

x_k	y_k	$x_k y_k$	x_k^2
-5	60	-300	25
0	50	0	0
5	30	150	25
10	20	200	100
15	15	225	225
Totals 25	175	275	375

Thus, $\sum\limits_{k=1}^{5} x_k = 25$, $\sum\limits_{k=1}^{5} y_k = 175$, $\sum\limits_{k=1}^{5} x_k y_k = 275$, $\sum\limits_{k=1}^{5} x_k^2 = 375$.

Substituting these values into formulas for m and d respectively (see Problem 2), we have:

$$m = \frac{5(275) - (25)(175)}{5(375) - (25)^2} = -2.4, \quad d = \frac{175 + 2.4(25)}{5} = 47$$

Thus, the least squares line is $y = -2.4x + 47$.
When $x = 20$, $y = -2.4(20) + 47 = -1$.

12.

x_k	y_k	$x_k y_k$	x_k^2
2	-4	-8	4
6	0	0	36
10	8	80	100
14	12	168	196
18	14	252	324
Totals 50	30	492	660

Thus, $\displaystyle\sum_{k=1}^{5} x_k = 50, \quad \sum_{k=1}^{5} y_k = 30, \quad \sum_{k=1}^{5} x_k y_k = 492, \quad \sum_{k=1}^{5} x_k^2 = 660.$

Substituting these values into formulas for m and d respectively (see Problem 2), we have:

$$m = \frac{5(492) - (50)(30)}{5(660) - (50)^2} = 1.2, \quad d = \frac{30 - 1.2(50)}{5} = -6$$

Thus, the least squares line is $y = 1.2x - 6$.
When $x = 15$, $y = 1.2(15) - 6 = 12$.

14.

x_k	y_k	$x_k y_k$	x_k^2
0	-15	0	0
2	-9	-18	4
4	-7	-28	16
6	-7	-42	36
8	-1	-8	64
12	11	132	144
14	13	182	196
16	19	304	256
18	25	450	324
20	33	660	400
Totals 100	62	1632	1440

Thus, $\displaystyle\sum_{k=1}^{10} x_k = 100, \quad \sum_{k=1}^{10} y_k = 62, \quad \sum_{k=1}^{10} x_k y_k = 1{,}632, \quad \sum_{k=1}^{10} x_k^2 = 1{,}440.$

Substituting these values into formulas for m and d respectively (see Problem 2), we have:

$$m = \frac{10(1632) - (100)(62)}{10(1440) - (100)^2} = 2.3, \quad d = \frac{62 - 2.3(100)}{10} = -16.8$$

Thus, the least squares line is $y = 2.3x - 16.8$.
When $x = 10$, $y = 2.3(10) - 16.8 = 6.2$.

16. Minimize

$$F(a, b, c) = (a - b + c + 2)^2 + (c - 1)^2$$
$$+ (a + b + c - 2)^2 + (4a + 2b + c)^2$$

$$F_a = 2(a - b + c + 2) + 2(a + b + c - 2) + 8(4a + 2b + c)$$

$$F_b = -2(a - b + c + 2) + 2(a + b + c - 2) + 4(4a + 2b + c)$$

$$F_c = 2(a - b + c + 2) + 2(c - 1) + 2(a + b + c - 2) + 2(4a + 2b + c)$$

The system is: $F_a(a, b, c) = 0$
$F_b(a, b, c) = 0$
$F_c(a, b, c) = 0$

or:
$36a + 16b + 12c = 0$
$16a + 12b + 4c = 8$
$12a + 4b + 8c = 2$

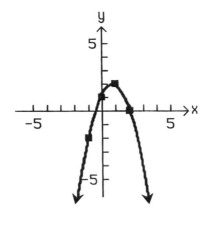

The solution is $(a, b, c) = (-1.25, 1.95, 1.15)$, which gives us the equation for the parabola shown at the right:

$y = ax^2 + bx + c$

or

$y = -1.25x^2 + 1.95x + 1.15$

The given points: $(-1, -2)$, $(0, 1)$, $(1, 2)$, and $(2, 0)$ also appear on the graph.

18. From formula (3) of the text:

$$b = \frac{\sum\limits_{k=1}^{n} y_k - a\left(\sum\limits_{k=1}^{n} x_k\right)}{n}$$

$$= \frac{1}{n}\sum\limits_{k=1}^{n} y_k - a\left(\frac{1}{n}\sum\limits_{k=1}^{n} x_k\right)$$

$$= \overline{y} - a\overline{x}$$

Thus, $\overline{y} = a\overline{x} + b$ and hence $(\overline{x}, \overline{y})$ satisfies the equation of the least squares.

20. (A) Consider the set of six data points $\{(-3, 2), (-2, 1), (-1, 2), (1, 1), (2, 2), (3, 1)\}$. The least squares line for this set of data is $y = -0.71x + 1.5$.

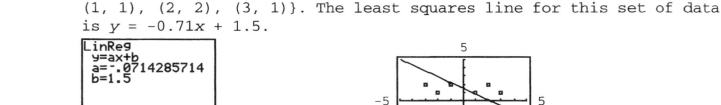

```
LinReg
 y=ax+b
 a=-.0714285714
 b=1.5
```

(B) Consider the data set $\{(-3, 0), (-2, 0), (-1, 0), (1, 6), (2, 0), (3, 0)\}$. The least squares line for this set of data is $y = 0.21x + 1$.

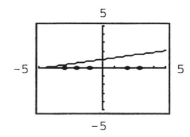

```
LinReg
 y=ax+b
 a=.2142857143
 b=1
```

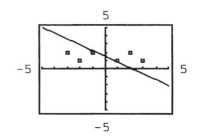

22. (A)
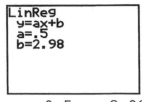

$y = 0.5x + 2.98$ $y = -0.11x^2 + 1.19x + 2.18$ $y = 3.24 + 1.29 \ln x$

(B)
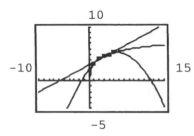

Conclusion: The logarithmic function best fits the data.

24. The normal equations form a system of 5 linear equations in the 5 variables a, b, c, d and e. The system can be solved using Gauss-Jordan elimination.

26. (A)

$y = 448.1x + 22,451$

(B) For $x = 22$,

$y = 448.1(22) + 22,451 \approx 32,309 \times 10^6$

Thus, the estimated annual production of beef in the United States in 2012 will be approximately $32,309 \times 10^6$ lbs.

28. (A)

x_k	y_k	$x_k y_k$	x_k^2
4.0	4.2	16.80	16.00
4.5	3.5	15.75	20.25
5.0	2.7	13.50	25.00
5.5	1.5	8.25	30.25
6.0	0.7	4.20	36.00
Totals 25	12.6	58.50	127.50

Thus, $\sum\limits_{k=1}^{5} x_k = 25$, $\sum\limits_{k=1}^{5} y_k = 12.6$, $\sum\limits_{k=1}^{5} x_k y_k = 85.50$, $\sum\limits_{k=1}^{5} x_k^2 = 127.50$.

Substituting these values in the formulas for m and d, we have:

$m = \dfrac{5(58.50) - (25)(12.6)}{5(127.50) - (25)^2} = -1.80$ and $d = \dfrac{12.6 + 1.80(25)}{5} = 11.52$

Thus, the least squares line is $y = -1.80x + 11.52$ which is the demand equation.

Let $C(y)$ be the cost for purchasing y cars. Then
$C(x) = 3y = 3(-1.80x + 11.52) = -5.40x + 34.56$

The revenue function $R(x) = xy = x(-1.80x + 11.52) = -1.80x^2 + 11.52$, and therefore the profit function $P(x)$ is given by:

$P(x) = R(x) - C(x) = -1.80x^2 + 16.92x + 34.56$
$P'(x) = -3.60x + 16.92$
Critical value(s) for P: $-3.60x + 16.92 = 0$

$$x = 4.70$$

$P''(x) = -3.60 < 0$, thus P has a maximum at $x = 4.70$.

Thus, the supermarket will achieve a maximum monthly profit if the price of each can of nuts is set at \$4.70.

30. (A)

h_k	d_k	$h_k d_k$	h_k^2
0	0	0	0
1	7	7	1
2	18	36	4
3	28	84	9
4	33	132	16
Totals 10	86	259	30

Thus, $\sum_{k=1}^{5} h_k = 10$, $\sum_{k=1}^{5} d_k = 86$, $\sum_{k=1}^{5} h_k d_k = 259$, $\sum_{k=1}^{5} h_k^2 = 30$.

Substituting these values into formulas for a and b, we have:

$a = \dfrac{5(259) - (10)(86)}{5(30) - (10)^2} = 8.7$, $b = \dfrac{86 - 8.7(10)}{5} = -0.2$

The least squares line for the data is $d = 8.7h - 0.2$.
Note: $d = 8h$ appears to be approximately correct.

(B) For $h = 3.5$, $d = 8.7(3.5) - 0.2 \approx 30$ days.

32. (A)

```
LinReg
y=ax+b
a=-2.259393939
b=177.4672727
```

$y = -2.26x + 177.47$

(B) For $x = 26$,
$y = -2.26(26) + 177.47 \approx 118.7 \times 10^6$
The estimated emissions of air pollutants in the U.S. in 2015 will be 118.7×10^6 short tons.

34. (A)

x_k	y_k	$x_k y_k$	x_k^2
2.0	1.5	3.00	4.00
2.2	1.5	3.30	4.84
2.4	1.6	3.84	5.76
2.7	1.8	4.86	7.29
2.9	2.1	6.09	8.41
3.0	2.3	6.90	9.00
3.1	2.5	7.75	9.61
3.3	2.9	9.57	10.89
3.4	3.2	10.88	11.56
3.7	3.5	12.95	13.69
Totals 28.7	22.9	69.14	85.05

Thus, $\sum_{k=1}^{10} x_k = 28.7$, $\sum_{k=1}^{10} y_k = 22.9$, $\sum_{k=1}^{10} x_k d_k = 69.14$, $\sum_{k=1}^{10} x_k^2 = 85.05$.

Substituting these values into the formulas for m (or a) and d (or b), we have:

$$m = \frac{10(69.14) - (28.7)(22.9)}{10(85.05) - (28.7)^2} \approx 1.27, \quad d = \frac{22.9 - 1.27(28.7)}{10} \approx -1.35$$

(<u>Note</u>: If we round m to 4 decimal places, i.e. $m = 1.2745$, then $d = -1.3678$ (to 4 decimal places). In this case, after rounding off for the second time to two decimal places, we get $m = 1.27$ and $d = -1.37$.)

The least squares line is $y = 1.27x - 1.35$.

(B) For $x = 3.5$, $y = 1.27(3.5) - 1.35 \approx 3.1$
Thus, an estimate of the college GPA for a student with high school GPA of 3.5 is 3.1.

(C) Here, $y = 2.7$ and we need to solve $2.7 = 1.27x - 1.35$ for x.
$$1.27x = 4.05$$
$$x = \frac{4.05}{1.27} \approx 3.2$$

Thus, an estimate of the high school GPA necessary for a college GPA of 2.7 is 3.2.

EXERCISE 8-6

2. (A) $\int 12x^2 y^3 \, dx = 12y^3 \int x^2 \, dx \qquad$ (y is treated as a constant.)

$$= 12y^3 \frac{x^3}{3} + E(y) \qquad \text{(The "constant" of integration is a function of y.)}$$

$$= 4y^3 x^3 + E(y)$$

(B) $\int_{-1}^{2} 12x^2 y^3 \, dx = 4y^3 (x^3) \Big|_{-1}^{2} = 4y^3(8 + 1) = 36y^3$

4. (A) $\int (4x + 6y + 5) \, dy = \int (4x + 5) \, dy + \int 6y \, dy$

$$= (4x + 5)y + 3y^2 + C(x)$$

(<u>Note</u>: x is treated as a constant and the "constant" of integration is a function of x.)

(B) $\int_{1}^{4} (4x + 6y + 5) \, dy = (4x + 5)(y) \Big|_{1}^{4} + (3y^2) \Big|_{1}^{4}$

$$= (4x + 5)(4 - 1) + 3(16 - 1)$$
$$= 12x + 60$$

6. (A) $\int \frac{x}{\sqrt{y + x^2}} \, dy = x \int (y + x^2)^{-1/2} \, dy$

Let $u = y + x^2$, then $du = dy$, and

$$\int \frac{x}{\sqrt{y + x^2}} = x \int u^{-1/2} \, du = x \frac{u^{1/2}}{\frac{1}{2}} + C(x)$$

$$= 2x\sqrt{y + x^2} + C(x)$$

(B) $\int_1^5 \dfrac{x}{\sqrt{y + x^2}}\, dy = 2x\left(\sqrt{y + x^2}\right)\Big|_1^5 = 2x\left(\sqrt{5 + x^2} - \sqrt{1 + x^2}\right)$

8. (A) $\displaystyle\int \dfrac{\ln x}{xy}\, dx = \dfrac{1}{y}\int \dfrac{\ln x}{x}\, dx$

Let $u = \ln x$, the $du = \dfrac{1}{x}\, dx$, and

$\displaystyle\int \dfrac{\ln x}{xy}\, dx = \dfrac{1}{y}\int \dfrac{\ln x}{x}\, dx = \dfrac{1}{y}\int (\ln x)\, \dfrac{1}{x}\, dx$

$= \dfrac{1}{y}\int u\, du$

$= \dfrac{1}{y} \cdot \dfrac{u^2}{2} + E(y)$

$= \dfrac{(\ln x)^2}{2y} + E(y)$

(B) $\displaystyle\int_1^e \dfrac{\ln x}{xy}\, dx = \dfrac{1}{2y}(\ln x)^2\Big|_1^e$

$= \dfrac{1}{2y}[(\ln e)^2 - (\ln 1)^2]$

$= \dfrac{1}{2y}$

10. $\displaystyle\int_0^1 \int_{-1}^2 12x^2 y^3\, dx\, dy = \int_0^1 \left[\int_{-1}^2 12x^2 y^3 dx\right] dy = \int_0^1 36y^3\, dy$ (see Problem 2)

$= 9y^4\Big|_0^1 = 9$

12. $\displaystyle\int_{-2}^3 \int_1^4 (4x + 6y + 5)\, dy\, dx = \int_{-2}^3 \left[\int_1^4 (4x + 6y + 5) dy\right] dx$

$= \int_{-2}^3 (12x + 60)\, dx$ (see Problem 4)

$= (6x^2 + 60x)\Big|_{-2}^3$

$= (54 + 180) - (24 - 120) = 330$

14. $\displaystyle\int_0^2 \int_1^5 \dfrac{x}{\sqrt{y + x^2}}\, dy\, dx = \int_0^2 \left[\int_1^5 \dfrac{x}{\sqrt{y + x^2}}\, dy\right] dx$

$= \int_0^2 2x\left(\sqrt{5 + x^2} - \sqrt{1 + x^2}\right) dx$ (see Problem 6)

$= \int_0^2 2x\sqrt{5 + x^2} - \int_0^2 2x\sqrt{1 + x^2}\, dx$

To compute $\displaystyle\int_0^2 2x\sqrt{5 + x^2}\, dx$ we make the substitution

$u = 5 + x^2,\ du = 2x\, dx$:

$$\int 2x\sqrt{5 + x^2}\, dx = \int u^{1/2}\, du = \frac{u^{3/2}}{3/2} + C = \frac{2u^{3/2}}{3} + C$$

$$= \frac{2}{3}(5 + x^2)^{3/2} + C$$

Thus, $\displaystyle\int_0^2 2x\sqrt{5 + x^2}\, dx = \frac{2}{3}(5 + x^2)^{3/2}\Big|_0^2 = \frac{2}{3}[(9)^{3/2} - (5)^{3/2}]$

$$= \frac{2}{3}(27 - 5\sqrt{5})$$

Similarly, $\displaystyle\int_0^2 2x\sqrt{1 + x^2}\, dx = \frac{2}{3}(1 + x^2)^{3/2}\Big|_0^2$

$$= \frac{2}{3}[(5)^{3/2} - 1]$$

$$= \frac{2}{3}(5\sqrt{5} - 1)$$

Therefore,

$$\int_0^2 \int_1^5 \frac{x}{\sqrt{y + x^2}}\, dx = \frac{2}{3}(27 - 5\sqrt{5}) - \frac{2}{3}(5\sqrt{5} - 1)$$

$$= \frac{2}{3}(27 - 5\sqrt{5} - 5\sqrt{5} + 1) = \frac{2}{3}(28 - 10\sqrt{5}) = \frac{56 - 20\sqrt{5}}{3}$$

16. $\displaystyle\int_1^{e^2} \int_1^e \frac{\ln x}{xy}\, dx\, dy = \int_1^{e^2}\left[\int_1^e \frac{\ln x}{xy}\, dx\right] dy$

$$= \int_1^{e^2} \frac{1}{2y}\, dy \quad \text{(see Problem 8)}$$

$$= \frac{1}{2}\ln y\Big|_1^{e^2} = \frac{1}{2}\ln e^2 = 1$$

18. $\displaystyle\iint\limits_R \sqrt{xy}\, dA = \int_1^4 \int_1^9 \sqrt{xy}\, dy\, dx = \int_1^4 \sqrt{x}\left(\frac{y^{3/2}}{3/2}\right)\Big|_1^9 dx$

$$= \int_1^4 \sqrt{x}\, \frac{2}{3}(9^{3/2} - 1)\, dx$$

$$= \frac{2}{3}(27 - 1)\int_1^4 x^{1/2}\, dx$$

$$= \frac{52}{3} \cdot \left(\frac{x^{3/2}}{3/2}\right)\Big|_1^4$$

$$= \frac{104}{9}(4^{3/2} - 1)$$

$$= \frac{104}{9}(8 - 1) = \frac{728}{9}$$

$$\iint\limits_{R} \sqrt{xy}\, dA = \int_{1}^{9} \int_{1}^{4} \sqrt{xy}\, dx\, dy = \int_{1}^{9} \sqrt{y} \left(\frac{x^{3/2}}{3/2}\right)\Bigg|_{1}^{4} dy$$

$$= \int_{1}^{9} \sqrt{y}\, \frac{2}{3}\, (4^{3/2} - 1)\, dy$$

$$= \frac{2}{3}\, (8 - 1) \int_{1}^{9} \sqrt{y}\, dy$$

$$= \frac{14}{3} \int_{1}^{9} y^{1/2}\, dy$$

$$= \frac{14}{3} \cdot \left(\frac{y^{3/2}}{3/2}\right)\Bigg|_{1}^{9}$$

$$= \frac{28}{9}\, (9^{3/2} - 1)$$

$$= \frac{28}{9}\, (27 - 1) = \frac{728}{9}$$

20.
$$\iint\limits_{R} xe^{y}\, dA = \int_{-2}^{3} \int_{0}^{2} xe^{y}\, dy\, dx = \int_{-2}^{3} (xe^{y})\Big|_{0}^{2} dx$$

$$= \int_{-2}^{3} x(e^{2} - 1)\, dx$$

$$= (e^{2} - 1) \int_{-2}^{3} x\, dx$$

$$= (e^{2} - 1) \left(\frac{x^{2}}{2}\right)\Bigg|_{-2}^{3}$$

$$= \frac{e^{2} - 1}{2}\, (9 - 4)$$

$$= \frac{5}{2}\, (e^{2} - 1)$$

$$\iint\limits_{R} xe^{y}\, dA = \int_{0}^{2} \int_{-2}^{3} xe^{y}\, dx\, dy = \int_{0}^{2} e^{y} \left(\frac{x^{2}}{2}\right)\Bigg|_{-2}^{3} dy$$

$$= \int_{0}^{2} e^{y}\, \frac{1}{2}\, (9 - 4)\, dy$$

$$= \frac{5}{2} \int_{0}^{2} e^{y}\, dy$$

$$= \frac{5}{2}\, (e^{y})\Big|_{0}^{2}$$

$$= \frac{5}{2}\, (e^{2} - 1)$$

22. Average value $= \dfrac{1}{[2 - (-1)\,]\,(4 - 1)} \displaystyle\iint_R (x^2 + y^2)\,dA$

$$= \frac{1}{9}\int_{-1}^{2}\int_{1}^{4} (x^2 + y^2)\,dy\,dx = \frac{1}{9}\int_{-1}^{2} \left(x^2 y + \frac{y^3}{3}\right)\Big|_{1}^{4}\,dx$$

$$= \frac{1}{9}\int_{-1}^{2} \left[\left(4x^2 + \frac{64}{3}\right) - \left(x^2 + \frac{1}{3}\right)\right]dx = \frac{1}{9}\int_{-1}^{2} (3x^2 + 21)\,dx$$

$$= \frac{1}{9}(x^3 + 21x)\Big|_{-1}^{2} = \frac{1}{9}[\,(8 + 42) - (-1 - 21)\,] = \frac{72}{9} = 8$$

24. Average value $= \dfrac{1}{[1 - (-1)\,]\,(2 - 0)} \displaystyle\iint_R x^2 y^3\,dA = \frac{1}{4}\int_{-1}^{1}\int_{0}^{2} x^2 y^3\,dy\,dx$

$$= \frac{1}{4}\int_{-1}^{1} x^2\left(\frac{y^4}{4}\right)\Big|_{0}^{2}\,dx = \frac{1}{4}\int_{-1}^{1} x^2\left(\frac{16}{4}\right)dx = \int_{-1}^{1} x^2\,dx$$

$$= \frac{1}{3}x^3\Big|_{-1}^{1} = \frac{2}{3}$$

26. $V = \displaystyle\iint_R (5 - x)\,dA = \int_{0}^{5}\int_{0}^{5} (5 - x)\,dy\,dx$

$$= \int_{0}^{5} (5 - x)(y)\Big|_{0}^{5}\,dx = \int_{0}^{5} 5(5 - x)\,dx = 5\left(-\frac{1}{2}(5 - x)^2\right)\Big|_{0}^{5}$$

$$= 5\left(0 + \frac{25}{2}\right) = \frac{125}{2}$$

28. $V = \displaystyle\iint_R e^{-x-y}\,dA = \int_{0}^{1}\int_{0}^{1} e^{-x-y}\,dy\,dx = \int_{0}^{1}\int_{0}^{1} e^{-x}e^{-y}\,dy\,dx$

$$= \int_{0}^{1} e^{-x}(-e^{-y})\Big|_{0}^{1}\,dx = \int_{0}^{1} e^{-x}(-e^{-1} + 1)\,dx = (1 - e^{-1})\int_{0}^{1} e^{-x}\,dx$$

$$= (1 - e^{-1})(-e^{-x})\Big|_{0}^{1}$$

$$= (1 - e^{-1})^2$$

30. $\displaystyle\iint_R xye^{x^2 y}\,dA = \int_{1}^{2}\left[\int_{0}^{1} xye^{x^2 y}dx\right]dy$

To compute the inner integral, we let $u = x^2 y$, then $du = 2xy\,dx$. Thus,

$$\int xye^{x^2 y}\,dx = \int e^{x^2 y}\frac{2}{2}xy\,dx = \frac{1}{2}\int e^u\,du$$

$$= \frac{1}{2}e^u + E(y)$$

$$= \frac{1}{2}e^{x^2 y} + E(y)$$

and

$$\int_{0}^{1} xye^{x^2 y}\,dx = \frac{1}{2}e^{x^2 y}\Big|_{0}^{1} = \frac{1}{2}(e^y - 1).$$

Therefore,

$$\iint\limits_R xye^{x^2y}\,dA = \int_1^2 \frac{1}{2}(e^y - 1)\,dy$$

$$= \frac{1}{2}(e^y - 1)\Big|_1^2 = \frac{1}{2}[(e^2 - 2) - (e - 1)]$$

$$= \frac{1}{2}(e^2 - e - 1)$$

32. $\displaystyle \iint\limits_R \frac{2x + 2y}{1 + 4y + y^2}\,dA = \int_0^1 \left[\int_1^3 \frac{2x + 2y}{1 + 4y + y^2}\,dx\right] dy$

$$= \int_0^1 \left(\frac{x^2 + 2xy}{1 + 4y + y^2}\right)\Big|_1^3 dy$$

$$= \int_0^1 \frac{1}{1 + 4y + y^2}[(9 + 6y) - (1 + 2y)]\,dy$$

$$= \int_0^1 \frac{4y + 8}{1 + 4y + y^2}\,dy$$

Let $u = 1 + 4y + y^2$, then $du = (4 + 2y)\,dy$, and

$$\int \frac{4y + 8}{1 + 4y + y^2}\,dy = 2\int \frac{(4 + 2y)}{1 + 4y + y^2}\,dy = 2\int \frac{1}{u}\,du = 2\ln|u| + C$$

$$= 2\ln|1 + 4y + y^2| + C$$

Therefore,

$$\iint\limits_R \frac{2x + 2y}{1 + 4y + y^2}\,dA = 2\ln|1 + 4y + y^2|\Big|_0^1$$

$$= 2(\ln 6 - \ln 1) = 2\ln 6$$

34. (A) $\underline{f(x, y) = x + y}$:

Average value $= \dfrac{1}{(1 - 0)(1 - 0)} \displaystyle\int_0^1 \int_0^1 (x + y)\,dx\,dy$

$$= \int_0^1 \left(\frac{x^2}{2} + yx\right)\Big|_0^1 dy = \int_0^1 \left(\frac{1}{2} + y\right)dy$$

$$= \left(\frac{1}{2}y + \frac{1}{2}y^2\right)\Big|_0^1 = 1$$

$\underline{g(x, y) = x^2 + y^2}$:

Average value $= \displaystyle\int_0^1 \int_0^1 (x^2 + y^2)\,dx\,dy$

$$= \int_0^1 \left(\frac{x^3}{3} + y^2x\right)\Big|_0^1 dy$$

$$= \int_0^1 \left(\frac{1}{3} + y^2\right)dy = \left(\frac{y}{3} + \frac{y^3}{3}\right)\Big|_0^1 = \frac{2}{3}$$

$\underline{h(x, y) = x^3 + y^3}$:

Average value $= \int_0^1 \int_0^1 (x^3 + y^3)\,dx\,dy$

$= \int_0^1 \left(\dfrac{x^4}{4} + y^3 x\right)\Big|_0^1 dy$

$= \int_0^1 \left(\dfrac{1}{4} + y^3\right)dy = \left(\dfrac{y}{4} + \dfrac{y^4}{4}\right)\Big|_0^1 = \dfrac{1}{2}$

(B) $\underline{k(x, y) = x^n + y^n}$:

Average value $= \dfrac{2}{n + 1}$, which decreases as n increases.

(C) $\underline{k(x, y) = x^n + y^n}$; $R_2 = \{(x, y) \mid 0 \le x \le 2,\ 0 \le y \le 2\}$

Average value $= \dfrac{1}{(2 - 0)(2 - 0)} \int_0^2 \int_0^2 (x^n + y^n)\,dx\,dy$

$= \dfrac{1}{4} \int_0^2 \left(\dfrac{x^{n+1}}{n + 1} + y^n x\right)\Big|_0^2 dy$

$= \dfrac{1}{4} \int_0^2 \left(\dfrac{2^{n+1}}{n + 1} + 2y^n\right)dy$

$= \dfrac{1}{4}\left(\dfrac{2^{n+1}}{n + 1} y + \dfrac{2y^{n+1}}{n + 1}\right)\Big|_0^2$

$= \dfrac{1}{4}\left(\dfrac{2^{n+2}}{n + 1} + \dfrac{2^{n+2}}{n + 1}\right) = \dfrac{2^{n+1}}{n + 1}$,

which increases as n increases.

36. Let $2a$ be the length of a side of the square. Then

Average value $= \dfrac{1}{(2a)(2a)} \int_{-a}^a \int_{-a}^a x^2 e^y\,dy\,dx$

$= \dfrac{1}{4a^2} \int_{-a}^a x^2 (e^y)\Big|_{-a}^a dx$

$= \dfrac{(e^a - e^{-a})}{4a^2} \int_{-a}^a x^2\,dx$

$= \dfrac{(e^a - e^{-a})}{4a^2} \cdot \left(\dfrac{x^3}{3}\right)\Big|_{-a}^a$

$= \dfrac{a^3(e^a - e^{-a})}{6a^2} = \dfrac{1}{6} a(e^a - e^{-a})$

Given Average value $= 100$: we now have to solve $100 = \dfrac{1}{6} a(e^a - e^{-a})$

for a. Using a graphing utility with $y_1 = x(e^x - e^{-x})$, $y_2 = 600$, $0 \le x \le 15$, $0 \le y \le 1{,}000$ the intersection of y_1 and y_2 has x-coordinate approximately equal to 4.82. Thus, $a = 4.82$ and the side of the square S is $2(4.82) = 9.64$.

38. $S(x, y) = \dfrac{y}{1 - x}$, $0.7 \le x \le 0.9$, $6 \le y \le 10$.

The average total amount of spending is given by:

$$T = \frac{1}{(0.9 - 0.7)(10 - 6)} \iint\limits_{R} \frac{y}{1 - x} \, dA = \frac{1}{0.8} \int_{0.7}^{0.9} \int_{6}^{10} \frac{y}{1 - x} \, dy \, dx$$

$$= \frac{1}{0.8} \int_{0.7}^{0.9} \left[\frac{1}{1 - x} \cdot \frac{y^2}{2} \right]_{6}^{10} dx = \frac{1}{0.8} \int_{0.7}^{0.9} \frac{1}{1 - x} \left(\frac{100}{2} - \frac{36}{2} \right) dx$$

$$= \frac{32}{0.4} \int_{0.7}^{0.9} \frac{1}{1 - x} \, dx = 40 \left[-\ln(1 - x) \right]_{0.7}^{0.9}$$

$$= 40 \left[-\ln(0.1) + \ln(0.3) \right] = 40 \ln 3 \approx 43.9 \text{ billion dollars.}$$

40. $N(x, y) = x^{0.5} y^{0.5}$, $10 \le x \le 30$ and $1 \le y \le 3$.

$$\text{Average value} = \frac{1}{(30 - 10)(3 - 1)} \int_{10}^{30} \int_{1}^{3} x^{0.5} y^{0.5} \, dy \, dx$$

$$= \frac{1}{40} \int_{10}^{30} x^{0.5} \left(\frac{y^{3/2}}{3/2} \right) \Big|_{1}^{3} dx$$

$$= \frac{1}{60} \int_{10}^{30} x^{0.5} (3\sqrt{3} - 1) \, dx$$

$$= \frac{(3\sqrt{3} - 1)}{60} \int_{10}^{30} x^{0.5} \, dx$$

$$= \frac{(3\sqrt{3} - 1)}{60} \left(\frac{x^{3/2}}{3/2} \right) \Big|_{10}^{30}$$

$$= \frac{(3\sqrt{3} - 1)}{90} (30\sqrt{30} - 1) \approx 6.187 \text{ or } 6,187$$

42. $C = 8 - \dfrac{1}{10} d^2 = 8 - \dfrac{1}{10}(x^2 + y^2)$, $-6 \le x \le 6$, $-6 \le y \le 6$

$$\text{Average Concentration} = \frac{1}{144} \int_{-6}^{6} \int_{-6}^{6} \left[8 - \frac{1}{10}(x^2 + y^2) \right] dx \, dy$$

$$= \frac{1}{144} \int_{-6}^{6} \left[8x - \frac{x^3}{30} - \frac{xy^2}{10} \right] \Big|_{-6}^{6} dy$$

$$= \frac{1}{144} \int_{-6}^{6} \left\{ \left[48 - \frac{216}{30} - \frac{6y^2}{10} \right] - \left[-48 + \frac{216}{30} + \frac{6y^2}{10} \right] \right\} dy$$

$$= \frac{1}{144} \int_{-6}^{6} \left\{ 48 - \frac{216}{30} - \frac{6y^2}{10} + 48 - \frac{216}{30} - \frac{6y^2}{10} \right\} dy$$

$$= \frac{1}{72} \int_{-6}^{6} \left\{ 48 - \frac{216}{30} - \frac{6y^2}{10} \right\} dy$$

$$= \frac{1}{72} \int_{-6}^{6} \left\{ \frac{1224}{30} - \frac{6y^2}{10} \right\} dy$$

$$= \frac{1}{72} \left(\frac{1224}{30} y - \frac{2y^3}{10} \right)\Big|_{-6}^{6}$$

$$= \frac{1}{72} \left[\left(\frac{1224}{5} - \frac{432}{10} \right) - \left(-\frac{1224}{5} + \frac{432}{10} \right) \right]$$

$$= \frac{1}{36} \left[\frac{1224}{5} - \frac{432}{10} \right] = \frac{2448 - 432}{360} = \frac{2016}{360} = \frac{28}{5}$$

44. $C = 100 - 3d^2 = 100 - 3(x^2 + y^2)$, $-4 \leq x \leq 4$, $-2 \leq y \leq 2$

Average concentration $= \frac{1}{32} \int_{-4}^{4} \int_{-2}^{2} [100 - 3(x^2 + y^2)] \, dy \, dx$

$$= \frac{1}{32} \int_{-4}^{4} [100y - 3x^2 y - y^3]\Big|_{-2}^{2} dx$$

$$= \frac{1}{32} \int_{-4}^{4} [(200 - 6x^2 - 8) - (-200 + 6x^2 + 8)] \, dx$$

$$= \frac{1}{32} \int_{-4}^{4} (400 - 12x^2 - 16) \, dx$$

$$= \frac{1}{32} \int_{-4}^{4} (384 - 12x^2) \, dx$$

$$= \frac{1}{8} \int_{-4}^{4} (96 - 3x^2) \, dx$$

$$= \frac{1}{8} (96x - x^3)\Big|_{-4}^{4}$$

$$= \frac{1}{8} [(384 - 64) - (-384 + 64)]$$

$$= \frac{1}{8} [640] = 80 \text{ part per million}$$

46. $L = 0.0000133xy^2$, $2,000 \leq x \leq 2,500$, $40 \leq y \leq 50$

Average length $= \frac{1}{5,000} \int_{2000}^{2500} \int_{40}^{50} 0.0000133xy^2 \, dy \, dx$

$$= \frac{1}{5,000} \int_{2000}^{2500} \left(\frac{0.0000133}{3} xy^3 \right)\Big|_{40}^{50} dx$$

$$= \frac{0.0000133}{15,000} \int_{2000}^{2500} x(125,000 - 64,000) \, dx$$

$$= \frac{(0.0000133)(61)}{15} \int_{2000}^{2500} x \, dx$$

$$= \frac{(0.0000133)(61)}{15} \left(\frac{x^2}{2} \right)\Big|_{2000}^{2500}$$

$$= \frac{(0.0000133)(61)}{30}(6,250,000 - 4,000,000)$$

$$= \frac{(0.0000133)(61)}{30}(225)10^4$$

$$= \frac{(0.0133)(61)(225)}{3}$$

$$= (0.0133)(61)(75) \approx 60.85 \text{ feet}$$

48. $Q(x, y) = 100\dfrac{x}{y}, \quad 6 \le x \le 14, \quad 8 \le y \le 10$

$$\text{Average intelligence} = \frac{1}{16}\int_6^{14}\int_8^{10} 100\left(\frac{x}{y}\right) dy \, dx$$

$$= \frac{25}{4}\int_6^{14} (x \ln y)\Big|_8^{10} dx$$

$$= \frac{25}{4}\ln\left(\frac{10}{8}\right)\int_6^{14} x \, dx$$

$$= \frac{25}{4}\ln\left(\frac{5}{4}\right)\left(\frac{x^2}{2}\right)\Big|_6^{14}$$

$$= \frac{25}{4}\ln\left(\frac{5}{4}\right)\left(\frac{196}{2} - \frac{36}{2}\right)$$

$$= \frac{25}{4}\ln\left(\frac{5}{4}\right)(80) = 500\ln\left(\frac{5}{4}\right) \approx 111.6$$

CHAPTER 9   TRIGONOMETRIC FUNCTIONS

2. $60° = \dfrac{\pi}{3}$ radians

4. $135° = \dfrac{3\pi}{4}$ radians

6. $360° = 2\pi$ radians

8. III

10. II

12. I

14. $\cos 180° = -1$
(see Figure 6)

16. $\sin\left(-\dfrac{3\pi}{2}\right) = 1$
(see Figure 6)

18. $\cos 360° = 1$
(see Figure 6)

20. $\dfrac{\pi}{4}$ radians $= \dfrac{180°}{4}$
$= 45°$

22. 3π radians $= 3(180°)$
$= 540°$

24. $\dfrac{5\pi}{3}$ radians $= \dfrac{5(180°)}{3}$
$= 300°$

26. $\sin 45° = \dfrac{\sqrt{2}}{2}$
(see Figure 7)

28. $\cos\left(-\dfrac{\pi}{6}\right) = \dfrac{\sqrt{3}}{2}$
(see Figure 7)

30. $\sin\left(\dfrac{5\pi}{6}\right) = \dfrac{1}{2}$
(see Figure 7)

32. $\cos 13 = 0.9074$

34. $\sin 325.9 = -0.7350$

36. $\cos(-502.3) = 0.9377$

38. $\theta° = 18°$
Degree-Radian Conversion
Formula:
$$\dfrac{\theta_{deg}}{180°} = \dfrac{\theta_{rad}}{\pi_{rad}}$$
$$\dfrac{18°}{180°} = \dfrac{\theta}{\pi \text{ radians}}$$
$$\theta = \dfrac{18\pi}{180} = \dfrac{\pi}{10} \text{ radians}$$

40. Using Degree-Radian Conversion
Formula:
$$\dfrac{\theta°}{180°} = \dfrac{\dfrac{\pi}{60}}{\pi}$$
Thus, $\dfrac{\pi}{60}$ radians $= \dfrac{180°}{60°} = 3°$

42. $\cot 45° = \dfrac{\cos 45°}{\sin 45°}$
From Figure 7:
$$\cot 45° = \dfrac{1/\sqrt{2}}{1/\sqrt{2}} = 1$$

44. $\csc\dfrac{\pi}{6} = \dfrac{1}{\sin\dfrac{\pi}{6}} = \dfrac{1}{\dfrac{1}{2}}$ (From Figure 7)
$$= 2$$

46. $\tan\dfrac{\pi}{6} = \dfrac{\sin\dfrac{\pi}{6}}{\cos\dfrac{\pi}{6}} = \dfrac{1/2}{\sqrt{3}/2} = \dfrac{1}{\sqrt{3}}$ or $\dfrac{\sqrt{3}}{3}$

48. (A) From Problem 47:

$(\sin x)^2 + (\cos x)^2 = 1$ (1)

Divide both sides of (1) by $(\cos x)^2$:

$$\frac{(\sin x)^2}{(\cos x)^2} + 1 = \frac{1}{(\cos x)^2}$$

Thus,

$$(\tan x)^2 + 1 = (\sec x)^2$$

(B) Divide both sides of (1) by $(\sin x)^2$:

$$1 + \frac{(\cos x)^2}{(\sin x)^2} = \frac{1}{(\sin x)^2}$$

Thus,

$$1 + (\cot x)^2 = (\csc x)^2$$

50. $y = -0.5 \cos 2x;$
$0 \le x \le 2\pi, \ -0.5 \le y \le 0.5$

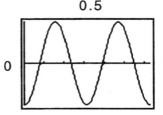

52. $y = 6 + 6 \sin \dfrac{\pi x}{26};$
$0 \le x \le 104, \ 0 \le y \le 12$

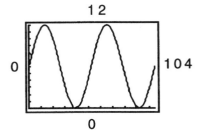

54. $R(t) = 4 - 3 \cos \dfrac{\pi t}{6}, \ 0 \le t \le 24$

(A) $R(0) = 4 - 3 \cos(0) = 4 - 3(1) = 4 - 3 = 1$

$R(2) = 4 - 3 \cos \dfrac{2\pi}{6} = 4 - 3 \cos \dfrac{\pi}{3} = 4 - 3\left(\dfrac{1}{2}\right) = 2.5$

$R(3) = 4 - 3 \cos \dfrac{3\pi}{6} = 4 - 3 \cos \dfrac{\pi}{2} = 4 - 3(0) = 4$

$R(18) = 4 - 3 \cos \dfrac{18\pi}{6} = 4 - 3 \cos(3\pi) = 4 - 3(-1) = 7$

(B) $R(5) = 4 - 3 \cos \dfrac{5\pi}{6} \approx 6.6$

$R(23) = 4 - 3 \cos \dfrac{23\pi}{6} \approx 1.46$

Thus, the soft drink company will have revenues of \$6.6 million for 1 month of sales 5 months after February 1 and revenues of \$1.4 million for 1 month of sales 23 months after February 1.

(C)

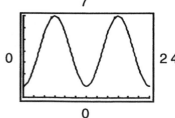

56. $P(n) = 1 + \cos \dfrac{\pi n}{26}$, $0 \le n \le 104$

(A) $P(0) = 1 + \cos(0) = 1 + 1 = 2$

$P(39) = 1 + \cos\left(\dfrac{39\pi}{26}\right) = 1 + \cos \dfrac{3\pi}{2} = 1$

$P(52) = 1 + \cos\left(\dfrac{52\pi}{26}\right) = 1 + \cos 2\pi = 1 + 1 = 2$

$P(65) = 1 + \cos\left(\dfrac{65\pi}{26}\right) = 1 + \cos\left(\dfrac{5\pi}{2}\right) = 1 + \cos \dfrac{\pi}{2} = 1 + 0 = 1$

(B) $P(10) = 1 + \cos \dfrac{10\pi}{26} = 1 + \cos \dfrac{5\pi}{13} \approx 1.35$

$P(95) = 1 + \cos \dfrac{95\pi}{26} \approx 1.46$

Thus, the amount of sulfur dioxide pollutant released into the atmosphere in a large city during the 10th week after January 1 is 1.35 tons and during the 95th week after January 1, 1.46 tons.

(C)

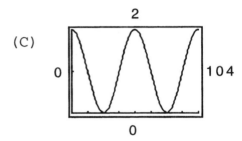

EXERCISE 9-2

2. $\dfrac{d}{dw} \sin w = \cos w$

4. $\dfrac{d}{dx} \cos(x^2 - 1) = -\sin(x^2 - 1)\, \dfrac{d}{dx}(x^2 - 1)$

$\qquad\qquad\qquad\qquad = -\sin(x^2 - 1)(2x)$

$\qquad\qquad\qquad\qquad = -2x \sin(x^2 - 1)$

6. $\dfrac{d}{du} u \cos u = \left(\dfrac{d}{du} u\right)\cos u + u\, \dfrac{d}{du} \cos u$

$\qquad\qquad = \cos u + u(-\sin u) = \cos u - u \sin u$

8. $\dfrac{d}{dx} \dfrac{\sin x}{\cos x} = \dfrac{\left(\dfrac{d}{dx} \sin x\right)\cos x - \left(\dfrac{d}{dx} \cos x\right)\sin x}{(\cos x)^2}$

$\qquad\qquad = \dfrac{(\cos x)(\cos x) - (-\sin x)(\sin x)}{(\cos x)^2} = \dfrac{(\cos x)^2 + (\sin x)^2}{(\cos x)^2}$

$\qquad\qquad\qquad\qquad\qquad = \dfrac{1}{(\cos x)^2}$

10. $\dfrac{d}{dx}(\cos x)^8 = 8(\cos x)^7 \left(\dfrac{d}{dx} \cos x\right)$

$\qquad\qquad = 8(\cos x)^7 (-\sin x) = -8(\cos x)^7 \sin x$

12. $\dfrac{d}{dx}\sqrt{\cos x} = \dfrac{d}{dx}(\cos x)^{1/2} = \dfrac{1}{2}(\cos x)^{-1/2}\left(\dfrac{d}{dx}\cos x\right)$

$$= \dfrac{1}{2}\cdot\dfrac{1}{(\cos x)^{1/2}}(-\sin x)$$

$$= \dfrac{-\sin x}{2\sqrt{\cos x}}$$

14. $\dfrac{d}{dx}\sin\sqrt{x} = (\cos\sqrt{x})\left(\dfrac{d}{dx}\sqrt{x}\right)$

$$= (\cos\sqrt{x})\left(\dfrac{d}{dx}x^{1/2}\right) = (\cos\sqrt{x})\left(\dfrac{1}{2}x^{-1/2}\right)$$

$$= \dfrac{\cos\sqrt{x}}{2x^{1/2}} = \dfrac{\cos\sqrt{x}}{2\sqrt{x}}$$

16. $f(x) = \cos x$
$f'(x) = -\sin x$

The slope of the graph of f at $x = \dfrac{\pi}{4}$ is: $f'\left(\dfrac{\pi}{4}\right) = -\sin\dfrac{\pi}{4} = -\dfrac{\sqrt{2}}{2}$.

18. f is decreasing on $\left[-\pi, -\dfrac{\pi}{2}\right]$ and $\left[\dfrac{\pi}{2}, \pi\right]$ ($f'(x) < 0$); f is increasing on

$\left[-\dfrac{\pi}{2}, \dfrac{\pi}{2}\right]$ ($f'(x) > 0$); f has a local minimum at $x = -\dfrac{\pi}{2}$ and a local

maximum at $x = \dfrac{\pi}{2}$; the graph of f is concave upward

on $[-\pi, 0]$ (f' is increasing on $[-\pi, 0]$); the graph
of f is concave downward on $[0, \pi]$ (f' is
decreasing on $[0, \pi]$); $f(x) = \sin x$, $f'(x) = \cos x$.

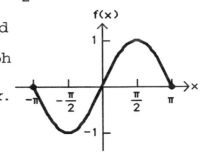

20. $\dfrac{d}{dx}\cot x = \dfrac{d}{dx}\dfrac{\cos x}{\sin x} = \dfrac{\left(\dfrac{d}{dx}\cos x\right)\sin x - \left(\dfrac{d}{dx}\sin x\right)\cos x}{(\sin x)^2}$

$$= \dfrac{(-\sin x)\sin x - (\cos x)\cos x}{(\sin x)^2}$$

$$= \dfrac{-(\sin x)^2 - (\cos x)^2}{(\sin x)^2}$$

$$= \dfrac{-[(\sin x)^2 + (\cos x)^2]}{(\sin x)^2} = -\dfrac{1}{(\sin x)^2}$$

22. $\dfrac{d}{dx} \cos\sqrt{x^4 - 1} = \left(-\sin\sqrt{x^4 - 1}\right)\left(\dfrac{d}{dx}\sqrt{x^4 - 1}\right)$

$$= -\sin\sqrt{x^4 - 1}\left(\dfrac{d}{dx}(x^4 - 1)^{1/2}\right)$$

$$= -\sin\sqrt{x^4 - 1}\left(\dfrac{1}{2}(x^4 - 1)^{-1/2}\dfrac{d}{dx}(x^4 - 1)\right)$$

$$= -\sin\sqrt{x^4 - 1}\left(\dfrac{1}{2}(x^4 - 1)^{-1/2}(4x^3)\right)$$

$$= -2\,\sin\sqrt{x^4 - 1}\left(\dfrac{x^3}{(x^4 - 1)^{1/2}}\right) = \dfrac{-2x^3\,\sin\sqrt{x^4 - 1}}{\sqrt{x^4 - 1}}$$

24. $f(x) = e^x \cos x$

$f'(x) = \left(\dfrac{d}{dx}e^x\right)\cos x + e^x\left(\dfrac{d}{dx}\cos x\right)$

$\qquad = e^x \cos x + e^x(-\sin x) = e^x \cos x - e^x \sin x = e^x(\cos x - \sin x)$

$f''(x) = \left(\dfrac{d}{dx}e^x\right)(\cos x - \sin x) + e^x\dfrac{d}{dx}(\cos x - \sin x)$

$\qquad = e^x(\cos x - \sin x) + e^x(-\sin x - \cos x)$

$\qquad = e^x(\cos x - \sin x - \sin x - \cos x)$

$\qquad = -2e^x \sin x$

26. $y = -x \cos \pi x;$

$\quad 0 \le x \le 9,\ -9 \le y \le 9$

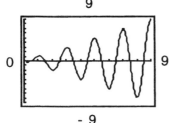

28. $y = \dfrac{\sin \pi x}{0.5x};$

$\quad 0 \le x \le 8,\ -2 \le y \le 3$

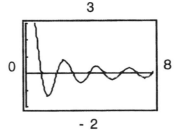

30. $y = e^{-0.2x} \cos \pi x,$
$\quad 0 \le x \le 10,\ -1 \le y \le 1$

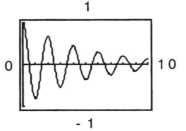

32. $R(t) = 4 - 3\cos\dfrac{\pi t}{6},\ 0 \le t \le 24$

(A) $R'(t) = -3\left(-\sin\dfrac{\pi t}{6}\right)\left(\dfrac{d}{dt}\dfrac{\pi t}{6}\right) = \left(3\sin\dfrac{\pi t}{6}\right)\left(\dfrac{\pi}{6}\right)$

$\qquad\qquad = \dfrac{\pi}{2}\sin\dfrac{\pi t}{6},\ 0 \le t \le 24$

(B) $R'(1) = \dfrac{\pi}{2} \sin \dfrac{\pi}{6} = \dfrac{\pi}{2} \cdot \dfrac{1}{2} = \dfrac{\pi}{4} \approx 0.79$ million or \$790,000 per month

$R'(6) = \dfrac{\pi}{2} \sin \dfrac{6\pi}{6} = \dfrac{\pi}{2} \sin \pi = \dfrac{\pi}{2}(0) = 0$ or \$0 per month

$R'(11) = \dfrac{\pi}{2} \sin \dfrac{11\pi}{6} = \dfrac{\pi}{2}\left(-\dfrac{1}{2}\right) = -\dfrac{\pi}{4}$

≈ -0.79 million or $-\$790,000$ per month

(C) $R'(t) = \dfrac{\pi}{2} \sin \dfrac{\pi t}{6} = 0, \ 0 < t < 24$

$\sin \dfrac{\pi t}{6} = 0$

Therefore, the critical values are:

$\dfrac{\pi t}{6} = \pi$ or $t = 6$; $\quad \dfrac{\pi t}{6} = 2\pi$ or $t = 12$; $\quad \dfrac{\pi t}{6} = 3\pi$ or $t = 18$.

Now,

$R''(t) = \dfrac{\pi^2}{12} \cos \dfrac{\pi t}{6}$

$R''(6) = \dfrac{\pi^2}{12} \cos \pi = -\dfrac{\pi^2}{12} < 0$

$R''(12) = \dfrac{\pi^2}{12} \cos 2\pi = \dfrac{\pi^2}{12} > 0$

$R''(18) = \dfrac{\pi^2}{12} \cos 3\pi = -\dfrac{\pi^2}{12} < 0$

Thus,

t	$R(t)$	
6	\$7,000,000	Local maximum
12	\$1,000,000	Local minimum
18	\$7,000,000	Local maximum

(D)

t	$R(t)$	
0	\$1,000,000	Absolute minimum
6	\$7,000,000	Absolute maximum
12	\$1,000,000	Absolute minimum
18	\$7,000,000	Absolute maximum
24	\$1,000,000	Absolute minimum

(E) The results in part (C) are illustrated by the graph of f shown at the right.

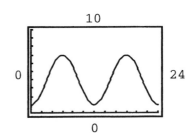

34. $P(n) = 1 + \cos \dfrac{\pi n}{26}, \quad 0 \leq n \leq 104$

(A) $P'(n) = \left(-\sin \dfrac{\pi n}{26}\right)\left(\dfrac{d}{dn}\dfrac{\pi n}{26}\right) = \left(-\sin \dfrac{\pi n}{26}\right)\left(\dfrac{\pi}{26}\right)$

$\qquad = -\dfrac{\pi}{26} \sin \dfrac{\pi n}{26}, \quad 0 \leq n \leq 104$

(B) $P'(13) = -\dfrac{\pi}{26} \sin \dfrac{13\pi}{26} = -\dfrac{\pi}{26} \sin \dfrac{\pi}{2} = -\dfrac{\pi}{26} \approx -0.12$ tons per week

$\quad P'(26) = -\dfrac{\pi}{26} \sin \dfrac{26\pi}{26} = -\dfrac{\pi}{26} \sin \pi = 0$ tons per week

$\quad P'(30) = -\dfrac{\pi}{26} \sin \dfrac{30\pi}{26} = -\dfrac{\pi}{26} \sin \dfrac{15\pi}{13} \approx 0.06$ tons per week

(C) $P'(n) = -\dfrac{\pi}{26} \sin \dfrac{\pi n}{26} = 0, \quad 0 < n < 104$

$\qquad\qquad \sin \dfrac{\pi n}{26} = 0$

Therefore, the critical values are:

$\dfrac{\pi n}{26} = \pi$ or $n = 26$; $\quad \dfrac{\pi n}{26} = 2\pi$ or $n = 52$; $\quad \dfrac{\pi n}{26} = 3\pi$ or $n = 78$.

Now,

$P''(n) = -\dfrac{\pi}{26} \cdot \dfrac{\pi}{26} \cos \dfrac{\pi n}{26} = -\left(\dfrac{\pi}{26}\right)^2 \cos \dfrac{\pi n}{26}$

$P''(26) = -\left(\dfrac{\pi}{26}\right)^2 \cos \pi = \left(\dfrac{\pi}{26}\right)^2 > 0$

$P''(52) = -\left(\dfrac{\pi}{26}\right)^2 \cos 2\pi = -\left(\dfrac{\pi}{26}\right)^2 < 0$

$P''(78) = -\left(\dfrac{\pi}{26}\right)^2 \cos 3\pi = \left(\dfrac{\pi}{26}\right)^2 > 0$

Thus,

n	$P(n)$	
26	0	Local minimum
52	2	Local maximum
78	0	Local minimum

(D)

n	$P(n)$	
0	2	Absolute maximum
26	0	Absolute minimum
52	2	Absolute maximum
78	0	Absolute minimum
104	2	Absolute maximum

(E) The results in part (C) are
illustrated by the graph of f shown
at the right.

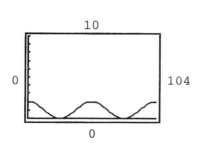

2. $\int \cos w \, dw = \sin w + C$

4. $\int \sin 2x \, dx = \dfrac{1}{2}\int \sin 2x \,(2\,dx)$ (Let $u = 2x$, then $du = 2\,dx$.)

$\qquad\qquad\quad = \dfrac{1}{2}\int \sin u \, du$

$\qquad\qquad\quad = \dfrac{1}{2}(-\cos u) + C$

$\qquad\qquad\quad = -\dfrac{1}{2}\cos 2x + C$

6. $\int \sin x \cos x \, dx = \dfrac{1}{2}\int 2 \sin x \cos x \, dx$

$\qquad\qquad\qquad = \dfrac{1}{2}\int \sin 2x \, dx$ ($\sin 2x = 2 \sin x \cos x$)

$\qquad\qquad\qquad = \dfrac{1}{2}\left(-\dfrac{1}{2}\cos 2x\right) + C$ (see Problem 4)

$\qquad\qquad\qquad = -\dfrac{1}{4}\cos 2x + C$

8. $\int \dfrac{\cos x}{\sqrt{\sin x}}\,dx = \int (\sin x)^{-1/2}\cos x \, dx$ (Let $u = \sin x$, then $du = \cos x \, dx$)

$\qquad\qquad\quad = \int u^{-1/2} \, du$

$\qquad\qquad\quad = \dfrac{u^{1/2}}{\frac{1}{2}} + C$

$\qquad\qquad\quad = 2u^{1/2} + C = 2(\sin x)^{1/2} + C$

$\qquad\qquad\quad = 2\sqrt{\sin x} + C$

10. $\int (x+1)\sin(x^2 + 2x)\,dx = \dfrac{1}{2}\int \sin(x^2 + 2x)\,(2(x+1)\,dx)$

$\qquad\qquad\qquad\qquad = \dfrac{1}{2}\int \sin u \, du$ $\left(\begin{array}{l}\text{Let } u = x^2 + 2x,\\ \text{then } du = 2(x+1)dx\end{array}\right)$

$\qquad\qquad\qquad\qquad = \dfrac{1}{2}(-\cos u) + C$

$\qquad\qquad\qquad\qquad = -\dfrac{1}{2}\cos(x^2 + 2x) + C$

12. $\displaystyle\int_0^{\pi/4} \cos x \, dx = (\sin x)\Big|_0^{\pi/4} = \sin\dfrac{\pi}{4} - \sin 0 = \dfrac{\sqrt{2}}{2} \approx 0.707$

14. $\displaystyle\int_{\pi/6}^{\pi/3} \sin x \, dx = (-\cos x)\Big|_{\pi/6}^{\pi/3} = -\cos\dfrac{\pi}{3} + \cos\dfrac{\pi}{6}$

$\qquad\qquad\qquad\qquad = -\dfrac{1}{2} + \dfrac{\sqrt{3}}{2} \approx 0.366$

16. The shaded area $= \int_{\pi/6}^{2\pi/3} \sin x \, dx = (-\cos x) \Big|_{\pi/6}^{2\pi/3} = -\cos \dfrac{2\pi}{3} + \cos \dfrac{\pi}{6}$

$$= -\left(-\dfrac{1}{2}\right) + \dfrac{\sqrt{3}}{2}$$

$$= \dfrac{1}{2} + \dfrac{\sqrt{3}}{2} \approx 1.366$$

18. $\int_{0}^{0.5} \cos x \, dx = (\sin x) \Big|_{0}^{0.5} = \sin 0.5 - \sin 0 \approx 0.4794$

20. $\int_{1}^{3} \sin x \, dx = (-\cos x) \Big|_{1}^{3} = -\cos 3 + \cos 1 \approx -(-0.9900) + 0.5403 = 1.5303$

22. $\int e^{\cos x} \sin x \, dx$ [Let $u = \cos x$, then $du = -\sin x \, dx$.]

$$= -\int e^{\cos x} (-\sin x \, dx) = -\int e^u \, du$$

$$= -e^u + C$$
$$= -e^{\cos x} + C$$

24. $\int \dfrac{\sin x}{\cos x} \, dx = -\int \dfrac{1}{\cos x} (-\sin x \, dx)$ [Let $u = \cos x$, then $du = -\sin x \, dx$.]

$$= -\int \dfrac{1}{u} \, du = -\ln|u| + C$$

$$= -\ln|\cos x| + C$$

26. $\int \cot x \, dx = \int \dfrac{\cos x}{\sin x} \, dx$

$$= \int \dfrac{1}{\sin x} (\cos x \, dx) \quad \text{[Let } u = \sin x, \text{ then } du = \cos x \, dx.]$$

$$= \int \dfrac{1}{u} \, du = \ln|u| + C = \ln|\sin x| + C$$

28. $f(x) = e^{-x} \cos x$

(A)

(B) $I = \int_{0}^{3} e^{-x} \cos x \, dx$ $[0, 3]$, $n = 6$, $\Delta x = \dfrac{1}{2}$

$R_6 = \dfrac{1}{2} \{ e^{-0.5} \cos(0.5) + e^{-1} \cos(1) + e^{-1.5} \cos(1.5)$

$\qquad\qquad + e^{-2} \cos(2) + e^{-2.5} \cos(2.5) + e^{-3} \cos(3) \}$

≈ 0.288

30. $R(t) = 4 - 3 \cos\dfrac{\pi t}{6}, \quad 0 \le t \le 24$

(A) Total revenue taken in over the two-year period:

$$T = \int_0^{24}\left[4 - 3\cos\frac{\pi t}{6}\right]dt = \int_0^{24} 4\ dt - 3\int_0^{24}\frac{\cos \pi t}{6}dt$$

$$= (4t)\Big|_0^{24} - 3\left(\frac{6}{\pi}\sin\frac{\pi t}{6}\right)\Big|_0^{24}$$

$$= 96 - 3\left(\frac{6}{\pi}\sin 4\pi - \frac{6}{\pi}\sin 0\right) = 96$$

Thus, $T = \$96$ million or $\$96,000,000$.

(B) Total revenue taken in from $t = 8$ to $t = 14$:

$$T = \int_8^{14}\left[4 - 3\cos\frac{\pi t}{6}\right]dt = \int_8^{14} 4\ dt - 3\int_8^{14}\cos\frac{\pi t}{6}dt$$

$$= (4t)\Big|_8^{14} - 3\left(\frac{6}{\pi}\sin\frac{\pi t}{6}\right)\Big|_8^{14}$$

$$= 4(14) - 4(8) - 3\left(\frac{6}{\pi}\sin\frac{7\pi}{3} - \frac{6}{\pi}\sin\frac{4\pi}{3}\right)$$

$$\approx \$14.076 \text{ million or } \$14,076,000$$

(C)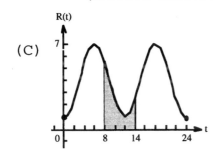

APPENDIX A   BASIC ALGEBRA REVIEW

2. $7 + x$ **4.** $(xy)z$ **5.** $9m$

8. T; Commutative property of multiplication

10. T; Distributive property   **12.** T; Multiplicative inverse property

14. F; Let $x = y = 1$, then $\dfrac{x}{3y} \div \dfrac{5y}{x} - \dfrac{1}{3} : \dfrac{5}{1} - \dfrac{1}{3} \cdot \dfrac{1}{5} = \dfrac{1}{15}, \dfrac{15y^2}{x^2} = 15$.

16. T; Property of negatives

18. T; Property of additive inverse   **20.** T; Property of negatives

22. F; Let $k = 2$, $b = 1$, then $\dfrac{k}{k + b} = \dfrac{2}{3}$, $\dfrac{1}{1 + b} = \dfrac{1}{2}$.

24. T; Distributive property

26. T; Zero property

28. Yes. If neither u nor v are zero, then $uv \neq 0$.

30. (A) True

    (B) False. For example, 4 is a real number, but is not irrational.

    (C) True

32. $\dfrac{3}{5}$ and -1.43 are two examples of infinitely many.

34. (A) $-3 \in Z, Q, R$ (B) $3.14 \in Q, R$

      (C) $\pi \in R$ (D) $\dfrac{2}{3} \in Q, R$

36. (A) True. This is the commutative property of addition.

    (B) False. For example, $5 - 3 \neq 3 - 5$.

    (C) True. This is the commutative property of multiplication.

    (D) False. For example, $9 \div 3 \neq 3 \div 9$.

38.

$$C = 0.181818\ldots$$
$$100C = 18.1818\ldots$$
$$100C - C = (18.1818\ldots) - (0.181818\ldots)$$
$$99C = 18$$
$$C = \frac{18}{99} = \frac{2}{11}$$

40. (A) $0.888888888\ldots$ (B) $0.27272727\ldots$ (C) $2.23606797\ldots$ (D) $1.375000000\ldots$

2. The term of highest degree in $2x - 3$ is $2x$ and the degree of this term is 1.

4. $(2x - 3) + (2x^2 - x + 2) = 2x^2 + x - 1$

6. $(2x^2 - x + 2) - (2x - 3) = 2x^2 - x + 5$

8. $(2x - 3)(x^3 + 2x^2 - x + 3) = 2x^4 + x^3 - 8x^2 + 9x - 9$

10. $2(x - 1) + 3(2x - 3) - (4x - 5) = 2x - 2 + 6x - 9 - 4x + 5 = 4x - 6$

12. $2y - 3y[4 - 2(y - 1)] = 2y - 3y[4 - 2y + 2]$
$$= 2y - 3y[6 - 2y]$$
$$= 2y - 18y + 6y^2$$
$$= 6y^2 - 16y$$

14. $(m - n)(m + n) = m^2 - n^2$ (Special product)

16. $(4t - 3)(t - 2) = 4t^2 - 8t - 3t + 6 = 4t^2 - 11t + 6$

18. $(3x + 2y)(x - 3y) = 3x^2 - 9xy + 2xy - 6y^2$
$$= 3x^2 - 7xy - 6y^2$$

20. $(2m - 7)(2m + 7) = (2m)^2 - (7)^2 = 4m^2 - 49$ (Special product)

22. $-(5 - 3x)^2 = -(25 - 30x + 9x^2) = -25 + 30x - 9x^2$

24. $(3x - 2y)(3x + 2y) = (3x)^2 - (2y)^2$
$$= 9x^2 - 4y^2 \quad \text{(Special product)}$$

26. $(4x - y)^2 = 16x^2 - 8xy + y^2$

28. $(a + b)(a^2 - ab + b^2) = a(a^2 - ab + b^2) + b(a^2 - ab + b^2)$
$$= a^3 - a^2b + ab^2 + a^2b - ab^2 + b^3$$
$$= a^3 + b^3$$

30. $[a - (2b - c)][a + (2b - c)] = a^2 - (2b - c)^2 = a^2 - (4b^2 - 4bc + c^2)$
$$= a^2 - 4b^2 + 4bc - c^2$$

32. $2x - 3\{x + 2[x - (x + 5)] + 1\} =$
$2x - 3\{x + 2[x - x - 5] + 1\} = 2x - 3\{x + 2(-5) + 1\}$
$$= 2x - 3\{x - 10 + 1\}$$
$$= 2x - 3\{x - 9\}$$
$$= 2x - 3x + 27$$
$$= -x + 27$$

34. $(3x - 2y)^2(2x + 5y) = (9x^2 - 12xy + 4y^2)(2x + 5y)$
$$= 18x^3 + 45x^2y - 24x^2y - 60xy^2 + 8xy^2 + 20y^3$$
$$= 18x^3 + 21x^2y - 52xy^2 + 20y^3$$

36. $(2x - 1)^2 - (3x + 2)(3x - 2) = (2x - 1)^2 - ((3x)^2 - (2)^2)$

$$= (4x^2 - 4x + 1) - (9x^2 - 4)$$
$$= 4x^2 - 4x + 1 - 9x^2 + 4$$
$$= -5x^2 - 4x + 5$$

38. $(x - 3)(x + 3) - (x - 3)^2 = x^2 - 9 - (x^2 - 6x + 9)$

$$= x^2 - 9 - x^2 + 6x - 9$$
$$= 6x - 18$$

40. $(3m + n)(m - 3n) - (m + 3n)(3m - n)$

$$= 3m^2 - 9mn + mn - 3n^2 - (3m^2 - mn + 9mn - 3n^2)$$
$$= 3m^2 - 9mn + mn - 3n^2 - 3m^2 + mn - 9mn + 3n^2$$
$$= -16mn$$

42. $(x - y)^3 = (x - y)(x - y)^2 = (x - y)(x^2 - 2xy + y^2)$

$$= x^3 - 2x^2y + xy^2 - x^2y + 2xy^2 - y^3$$
$$= x^3 - 3x^2y + 3xy^2 - y^3$$

44. $(2m - n)^3 = (2m - n)(2m - n)^2 = (2m - n)(4m^2 - 4mn + n^2)$

$$= 8m^3 - 8m^2n + 2mn^2 - 4m^2n + 4mn^2 - n^3$$
$$= 8m^3 - 12m^2n + 6mn^2 - n^3$$

46. $\{(3m^2 - 3m - 2) + (m^3 + m^2 + 2)\} - \{(3m^2 - 2m + 5) + (4m^2 - m)\}$

$$= \{3m^2 - 3m - 2 + m^3 + m^2 + 2\} - \{3m^2 - 2m + 5 + 4m^2 - m\}$$
$$= \{m^3 + 4m^2 - 3m\} - \{7m^2 - 3m + 5\}$$
$$= m^3 + 4m^2 - 3m - 7m^2 + 3m - 5 = m^3 - 3m^2 - 5$$

48. $[5x(3x + 1) - 5(2x - 1)^2]^2 = [15x^2 + 5x - 5(4x^2 - 4x + 1)]^2$

$$= [15x^2 + 5x - 20x^2 + 20x - 5]^2$$
$$= [-5x^2 + 25x - 5]^2$$
$$= 25x^4 + 625x^2 + 25 - 250x^3 + 50x^2 - 250x$$
$$= 25x^4 - 250x^3 + 675x^2 - 250x + 25$$

50. $-3x\{x[x - x(2 - x)] - (x + 2)(x^2 - 3)\}$

$$= -3x\{x[x - 2x + x^2] - [x^3 - 3x + 2x^2 - 6]\}$$
$$= -3x\{x[-x + x^2] - x^3 + 3x - 2x^2 + 6\}$$
$$= -3x\{-x^2 + x^3 - x^3 + 3x - 2x^2 + 6\}$$
$$= -3x\{-3x^2 + 3x + 6\} = 9x^3 - 9x^2 - 18x$$

52. m

54. Now the degree is less than or equal to m.

56. $(2 - 1)^2 \neq 2^2 - 1^2$; since
$(a - b)^2 = a^2 - 2ab + b^2$, $(a - b)^2 = a^2 - b^2$ only when
$a = b$ in which case $a^2 - 2ab + b^2 = a^2 - 2a^2 + a^2 = 0$ or
$b = 0$ in which case $a^2 - 2ab + b^2 = a^2$.

58. Let x = amount invested at 7%,
$2x$ = amount invested at 9%,
and $100,000 - 3x$ = amount invested at 11%.
$I = 0.07x + (0.09)(2x) + 0.11(100,000 - 3x)$
$= 11,000 - 0.08x$

60. Let x = number of tickets at \$9.
Then $6,000$ = number of tickets at \$15.
The total receipts R are:

$$R = 9x + 15(6,000 - x) = 90,000 - 6x$$

62. Let x = number of ounces of food M used.
Then $160 - x$ = number of ounces of food N used.
The total number of units of calcium, C, in the diet mix is given by:
$$C = 8x + 5(160 - x) = 800 + 3x$$

EXERCISE A-3

2. $2x^2$ is a common factor: $6x^4 - 8x^3 - 2x^2 = 2x^2(3x^2 - 4x - 1)$

4. $5xy$ is a common factor: $10x^3y + 20x^2y^2 - 15xy^3 = 5xy(2x^2 + 4xy - 3y^2)$

6. $(x + 1)$ is a common factor: $5x(x + 1) - 3(x + 1) = (x + 1)(5x - 3)$

8. $3(b - 2c)$ is a common factor:
$12a(b - 2c) - 15b(b - 2c) = 3(b - 2c)[4a - 5b]$
$= 3(b - 2c)(4a - 5b)$

10. $x^2 - 3x + 2x - 6 = (x^2 - 3x) + (2x - 6)$
$= x(x - 3) + 2(x - 3)$
$= (x - 3)(x + 2)$

12. $2x^2 - x + 6x - 3 = (2x^2 - x) + (6x - 3)$
$= x(2x - 1) + 3(2x - 1)$
$= (2x - 1)(x + 3)$

14. $6x^2 + 9x - 2x - 3 = (6x^2 + 9x) + (-2x - 3)$
$= 3x(2x + 3) - (2x + 3)$
$= (2x + 3)(3x - 1)$

16. $ac + ad + bc + bd = (ac + ad) + (bc + bd)$
$= a(c + d) + b(c + d)$
$= (a + b)(c + d)$

18. $ab + 6 + 2a + 3b = (ab + 2a) + (6 + 3b)$
$= a(b + 2) + 3(b + 2)$
$= (a + 3)(b + 2)$

20. $2x^2 + 5x - 3$

$a = 2, \ b = 5, \ c = -3$

Step 1. Use the ac-test to test for factorability

$ac = (2)(-3) = -6$

$$\underline{pq}$$
$$(1)(-6)$$
$$\boxed{(-1)(6)}$$
$$(2)(-3)$$
$$(-2)(3)$$

Note that $-1 + 6 = 5 = b$. Thus, $2x^2 + 5x - 3$ has first-degree factors with integer coefficients.

Step 2. Split the middle term using $b = p + q$ and factor by grouping.

$5 = -1 + 6$

$$\begin{aligned}
2x^2 + 5x - 3 &= (2x^2 - x) + (6x - 3) \\
&= x(2x - 1) + 3(2x - 1) \\
&= (2x - 1)(x + 3)
\end{aligned}$$

22. $x^2 - 4xy - 12y^2$

$a = 1, \ b = -4, \ c = -12$

Step 1. Use the ac-test

$ac = 1(-12) = -12$

$$\underline{pq}$$
$$(1)(-12)$$
$$(-1)(12)$$
$$(-2)(6)$$
$$\boxed{(2)(-6)}$$
$$(-3)(4)$$
$$(3)(-4)$$

Note that $2 + (-6) = -4 = b$. Thus $x^2 - 4xy - 12y^2$ has first-degree factors with integer coefficients.

Step 2. Factor by grouping

$-4 = 2 + (-6)$

$$\begin{aligned}
x^2 + 2xy - 6xy - 12y^2 &= (x^2 + 2xy) - (6xy + 12y^2) \\
&= x(x + 2y) - 6y(x + 2y) \\
&= (x + 2y)(x - 6y)
\end{aligned}$$

24. $x^2 + x - 4$

$a = 1, \ b = 1, \ c = -4$

Step 1. Use the ac-test

$ac = (1)(1) = 1$

$$\underline{pq}$$
$$(1)(1)$$
$$(-1)(-1)$$

None of the factors add up to $1 = b$. Thus, this polynomial is *not factorable*.

26. $25m^2 - 16n^2 = (5m - 4n)(5m + 4n)$ (difference of squares)

28. $x^2 + 10xy + 25y^2 = (x + 5y)^2$ (perfect square)

30. $u^2 + 81$
$a = 1, \ b = 0, \ c = 81$
Step 1. Use the ac-test
$$ac = (1)(81) = 81$$

$$
\begin{array}{c}
\underline{pq} \\
(1)(81) \\
(-1)(-81) \\
(3)(27) \\
(-3)(-27) \\
(9)(9) \\
(-9)(-9)
\end{array}
$$

None of the factors add up to $0 = b$. Thus this polynomial is *not factorable*.

32. $6x^2 + 48x + 72 = 6(x^2 + 8x + 12) = 6(x + 2)(x + 6)$

34. $2y^3 - 22y^2 + 48y = 2y(y^2 - 11y + 24)$
$\qquad\qquad\qquad\qquad = 2y(y - 3)(y - 8)$

36. $16x^2y - 8xy + y = y(16x^2 - 8x + 1)$
$\qquad\qquad\qquad\quad = y(4x - 1)^2$

38. $6s^2 + 7st - 3t^2 = (3s - t)(2s + 3t)$

40. $x^3y - 9xy^3 = xy(x^2 - 9y^2) = xy(x - 3y)(x + 3y)$

42. $3m^3 - 6m^2 + 15m = 3m(m^2 - 2m + 5)$ [Note: $m^2 - 2m + 5$ is *not factorable*.]

44. $5x^3 + 40y^3 = 5(x^3 + 8y^3)$
$\qquad\qquad\quad = 5[x^3 + (2y)^3]$
$\qquad\qquad\quad = 5(x + 2y)(x^2 - 2xy + y^2)$ (sum of cubes)

46. $8a^3 - 1 = (2a)^3 - (1)^3$
$\qquad\qquad = (2a - 1)(4a^2 + 2a + 1)$ (difference of cubes)

48. $(a - b)^2 - 4(c - d)^2 = [(a - b) - 2(c - d)][(a - b) + 2(c - d)]$

50. $3x^2 - 2xy - 4y^2$ is *not factorable*

52. $4(A + B)^2 - 5(A + B) - 6$
Let $x = A + B$, then $4x^2 - 5x - 6$ can be written as
$4x^2 - 5x - 6 = (2x + 3)(x - 2)$. Now, replace x with $A + B$ to obtain:
$4(A + B)^2 - 5(A + B) - 6 = [2(A + B) + 3][(A + B) - 2]$

54. $m^4 - n^4 = (m^2 - n^2)(m^2 + n^2)$
$\qquad\qquad = (m - n)(m + n)(m^2 + n^2)$ [Note: $m^2 + n^2$ is not factorable.]

56. $15x^2$ and $(3x - 1)^3$ are common factors:

$$15x^2(3x - 1)^4 + 60x^3(3x - 1)^3 = 15x^2(3x - 1)^3[(3x - 1) + 4x]$$
$$= 15x^2(3x - 1)^3[3x - 1 + 4x]$$
$$= 15x^2(3x - 1)^3(7x - 1)$$

58. False. Here is a counterexample. Consider $u^4 - v^2$, $m = 4$, $n = 2$, $m \neq n$, but $u^4 - v^2 = (u^2 - v)(u^2 + v)$.

60. True. $u^{2k+1} + v^{2k+1} = (u + v)(u^{2k} - u^{2k-1}v + u^{2k-2}v^2 - \dots + v^{2k})$. For example, if $k = 2$, then as you know $u^3 + v^3 = (u + v)(u^2 - uv + v^2)$.

EXERCISE A-4

2. $\left(\dfrac{d^5}{3a} \div \dfrac{d^2}{6a^2}\right) \cdot \dfrac{a}{4d^3} = \left(\dfrac{d^5}{3a} \cdot \dfrac{6a^2}{d^2}\right) \cdot \dfrac{a}{4d^3} = (2ad^3) \cdot \dfrac{a}{4d^3} = \dfrac{a^2}{2}$

4. $\dfrac{2y}{18} - \dfrac{-1}{28} - \dfrac{y}{42}$

$= \dfrac{28y}{252} - \dfrac{-9}{252} - \dfrac{6y}{252}$

$= \dfrac{28y + 9 - 6y}{252} = \dfrac{22y + 9}{252}$

We find the LCD of 18, 28, 42:
$18 = 2 \cdot 3^2$, $28 = 2^2 \cdot 7$, $42 = 2 \cdot 3 \cdot 7$.
Thus, LCD $= 2^2 \cdot 3^2 \cdot 7 = 252$.

6. $\dfrac{3x + 8}{4x^2} - \dfrac{2x - 1}{x^3} - \dfrac{5}{8x}$

$= \dfrac{2x(3x + 8)}{8x^3} - \dfrac{8(2x - 1)}{8x^3} - \dfrac{5x^2}{8x^3}$

$= \dfrac{6x^2 + 16x - 16x + 8 - 5x^2}{8x^3}$

$= \dfrac{x^2 + 8}{8x^3}$

Find the LCD of $4x^2$, x^3, $8x$:
$4x^2 = 2^2 x^2$, $x^3 = x^3$, $8x = 2^3 \cdot x$.
Thus, LCD $= 8x^3$.

8. $\dfrac{2x^2 + 7x + 3}{4x^2 - 1} \div (x + 3)$

$= \dfrac{(2x^2 + 7x + 3)}{(4x^2 - 1)(x + 3)} = \dfrac{(2x + 1)(x + 3)}{(2x - 1)(2x + 1)(x + 3)} = \dfrac{1}{2x - 1}$

10. $\dfrac{5}{m - 2} - \dfrac{3}{2m + 1} = \dfrac{5(2m + 1) - 3(m - 2)}{(m - 2)(2m + 1)} = \dfrac{10m + 5 - 3m + 6}{(m - 2)(2m + 1)} = \dfrac{7m + 11}{(m - 2)(2m + 1)}$

12. $\dfrac{3}{x^2 - 5x + 6} - \dfrac{5}{(x - 2)^2} = \dfrac{3}{(x - 2)(x - 3)} - \dfrac{5}{(x - 2)^2}$ $\text{LCD} = (x - 2)^2(x - 3)$

$$= \dfrac{3(x - 2) - 5(x - 3)}{(x - 2)^2(x - 3)} = \dfrac{3x - 6 - 5x + 15}{(x - 2)^2(x - 3)}$$

$$= \dfrac{-2x + 9}{(x - 2)^2(x - 3)}$$

14. $m - 3 - \dfrac{m - 1}{m - 2} = \dfrac{(m - 3)(m - 2)}{m - 2} - \dfrac{m - 1}{m - 2}$ $\text{LCD} = m - 2$

$$= \dfrac{(m - 3)(m - 2) - (m - 1)}{(m - 2)}$$

$$= \dfrac{m^2 - 2m - 3m + 6 - m + 1}{m - 2} = \dfrac{m^2 - 6m + 7}{m - 2}$$

16. $\dfrac{5}{x - 3} - \dfrac{2}{3 - x} = \dfrac{5}{(x - 3)} - \dfrac{-2}{(x - 3)}$ (property of negatives)

$$= \dfrac{5 - (-2)}{x - 3} = \dfrac{7}{x - 3}$$

18. $\dfrac{m + 2}{m^2 - 2m} - \dfrac{m}{m^2 - 4} = \dfrac{m + 2}{m(m - 2)} - \dfrac{m}{(m - 2)(m + 2)}$ $\text{LCD} = m(m - 2)(m + 2)$

$$= \dfrac{(m + 2)^2}{m(m - 2)(m + 2)} - \dfrac{m^2}{m(m - 2)(m + 2)}$$

$$= \dfrac{(m + 2)^2 - m^2}{m(m - 2)(m + 2)} = \dfrac{m^2 + 4m + 4 - m^2}{m(m - 2)(m + 2)}$$

$$= \dfrac{4(m + 1)}{m(m - 2)(m + 2)}$$

20. $\dfrac{y}{y^2 - y - 2} - \dfrac{1}{y^2 + 5y - 14} - \dfrac{2}{y^2 + 8y + 7}$

$= \dfrac{y}{(y - 2)(y + 1)} - \dfrac{1}{(y + 7)(y - 2)} - \dfrac{2}{(y + 1)(y + 7)}$ $\text{LCD} = (y - 2)(y + 1)(y + 7)$

$= \dfrac{y(y + 7)}{(y - 2)(y + 1)(y + 7)} - \dfrac{(y + 1)}{(y - 2)(y + 1)(y + 7)} - \dfrac{2(y - 2)}{(y - 2)(y + 1)(y + 7)}$

$= \dfrac{y(y + 7) - (y + 1) - 2(y - 2)}{(y - 2)(y + 1)(y + 7)} = \dfrac{y^2 + 7y - y - 1 - 2y + 4}{(y - 2)(y + 1)(y + 7)}$

$$= \dfrac{y^2 + 4y + 3}{(y - 2)(y + 1)(y + 7)}$$

$$= \dfrac{(y + 1)(y + 3)}{(y - 2)(y + 1)(y + 7)}$$

$$= \dfrac{y + 3}{(y - 2)(y + 7)}$$

22. $\dfrac{2}{5 - \dfrac{3}{4x + 1}} = \dfrac{2}{\dfrac{5(4x + 1) - 3}{4x + 1}} = \dfrac{2}{\dfrac{20x + 5 - 3}{4x + 1}} = \dfrac{2}{20x + 2} \cdot \dfrac{4x + 1}{1}$

$$= \dfrac{1}{10x + 1} \cdot \dfrac{4x + 1}{1} = \dfrac{4x + 1}{10x + 1}$$

24. $\dfrac{x + 7}{ax - bx} + \dfrac{y + 9}{by - ay} = \dfrac{x + 7}{x(a - b)} + \dfrac{y + 9}{-y(a - b)}$ $\text{LCD} = xy(a - b)$

$$= \dfrac{y(x + 7)}{xy(a - b)} - \dfrac{x(y + 9)}{xy(a - b)}$$

$$= \dfrac{y(x + 7) - x(y + 9)}{xy(a - b)} = \dfrac{xy + 7y - xy - 9x}{xy(a - b)} = \dfrac{7y - 9x}{xy(a - b)}$$

26. $\dfrac{1 - \dfrac{y^2}{x^2}}{1 - \dfrac{y}{x}} = \dfrac{\dfrac{x^2 - y^2}{x^2}}{\dfrac{x - y}{x}} = \dfrac{x^2 - y^2}{x^2} \cdot \dfrac{x}{x - y}$

$$= \dfrac{(x - y)(x + y)}{x^2} \cdot \dfrac{x}{x - y}$$

$$= \dfrac{x(x - y)(x + y)}{x^2(x - y)}$$

$$= \dfrac{x + y}{x}$$

28. $\dfrac{\dfrac{1}{x + h} - \dfrac{1}{x}}{h} = \dfrac{\dfrac{x}{x(x + h)} - \dfrac{x + h}{x(x + h)}}{h} = \dfrac{\dfrac{x - (x + h)}{x(x + h)}}{h}$

$$= \dfrac{\dfrac{-h}{x(x + h)}}{h} = -\dfrac{h}{x(x + h)} \cdot \dfrac{1}{h}$$

$$= -\dfrac{1}{x(x + h)}$$

30. $\dfrac{1 + \dfrac{2}{x} - \dfrac{15}{x^2}}{1 + \dfrac{4}{x} - \dfrac{5}{x^2}} = \dfrac{\dfrac{x^2}{x^2} + \dfrac{2x}{x^2} - \dfrac{15}{x^2}}{\dfrac{x^2}{x^2} + \dfrac{4x}{x^2} - \dfrac{5}{x^2}} = \dfrac{\dfrac{x^2 + 2x - 15}{x^2}}{\dfrac{x^2 + 4x - 5}{x^2}}$

$$= \dfrac{x^2 + 2x - 15}{x^2} \cdot \dfrac{x^2}{x^2 + 4x - 5}$$

$$= \dfrac{(x + 5)(x - 3)}{x^2} \cdot \dfrac{x^2}{(x + 5)(x - 1)}$$

$$= \dfrac{x^2(x + 5)(x - 3)}{x^2(x + 5)} = \dfrac{x - 3}{x - 1}$$

32. (A) $\dfrac{x^2 - 3x - 4}{x - 4} = x - 3$: Incorrect

(B) $\dfrac{x^2 - 3x - 4}{x - 4} = \dfrac{(x - 4)(x + 1)}{x - 4} = x + 1$

34. (A) $\dfrac{(x + h)^3 - x^3}{h} = 3x^2 + 3x + 1$: Incorrect

(B) $\dfrac{(x + h)^3 - x^3}{h} = \dfrac{((x + h) - x)((x + h)^2 + x(x + h) + x^2)}{h}$

$\qquad = \dfrac{(x + h - x)(x^2 + 2hx + h^2 + x^2 + xh + x^2)}{h}$

$\qquad = \dfrac{h(3x^2 + 3hx + h^2)}{h}$

$\qquad = 3x^2 + 3hx + h^2$

36. (A) $\dfrac{2}{x - 1} - \dfrac{x + 3}{x^2 - 1} = \dfrac{1}{x + 1}$: Correct

38. (A) $x + \dfrac{x - 2}{x^2 - 3x + 2} = \dfrac{2}{x - 2}$: Incorrect

(B) $x + \dfrac{x - 2}{x^2 - 3x + 2} = x + \dfrac{x - 2}{(x - 2)(x - 1)}$

$\qquad = x + \dfrac{1}{x - 1} \qquad \text{LCD} = x - 1$

$\qquad = \dfrac{x(x - 1)}{x - 1} + \dfrac{1}{x - 1}$

$\qquad = \dfrac{x(x - 1) + 1}{x - 1} = \dfrac{x^2 - x + 1}{x - 1}$

40. $\dfrac{\dfrac{1}{(x + h)^2} - \dfrac{1}{x^2}}{h} = \left[\dfrac{1}{(x + h)^2} - \dfrac{1}{x^2}\right] \div \dfrac{h}{1}$

$\qquad = \dfrac{x^2 - (x + h)^2}{x^2(x + h)^2} \cdot \dfrac{1}{h}$

$\qquad = \dfrac{x^2 - (x^2 + 2xh + h^2)}{x^2(x + h)^2 h}$

$\qquad = \dfrac{x^2 - x^2 - 2xh - h^2}{x^2(x + h)^2 h}$

$\qquad = \dfrac{-2xh - h^2}{x^2(x + h)^2 h} = \dfrac{-h(2x + h)}{x^2(x + h)^2 h}$

$\qquad = -\dfrac{2x + h}{x^2(x + h)^2}$

42. $2 - \dfrac{1}{1 - \dfrac{2}{a+2}} = 2 - \dfrac{1}{\dfrac{a+2-2}{a+2}} = 2 - \dfrac{1}{\dfrac{a}{a+2}}$

$\qquad\qquad = 2 - \dfrac{1}{1} \cdot \dfrac{a+2}{a} = 2 - \dfrac{a+2}{a}$

$\qquad\qquad = \dfrac{2a - (a+2)}{a} = \dfrac{2a - a - 2}{a} = \dfrac{a-2}{a}$

EXERCISE A-5

2. $3y^{-5} = \dfrac{3}{y^5}$

4. $\dfrac{5}{4x^{-9}} = \dfrac{5x^9}{4}$

6. $3c^{-9}c^4 = 3c^{-9+4} = 3c^{-5} = \dfrac{3}{c^5}$

8. $\dfrac{m^{-11}}{m^{-5}} = m^{-11}m^5 = m^{-11+5} = m^{-6} = \dfrac{1}{m^6}$

10. $7d^{-4}d^4 = 7d^{-4+4} = 7d^0 = 7$

12. $(5b^{-2})^2 = \left(\dfrac{5}{b^2}\right)^2 = \dfrac{25}{b^4}$

14. $(a^{-3}b^4)^{-3} = a^{(-3)(-3)}b^{4(-3)} = a^9b^{-12} = \dfrac{a^9}{b^{12}}$

16. $5{,}380{,}000 = 5.38 \times 10^6$

18. $0.019 = 1.9 \times 10^{-2}$

20. $0.000\,000\,007\,832 = 7.832 \times 10^{-9}$

22. $9 \times 10^6 = 9{,}000{,}000$

24. $2 \times 10^{-5} = 0.00002$

26. $3.044 \times 10^3 = 3{,}044$

28. $1.13 \times 10^{-2} = 0.0113$

30. $(2x^3y^4)^0 = 1$

32. $\dfrac{10^{-17} \cdot 10^{-5}}{10^{-3} \cdot 10^{-14}} = \dfrac{10^{-22}}{10^{-17}} = 10^{-22} \cdot 10^{17} = 10^{-5} = \dfrac{1}{10^5}$

34. $(2m^{-3}n^2)^{-3} = \dfrac{1}{(2m^{-3}n^2)^3} = \dfrac{1}{8m^{-9}n^6} = \dfrac{m^9}{8n^6}$

36. $\left(\dfrac{2a}{3b^2}\right)^{-3} = \dfrac{1}{\left(\dfrac{2a}{3b^2}\right)^3} = \dfrac{1}{\dfrac{8a^3}{27b^6}} = \dfrac{27b^6}{8a^3}$

38. $\dfrac{9m^{-4}n^3}{12m^{-1}n^{-1}} = \dfrac{3}{4}m^{-4}n^3mn = \dfrac{3}{4}m^{-4+1}n^{3+1} = \dfrac{3}{4}m^{-3}n^4 = \dfrac{3n^4}{4m^3}$

40. $\dfrac{5x^3 - 2}{3x^2} = \dfrac{5x^3}{3x^2} - \dfrac{2}{3x^2} = \dfrac{5}{3}x - \dfrac{2}{3}x^{-2}$

42. $\dfrac{2x^3 - 3x^2 + x}{2x^2} = \dfrac{2x^3}{2x^2} - \dfrac{3x^2}{2x^2} + \dfrac{x}{2x^2} = x - \dfrac{3}{2} + \dfrac{1}{2}x^{-1}$

44. $\dfrac{5x^4(x + 3)^2 - 2x^5(x + 3)}{(x + 3)^4} = \dfrac{x^4(x + 3)\,[5(x + 3) - 2x]}{(x + 3)^4}$

$$= \dfrac{x^4(x + 3)\,[5x + 15 - 2x]}{(x + 3)^4}$$

$$= \dfrac{x^4(x + 3)\,(3x + 15)}{(x + 3)^4}$$

$$= \dfrac{3x^4(x + 3)\,(x + 5)}{(x + 3)^4}$$

$$= \dfrac{3x^4(x + 5)}{(x + 3)^3}$$

46. $2x(x + 3)^{-1} - x^2(x + 3)^{-2} = \dfrac{2x}{x + 3} - \dfrac{x^2}{(x + 3)^2}$

$$= \dfrac{2x(x + 3) - x^2}{(x + 3)^2}$$

$$= \dfrac{2x^2 + 6x - x^2}{(x + 3)^2}$$

$$= \dfrac{x^2 + 6x}{(x + 3)^2} = \dfrac{x(x + 6)}{(x + 3)^2}$$

48. $\dfrac{(60,000)\,(0.000003)}{(0.0004)\,(1,500,000)} = \dfrac{(6 \times 10^4)\,(3 \times 10^{-6})}{(4 \times 10^{-4})\,(1.5 \times 10^6)}$

$$= \dfrac{18 \times 10^{-2}}{6 \times 10^2} = 3 \times 10^{-4};\ \ 0.0003$$

50. $\dfrac{(0.00000082)\,(230,000)}{(625,000)\,(0.0082)} = \dfrac{(8.2 \times 10^{-7})\,(2.3 \times 10^5)}{(6.25 \times 10^5)\,(8.2 \times 10^{-3})}$

$$= \dfrac{2.3 \times 10^{-2}}{6.25 \times 10^2} = 0.368 \times 10^{-4}$$

$$= 3.68 \times 10^{-5};\ \ 0.000\ 0368$$

52. $2^{(3^2)} = 2^9 = 512$ while $(2^3)^2 = 8^2 = 64$ which is the calculator result.

56. $\dfrac{x^{-2} - y^{-2}}{x^{-1} + y^{-1}} = \dfrac{\dfrac{1}{x^2} - \dfrac{1}{y^2}}{\dfrac{1}{x} + \dfrac{1}{y}} = \dfrac{\dfrac{y^2 - x^2}{x^2 y^2}}{\dfrac{y + x}{xy}} = \dfrac{y^2 - x^2}{x^2 y^2} \cdot \dfrac{xy}{y + x} = \dfrac{(y - x)\,(y + x)xy}{x^2 y^2(y + x)}$

$$= \dfrac{y - x}{xy}$$

58. $\dfrac{xy^{-2} - yx^{-2}}{y^{-1} - x^{-1}} = [xy^{-2} - yx^{-2}] \div [y^{-1} - x^{-1}]$

$$= \left[\dfrac{x}{y^2} - \dfrac{y}{x^2}\right] \div \left[\dfrac{1}{y} - \dfrac{1}{x}\right] = \dfrac{x^3 - y^3}{x^2 y^2} \div \dfrac{x - y}{xy}$$

$$= \dfrac{(x - y)(x^2 + xy + y^2)}{x^2 y^2} \cdot \dfrac{xy}{x - y} = \dfrac{x^2 + xy + y^2}{xy}$$

60. (A) $617,679,000,000 = 6.17679 \times 10^{11}$

(B) $261,067,000,000 = 2.61067 \times 10^{11}$

$$\dfrac{6.17679 \times 10^{11}}{2.61067 \times 10^{11}} = \dfrac{6.17679}{2.61067} = 2.366$$

(C) $\dfrac{1}{2.366} = 0.4227$

62. (A) $\dfrac{3,233,300,000,000}{248,765,170} = \dfrac{3.233 \times 10^{12}}{2.4876517 \times 10^8} = 1.2997 \times 10^4 = \$12,997$

(B) $\dfrac{264,800,000,000}{248,765,170} = \dfrac{2.648 \times 10^{11}}{2.4876517 \times 10^8} = 1.064 \times 10^3 = \$1,064$

(C) $\dfrac{264,800,000,000}{3,233,300,000,000} = \dfrac{2.648 \times 10^{11}}{3.2333 \times 10^{12}} = 0.0819$ or 8.19%

64. (A) 0.03 ppm $= \dfrac{0.03}{1,000,000} = \dfrac{3 \times 10^{-2}}{10^6} = 3 \times 10^{-8}$

(B) $0.000\ 000\ 03$ (C) $0.000\ 003\%$

66. $\dfrac{270,300,000}{3,539,000} = \dfrac{2.703 \times 10^8}{3.539 \times 10^6} = 0.764 \times 10^2$ or 76.4 persons per square mile

EXERCISE A-6

2. $7y^{2/5} = 7\sqrt[5]{y^2}$

4. $(7x^2 y)^{5/7} = \sqrt[7]{(7x^2 y)^5}$

6. $x^{1/2} + y^{1/2} = \sqrt{x} + \sqrt{y}$

8. $7m\sqrt[5]{n^2} = 7mn^{2/5}$

10. $\sqrt[7]{(8x^4 y)^3} = ((8x^4 y)^3)^{1/7} = (8^3 x^{12} y^3)^{1/7} = (2^9 x^{12} y^3)^{1/7}$

12. $\sqrt[3]{x^2 + y^2} = (x^2 + y^2)^{1/3}$

14. $64^{1/3} = (4^3)^{1/3} = 4$

16. $16^{3/4} = (16^{1/4})^3 = ((2^4)^{1/4})^3 = 2^3 = 8$

18. $(-49)^{1/2}$ is not a real number.

20. $(-64)^{2/3} = (-2^6)^{2/3} = ((-2^6)^2)^{1/3} = (2^{12})^{1/3} = 2^{12/3} = 2^4 = 16$

22. $\left(\dfrac{8}{27}\right)^{2/3} = \left(\dfrac{2^3}{3^3}\right)^{2/3} = \dfrac{2^2}{3^2} = \dfrac{4}{9}$

24. $8^{-2/3} = (8^{1/3})^{-2} = ((2^3)^{1/3})^{-2} = (2)^{-2} = \dfrac{1}{4}$

26. $y^{-3/7}y^{4/7} = y^{(-3/7) \; + (4/7)} = y^{1/7}$

28. $\dfrac{x^{1/4}}{x^{3/4}} = \dfrac{1}{x^{3/4}x^{-1/4}} = \dfrac{1}{x^{(3/4)-(1/4)}} = \dfrac{1}{x^{1/2}}$

30. $(4u^{-2}v^4)^{1/2} = 4^{1/2}u^{-2 \times (1/2)} v^{4 \times (1/2)} = 2u^{-1}v^2 = \dfrac{2v^2}{u}$

32. $\left(\dfrac{w^4}{9x^{-2}}\right)^{-1/2} = \dfrac{w^{4(-1/2)}}{(9x^{-2})^{-1/2}} = \dfrac{w^{-2}}{9^{-1/2}x} = \dfrac{3}{xw^2}$

34. $\dfrac{6a^{3/4}}{15a^{-1/3}} = \dfrac{2}{5}a^{(3/4) \; + (1/3)} = \dfrac{2}{5}a^{13/12}$

36. $\sqrt[3]{(7 + 2y)^3} = (7 + 2y)^{3/3} = 7 + 2y$

38. $\sqrt[5]{16a^4}\,\sqrt[5]{4a^2}\,\sqrt[5]{8a^3} = \sqrt[5]{(16a^4)(4a^2)(8a^3)} = \sqrt[5]{16 \cdot 4 \cdot 8\,a^9}$

$\qquad\qquad\qquad\qquad\qquad = \sqrt[5]{(2^5a^5) \cdot 16a^4} = 2a\sqrt[5]{16a^4}$

40. $\dfrac{\sqrt{8}\sqrt{12y}}{\sqrt{6y}} = \dfrac{\sqrt{96y}}{\sqrt{6y}} = \sqrt{\dfrac{96y}{6y}} = \sqrt{16} = 4$

42. $2m^{1/3}(3m^{2/3} - m^6) = 6m^{(1/3)+(2/3)} - 2m^{(1/3)+6} = 6m - 2m^{19/3}$

44. $(a^{1/2} + 2b^{1/2})(a^{1/2} - 3b^{1/2})$

$\qquad\qquad = a^{(1/2) \; +(1/2)} - 3a^{1/2}b^{1/2} + 2a^{1/2}b^{1/2} - 6b^{(1/2) \; +(1/2)}$

$\qquad\qquad = a - (ab)^{1/2} - 6b$

46. $(2x - 3y^{1/3})(2x^{1/3} + 1) = 4x^{4/3} + 2x - 6x^{1/3}y^{1/3} - 3y^{1/3}$

48. $(x^{1/2} + 2y^{1/2})^2 = (x^{1/2})^2 + 4(x^{1/2})(y^{1/2}) + (2y^{1/2})^2 = x + 4x^{1/2}y^{1/2} + 4y$

50. $\dfrac{12\sqrt{x} - 3}{4\sqrt{x}} = \dfrac{12x^{1/2} - 3}{4x^{1/2}} = \dfrac{12x^{1/2}}{4x^{1/2}} - \dfrac{3}{4x^{1/2}} = 3 - \dfrac{3}{4}x^{-1/2}$

52. $\dfrac{3\sqrt[3]{x^2} + \sqrt{x}}{5x} = \dfrac{3x^{2/3} + x^{1/2}}{5x} = \dfrac{3x^{2/3}}{5x} + \dfrac{x^{1/2}}{5x}$

$\qquad\qquad\qquad\qquad = \dfrac{3}{5}x^{2/3}x^{-1} + \dfrac{1}{5}x^{1/2}x^{-1}$

$\qquad\qquad\qquad\qquad = \dfrac{3}{5}x^{-1/3} + \dfrac{1}{5}x^{-1/2}$

54. $\dfrac{x^2 - 4\sqrt{x}}{2\sqrt[3]{x}} = \dfrac{x^2 - 4x^{1/2}}{2x^{1/3}} = \dfrac{x^2}{2x^{1/3}} - \dfrac{4x^{1/2}}{2x^{1/3}}$

$$= \dfrac{1}{2}x^2 x^{-1/3} - 2x^{1/2}x^{-1/3}$$

$$= \dfrac{1}{2}x^{5/3} - 2x^{1/6}$$

56. $\dfrac{14x^2}{\sqrt{7x}} = \dfrac{14x^2}{\sqrt{7x}} \cdot \dfrac{\sqrt{7x}}{\sqrt{7x}} = \dfrac{14x^2\sqrt{7x}}{7x} = 2x\sqrt{7x}$

58. $\dfrac{3(x + 1)}{\sqrt{x + 4}} = \dfrac{3(x + 1)}{\sqrt{x + 4}} \cdot \dfrac{\sqrt{x + 4}}{\sqrt{x + 4}} = \dfrac{3(x + 1)\sqrt{x + 4}}{x + 4}$

60. $\dfrac{3a - 3b}{\sqrt{a} + \sqrt{b}} = \dfrac{3(a - b)}{\sqrt{a} + \sqrt{b}} \cdot \dfrac{\sqrt{a} - \sqrt{b}}{\sqrt{a} - \sqrt{b}} = \dfrac{3(a - b)(\sqrt{a} - \sqrt{b})}{(\sqrt{a})^2 - (\sqrt{b})^2}$

$$= \dfrac{3(a - b)(\sqrt{a} - \sqrt{b})}{a - b} = 3(\sqrt{a} - \sqrt{b})$$

62. $\dfrac{\sqrt{3mn}}{3mn} = \dfrac{\sqrt{3mn}}{3mn} \cdot \dfrac{\sqrt{3mn}}{\sqrt{3mn}} = \dfrac{3mn}{3mn\sqrt{3mn}} = \dfrac{1}{\sqrt{3mn}}$

64. $\dfrac{\sqrt{2(a + h)} - \sqrt{2a}}{h} = \dfrac{\sqrt{2(a + h)} - \sqrt{2a}}{h} \cdot \dfrac{\sqrt{2(a + h)} + \sqrt{2a}}{\sqrt{2(a + h)} + \sqrt{2a}}$

$$= \dfrac{2(a + h) - 2a}{h[\sqrt{2(a + h)} + \sqrt{2a}]}$$

$$= \dfrac{2a + 2h - 2a}{h[\sqrt{2(a + h)} + \sqrt{2a}]}$$

$$= \dfrac{2}{\sqrt{2(a + h)} + \sqrt{2a}}$$

66. $\dfrac{\sqrt{x} - \sqrt{y}}{\sqrt{x} + \sqrt{y}} = \dfrac{\sqrt{x} - \sqrt{y}}{\sqrt{x} + \sqrt{y}} \cdot \dfrac{\sqrt{x} + \sqrt{y}}{\sqrt{x} + \sqrt{y}} = \dfrac{x - y}{(\sqrt{x} + \sqrt{y})^2} = \dfrac{x - y}{x + 2\sqrt{xy} + y}$

68. $(x^3 + y^3)^{1/3} \overset{?}{=} x + y$

Let $x = y = 1$, then $(x^3 + y^3)^{1/3} = (1 + 1)^{1/3} = 2^{1/3}$
$1 + 1 = 2$; $2^{1/3} \neq 2$

70. $(x + y)^{-1/2} \overset{?}{=} \dfrac{1}{(x + y)^2}$

Let $x = y = 1$, then $(x + y)^{-1/2} = (2)^{-1/2} = \dfrac{1}{\sqrt{2}}$,

$\dfrac{1}{(x + y)^2} = \dfrac{1}{(1 + 1)^2} = \dfrac{1}{4}$; $\dfrac{1}{\sqrt{2}} \neq \dfrac{1}{4}$

72. True; $\sqrt{x^2} = \sqrt{|x|^2} = |x|$

74. True; $\sqrt[3]{x^3} = (x^3)^{1/3} = x^{3/3} = x$

76. False. $r = 2\sqrt{6} - 5 < 0$ and negative numbers do not have square roots.

78. True. $(1 - \sqrt{2})^3 = -.0710678119$ and $7 - 5\sqrt{2} = -.0710678119$. Therefore, $1 - \sqrt{2}$ is a cube root of $7 - 5\sqrt{2}$.

80. $2(x - 2)^{-1/2} - \dfrac{1}{2}(2x + 3)(x - 2)^{-3/2} = \dfrac{2}{(x - 2)^{1/2}} - \dfrac{2x + 3}{2(x - 2)^{3/2}}$

$$= \dfrac{4(x - 2) - (2x + 3)}{2(x - 2)^{3/2}}$$

$$= \dfrac{4x - 8 - 2x - 3}{2(x - 2)^{3/2}}$$

$$= \dfrac{2x - 11}{2(x - 2)^{3/2}}$$

82. $\dfrac{(2x - 1)^{1/2} - (x + 2)\left(\dfrac{1}{2}\right)(2x - 1)^{-1/2}(2)}{2x - 1}$

$$= \dfrac{(2x - 1)^{1/2}}{2x - 1} - \dfrac{(x + 2)(2x - 1)^{-1/2}}{2x - 1}$$

$$= \dfrac{1}{(2x - 1)^{1/2}} - \dfrac{x + 2}{(2x - 1)^{3/2}} = \dfrac{(2x - 1) - (x + 2)}{(2x - 1)^{3/2}}$$

$$= \dfrac{2x - 1 - x - 2}{(2x - 1)^{3/2}} = \dfrac{x - 3}{(2x - 1)^{3/2}}$$

84. $\dfrac{2(3x - 1)^{1/3} - (2x + 1)\left(\dfrac{1}{3}\right)(3x - 1)^{-2/3}(3)}{(3x - 1)^{2/3}}$

$$= \dfrac{2(3x - 1)^{1/3}}{(3x - 1)^{2/3}} - \dfrac{(2x + 1)(3x - 1)^{-2/3}}{(3x - 1)^{2/3}}$$

$$= \dfrac{2}{(3x - 1)^{1/3}} - \dfrac{2x + 1}{(3x - 1)^{4/3}} = \dfrac{2(3x - 1) - (2x + 1)}{(3x - 1)^{4/3}}$$

$$= \dfrac{6x - 2 - 2x - 1}{(3x - 1)^{4/3}} = \dfrac{4x - 3}{(3x - 1)^{4/3}}$$

86. $15^{5/4} = 15^{1.25} = 29.52$

88. $103^{-3/4} = \dfrac{1}{103^{3/4}} = \dfrac{1}{(103)^{0.75}} = 0.03093$

90. $2.876^{8/5} = (2.876)^{1.6} = 5.421$

92. (A) $2\sqrt[3]{2 + \sqrt{5}} = 3.236$ (B) $\sqrt{8} = 2.828$ (C) $\sqrt{3} + \sqrt{7} = 4.378$
(D) $\sqrt{3 + \sqrt{8}} + \sqrt{3 - \sqrt{8}} = 2.828$ (E) $\sqrt{10 + \sqrt{84}} = 4.378$
(F) $1 + \sqrt{5} = 3.236$

(A) and (F) have the same value:
$$\left(2\sqrt[3]{2 + \sqrt{5}}\right)^3 = 8(2 + \sqrt{5}) = 16 + 8\sqrt{5}$$
$$(1 + \sqrt{5})^3 = 1 + 3\sqrt{5} + 15 + 5\sqrt{5} = 16 + 8\sqrt{5}$$

(B) and (D) have the same value:
$$(\sqrt{8})^2 = 8$$
$$\left(\sqrt{3 + \sqrt{8}} + \sqrt{3 - \sqrt{8}}\right)^2 = 3 + \sqrt{8} + 3 - \sqrt{8} + 2\sqrt{(3 + \sqrt{8})(3 - \sqrt{8})}$$
$$= 6 + 2\sqrt{9 - 8} = 6 + 2 = 8$$

(C) and (E) have the same value:
$$(\sqrt{3} + \sqrt{7})^2 = 3 + 7 + 2\sqrt{21} = 10 + 2\sqrt{21}$$
$$\left(\sqrt{10 + \sqrt{84}}\right)^2 = 10 + \sqrt{84} = 10 + \sqrt{4 \times 21} = 10 + 2\sqrt{21}$$

EXERCISE A-7

2.
$$3y - 4 = 6y - 19$$
$$3y - 4 + 4 = 6y - 19 + 4$$
$$3y = 6y - 15$$
$$3y - 6y = -15$$
$$-3y = -15$$
$$y = \frac{-15}{-3} = 5$$

4. $5x + 2 > 1$
$$5x > -1$$
$$x > -\frac{1}{5}$$

6. $-4x \leq 8$
$$\frac{-4x}{-4} \geq \frac{8}{-4} \quad \text{(Dividing by a negative number)}$$
$$x \geq -2$$

8.
$$-2x + 8 < 4$$
$$-2x + 8 - 8 < 4 - 8$$
$$-2x < -4$$
$$\frac{-2x}{-2} > \frac{-4}{-2} \quad \text{(Dividing by a negative number)}$$
$$x > 2 \quad \text{or} \quad (2, \infty)$$

10. $-4 < 2y - 3 < 9$
$$-1 < 2y < 12$$
$$-\frac{1}{2} < y < 6$$

12. $\dfrac{m}{5} - 2 = \dfrac{3}{5}$

Multiply both sides of the equation by 5 to obtain:
$m - 10 = 3$
$\qquad m = 13$

16. $\dfrac{x}{4} = 9 - \dfrac{x}{2}$

Multiply both sides of the equation by 4 to obtain:
$\quad x = 36 - 2x$
$3x = 36, \; x = 12$

20.
$$x - 2 \geq 2(x - 5)$$
$$x - 2 \geq 2x - 10$$
$$x - 2 + 2 \geq 2x - 10 + 2$$
$$x \geq 2x - 8$$
$$x \leq 8$$

24.
$$\dfrac{u}{2} - \dfrac{2}{3} < \dfrac{u}{3} + 2$$
$$\dfrac{u}{2} - \dfrac{u}{3} < 2 + \dfrac{2}{3}$$
$$\dfrac{u}{6} < \dfrac{8}{3}$$
$$u < 16$$

28.
$$-4 \leq 5x + 6 < 21$$
$$-6 - 4 \leq 5x < 21 - 6$$
$$-10 \leq 5x < 15$$
$$-2 \leq x < 3 \quad \text{or} \quad [-2, 3)$$

32. $y = -\dfrac{2}{3}x + 8$

$y - 8 = -\dfrac{2}{3}x + 8 - 8$

$-\dfrac{2}{3}x = y - 8$

$-2x = 3y - 24$

$x = \dfrac{3y - 24}{-2} = -\dfrac{3}{2}y + 12$

14. $\dfrac{y}{-2} \leq -1$

Multiply both sides by (-2) which will result in changing the direction of the inequality as well.
$\quad y \geq 2$

18.
$$-3(4 - x) = 5 - (x + 1)$$
$$-12 + 3x = 5 - x - 1$$
$$-12 + 3x = 4 - x$$
$$12 - 12 + 3x = 12 + 4 - x$$
$$3x = 16 - x$$
$$4x = 16$$
$$x = 4$$

22. $\dfrac{y}{4} - \dfrac{y}{3} = \dfrac{1}{2}$

Multiply both sides by 12:
$3y - 4y = 6$
$\qquad -y = 6$
$\qquad\quad y = -6$

26.
$$0.03(2x + 1) - 0.05x = 12$$
$$0.06x + 0.03 - 0.05x = 12$$
$$0.01x = 12 - 0.03 = 11.97$$
$$x = \dfrac{11.97}{0.01} = 1{,}197$$

30. $-1 \leq \dfrac{2}{3}t + 5 \leq 11$

$-5 - 1 \leq \dfrac{2}{3}t \leq 11 - 5$

$-6 \leq \dfrac{2}{3}t \leq 6$

$-18 \leq 2t \leq 18$

$-9 \leq t \leq 9$

34.
$$y = mx + b$$
$$y - b = mx + b - b$$
$$mx = y - b$$
$$m = \dfrac{y - b}{x}$$

36. $C = \dfrac{5}{9}(F - 32)$

$\dfrac{9}{5}C = F - 32$

$32 + \dfrac{9}{5}C = F$

$F = \dfrac{9}{5}C + 32$

38. $U = 3C - 2CD$

$U = C(3 - 2D)$

$C = \dfrac{U}{3 - 2D}$

40. $-10 \le 8 - 3u \le -6$

$-18 \le -3u \le -14$

$18 \ge 3u \ge 14$

$6 \ge u \ge \dfrac{14}{3}$

42. (A) Two must be negative and one positive or all three must be positive.

(B) Two must be positive and one negative or all three must be negative.

(C) Two must be negative and one positive or all three must be positive.

(D) $a \ne 0$ and b and c must have opposite signs.

44. $c + d < c - d$ for all real c and $d < 0$.

46. If a and b are negative and $\dfrac{b}{a} > 1$, then multiplying both sides by the negative number a we obtain $b < a$ and hence $a - b > 0$.

48. False. Consider the two closed intervals [1, 2] and [2, 3]. Their intersection is {2} which is not an interval.

50. False. Consider the two closed intervals [-1, 0] and [1, 2]. Their union is [-1, 0] $\cup$ [1, 2] which is not an interval.

52. True. Let $A = [a, b]$, $B = [c, d]$, where $a < c < b < d$, so that $A \cap B \ne \varnothing$. Then $A \cap B = [c, b]$ which is a closed interval.

54. Let x = number of quarters in the meter. Then
$100 - x$ = number of dimes in the meter.

Now, $0.25x + 0.10(100 - x) = 14.50$ or

$0.25x + 10 - 0.10x = 14.50$

$0.15x = 4.50$

$x = \dfrac{4.50}{0.15} = 30$

Thus, there will be 30 quarters and 70 dimes.

56. Let x = the amount invested at 8%. Then $20,000 - x$ is the amount invested at 12%.

Required total yield = 11% of $20,000 = $(0.11) \cdot (20,000) = \$2,200$.
Thus,
$$0.08x + 0.12(20,000 - x) = 2,200$$
$$0.08x + 2,400 - 0.12x = 2,200$$
$$-0.04x = -200$$
$$x = \frac{200}{0.04} = \$5,000$$

Thus, we get $5,000 invested at 8% and $20,000 - 5,000 = \$15,000$ invested at 12%.

58. Let x be the price of the house in 1960. Then
$$\frac{29.6}{172.2} = \frac{x}{200,000} \quad \text{(refer to Table 2, Example 9)}$$
$$x = 200,000 \cdot \frac{29.6}{172.2} \approx \$34,379$$

To the nearest dollar, the house would be valued $34,379 in 1960.

60. Let x = number of books produced. Then

Costs: $C = 2.10x + 92,000$

Revenue: $R = 15x$

To find the break-even point, set $R = C$:
$$15x = 2.10x + 92,000$$
$$12.9x = 92,000$$
$$x = \frac{92,000}{12.9} \approx 7,132$$

Thus, 7,132 books will have to be sold for the publisher to break even.

62. Let x = number of books produced.

Costs: $C(x) = 92,000 + 2.70x$

Revenue: $R(x) = 15x$

(A) The obvious strategy is to raise the price of the book.

(B) To find the break-even point, set $R(x) = C(x)$:
$$15x = 92,000 + 2.70x$$
$$12.30x = 92,000$$
$$x = 7,480$$

The company must sell more than 7,480 books to make a profit.

(C) From Problem 60, the production level at the break-even point is: 7,132 books. At this production level, the costs are
$$C(7,132) = 92,000 + 2.70(7,132) = \$111,256.40$$

If p is the new price of the book, then we need
$$7,132p = 111,256.40$$
and $\quad p \approx \$15.60$

The company should increase the price at least $0.60 (60 cents).

64. $-49 \leq F \leq 14$

$$-49 \leq \frac{9}{5}C + 32 \leq 14$$

$$-32 - 49 \leq \frac{9}{5}C \leq 14 - 32$$

$$-81 \leq \frac{9}{5}C \leq -18$$

$$(-81) \cdot 5 \leq 9C \leq (-18) \cdot 5$$

$$\frac{(-81) \cdot 5}{9} \leq C \leq \frac{(-18) \cdot 5}{9}$$

$$-45 \leq C \leq -10$$

66. $C = \dfrac{100W}{L}$

For $C = 66$, $W = 6.6$, we have

$$66 = \frac{(100)(6.6)}{L}$$

$$L = \frac{660}{66} = 10 \text{ inches}$$

EXERCISE A-8
_____

2. $3m^2 - 21 = 0$

$$3m^2 = 21$$

$$m^2 = 7$$

$$m = \pm\sqrt{7}$$

4. $(2x + 1)^2 = 16$

$$2x + 1 = \pm 4$$

$$2x = \pm 4 - 1$$

$$x = \frac{\pm 4 - 1}{2}$$

$$x = -\frac{5}{2} \text{ and } x = \frac{3}{2}$$

6. $3x^2 - 18x + 15 = 0$

$$x^2 - 6x + 5 = 0$$

$$(x - 1)(x - 5) = 0$$

$$x - 1 = 0 \quad \text{or} \quad x - 5 = 0$$

$$x = 1 \quad \text{or} \quad x = 5$$

8. $n^2 = 3n$

$$n^2 - 3n = 0$$

$$n(n - 3) = 0$$

$$n = 0 \quad \text{or} \quad n - 3 = 0$$

$$n = 0 \quad \text{or} \quad n = 3$$

10. $m^2 + 8m + 3 = 0$

$$m = \frac{-b \pm \sqrt{b^2 - 4ac}}{2a}, \quad a = 1, \ b = 8, \ c = 3$$

$$= \frac{-8 \pm \sqrt{64 - 12}}{2} = \frac{-8 \pm \sqrt{52}}{2} = \frac{-8 \pm 2\sqrt{13}}{2} = -4 \pm \sqrt{13}$$

12. $2x^2 - 20x - 6 = 0$

$$x^2 - 10x - 3 = 0$$

$$x = \frac{-b \pm \sqrt{b^2 - 4ac}}{2a}, \quad a = 1, \ b = -10, \ c = -3$$

$$= \frac{-(-10) \pm \sqrt{100 + 12}}{2} = \frac{10 \pm \sqrt{112}}{2} = \frac{10 \pm 4\sqrt{7}}{2} = 5 \pm 2\sqrt{7}$$

14. $$x^2 = -\frac{3}{4}x$$

$$x^2 + \frac{3}{4}x = 0$$

$$x\left(x + \frac{3}{4}\right) = 0$$

$$x = 0 \text{ and } x = -\frac{3}{4}$$

16. $$9y^2 - 25 = 0$$

$$9y^2 = 25$$

$$y^2 = \frac{25}{9}$$

$$y = \pm\sqrt{\frac{25}{9}} = \pm\frac{5}{3}$$

18. $$9x^2 - 6 = 15x$$

$$3x^2 - 2 = 5x$$

$$3x^2 - 5x - 2 = 0$$

$$x = \frac{-b \pm \sqrt{b^2 - 4ac}}{2a}, \quad a = 3, \ b = -5, \ c = -2$$

$$= \frac{5 \pm \sqrt{25 + 24}}{6} = \frac{5 \pm \sqrt{49}}{6} = \frac{5 \pm 7}{6}$$

$$x = \frac{5 - 7}{6} = -\frac{1}{3}, \quad x = \frac{5 + 7}{6} = 2$$

20. $$m^2 = 1 - 3m$$

$$m^2 + 3m - 1 = 0$$

$$m = \frac{-b \pm \sqrt{b^2 - 4ac}}{2a}, \quad a = 1, \ b = 3, \ c = -1$$

$$= \frac{-3 \pm \sqrt{9 + 4}}{2} = \frac{-3 \pm \sqrt{13}}{2}$$

22. $$2x^2 = 4x - 1$$

$$2x^2 - 4x + 1 = 0$$

$$x = \frac{-b \pm \sqrt{b^2 - 4ac}}{2a}, \quad a = 2, \ b = -4, \ c = 1$$

$$x = \frac{4 \pm \sqrt{16 - 8}}{4} = \frac{4 \pm \sqrt{8}}{4} = \frac{4 \pm 2\sqrt{2}}{4} = \frac{2 \pm \sqrt{2}}{2}$$

24. $$x^2 - 2x = -3$$

$$x^2 - 2x + 3 = 0$$

$$x = \frac{-b \pm \sqrt{b^2 - 4ac}}{2a}, \quad a = 1, \ b = -2, \ c = 3$$

$$b^2 - 4ac = 4 - 12 = -8$$

Since $b^2 - 4ac < 0$, there are no real solutions.

26. $(5x - 2)^2 = 7$

$$5x - 2 = \pm\sqrt{7}$$

$$5x = \pm\sqrt{7} + 2$$

$$x = \frac{\pm\sqrt{7} + 2}{5}$$

$$x = \frac{2 - \sqrt{7}}{5} \text{ and } x = \frac{2 + \sqrt{7}}{5}$$

28. $x - \dfrac{7}{x} = 0$

Since $x \neq 0$, $\dfrac{x^2 - 7}{x} = 0$ will be determined and $x^2 - 7 = 0$

implies $x = \pm\sqrt{7}$.

30. $2 + \dfrac{5}{u} = \dfrac{3}{u^2}$

Multiply both sides by $u^2 \neq 0$.

$$2u^2 + 5u = 3$$

$$2u^2 + 5u - 3 = 0$$

$$u = \frac{-5 \pm \sqrt{25 + 24}}{4} = \frac{-5 \pm \sqrt{49}}{4} = \frac{-5 \pm 7}{4}$$

$$u = \frac{-5 - 7}{4} = -3 \text{ and } u = \frac{-5 + 7}{4} = \frac{1}{2}$$

32. $x^2 - 28x - 128$

<u>Step 1</u>. Test for factorability

$$\sqrt{b^2 - 4ac} = \sqrt{(-28)^2 - 4(1)(-128)} = 36$$

Since the result is an integer, the polynomial has first-degree factors with integer coefficients.

<u>Step 2</u>. Use the factor theorem

$$x^2 - 28x - 128 = 0$$

$$x = \frac{28 \pm 36}{2} = -4, \ 32 \quad \text{(by the quadratic formula)}$$

Thus, $x^2 - 28x - 128 = [x - (-4)](x - 32) = (x + 4)(x - 32)$

34. $x^2 + 52x + 208$

<u>Step 1</u>. Test for factorability

$$\sqrt{b^2 - 4ac} = \sqrt{(52)^2 - 4(1)(208)} = \sqrt{1872} \approx 43.27$$

Since this is not an integer, the polynomial is not factorable.

36. $3x^2 - 32x - 140$

Step 1. Test for factorability
$$\sqrt{b^2 - 4ac} = \sqrt{(-32)^2 - 4(3)(-140)} = 52$$
Thus, the polynomial has first-degree factors with integer coefficients.

Step 2. Use the factor theorem
$$3x^2 - 32x - 140 = 0$$
$$x = \frac{32 \pm 52}{6} = -\frac{10}{3}, \ 14$$
Thus, $3x^2 - 32x - 140 = 3\left[x - \left(-\frac{10}{3}\right)\right](x - 14)$
$$= 3 \cdot \frac{(3x + 10)}{3} \cdot (x - 14)$$
$$= (3x + 10)(x - 14)$$

38. $6x^2 - 427x - 360$

Step 1. Test for factorability
$$\sqrt{b^2 - 4ac} = \sqrt{(-427)^2 - 4(6)(-360)} = 437$$
Thus, the polynomial has first-degree factors with integer coefficients.

Step 2. Use the factor theorem
$$6x^2 - 427x - 360 = 0$$
$$x = \frac{427 \pm 437}{12} = -\frac{5}{6}, \ 72$$
Thus, $6x^2 - 427x - 360 = 6\left[x - \left(-\frac{5}{6}\right)\right](x - 72) = (6x + 5)(x - 72)$

40. $x^2 + 3mx - 3n = 0$
$$x = \frac{-3m \pm \sqrt{9m^2 + 12n}}{2}$$
$$x = \frac{-3m - \sqrt{9m^2 + 12n}}{2} \quad \text{and} \quad x = \frac{-3m + \sqrt{9m^2 + 12n}}{2}$$

42. $x^2 - 2x + C = 0$

The discriminant is: $4 - 4c$

(A) If $4 - 4c > 0$, i.e., if $c < 1$, then the equation has two distinct real roots.

(B) If $4 - 4c = 0$, i.e., if $c = 1$, then the equation has one real double root.

(C) If $4 - 4c < 0$, i.e., if $c > 1$, then there are no real roots.

44. Setting the supply equation equal to the demand equation, we have

$$\frac{x}{6} + 9 = \frac{24,840}{x}$$

$$\frac{1}{6}x^2 + 9x = 24,840$$

$$x^2 + 54x - 149,040 = 0$$

$$x = \frac{-54 \pm \sqrt{(54)^2 - 4(1)(149,040)}}{2}$$

$$= \frac{-54 \pm 774}{2} = 360 \text{ units}$$

Note, we discard the negative root since a negative number of units cannot be produced or sold. Substituting $x = 360$ into either equation (we use the demand equation), we get

$$p = \frac{24,840}{1,360} = 69$$

Supply equals demand at $69 per unit.

46. $A = P(1 + r)^2 = P(1 + 2r + r^2)$
Let $P = \$1,000$, $A = \$1,210$. Then,

$$1,210 = 1,000(1 + 2r + r^2)$$

$$r^2 + 2r + 1 = \frac{1210}{1000} = 1.21$$

$$r^2 + 2r - .21 = 0$$

$$r = \frac{-2 \pm \sqrt{4 - 4(-.21)}}{2} = \frac{-2 \pm \sqrt{4 + .84}}{2}$$

$$= \frac{-2 \pm \sqrt{4.84}}{2} = \frac{-2 \pm 2.2}{2}$$

$$= 0.10 \text{ or } 10\%$$

48. $d = 0.044v^2 + 1.1v$
For $d = 550$ we have

$$0.044v^2 + 1.1v - 550 = 0$$

$$44v^2 + 1100v - 550,000 = 0$$

$$v^2 + 25v - 12,500 = 0$$

$$v = \frac{-25 \pm \sqrt{625 + 50,000}}{2} = \frac{-25 \pm 225}{2}$$

$$= \frac{200}{2}$$

$$= 100 \text{ miles per hour}$$

EXERCISE B-1

2. $a_n = 4n - 3$; $a_1 = 4 \cdot 1 - 3 = 1$
$a_2 = 4 \cdot 2 - 3 = 5$
$a_3 = 4 \cdot 3 - 3 = 9$
$a_4 = 4 \cdot 4 - 3 = 13$

4. $a_n = \dfrac{2n + 1}{2n}$; $a_1 = \dfrac{2 \cdot 1 + 1}{2 \cdot 1} = \dfrac{3}{2}$
$a_2 = \dfrac{2 \cdot 2 + 1}{2 \cdot 2} = \dfrac{5}{4}$
$a_3 = \dfrac{2 \cdot 3 + 1}{2 \cdot 3} = \dfrac{7}{6}$
$a_4 = \dfrac{2 \cdot 4 + 1}{2 \cdot 4} = \dfrac{9}{8}$

6. $a_n = \left(-\dfrac{1}{4}\right)^{n-1}$; $a_1 = \left(-\dfrac{1}{4}\right)^{1-1} = \left(-\dfrac{1}{4}\right)^0 = 1$

$a_2 = \left(-\dfrac{1}{4}\right)^{2-1} = \left(-\dfrac{1}{4}\right)^1 = -\dfrac{1}{4}$

$a_3 = \left(-\dfrac{1}{4}\right)^{3-1} = \left(-\dfrac{1}{4}\right)^2 = \dfrac{1}{16}$

$a_4 = \left(-\dfrac{1}{4}\right)^{4-1} = \left(-\dfrac{1}{4}\right)^3 = -\dfrac{1}{64}$

8. $a_n = 4n - 3$; $a_{15} = 4 \cdot 15 - 3 = 57$

10. $a_n = \dfrac{2n + 1}{2n}$; $a_{200} = \dfrac{2 \cdot 200 + 1}{2 \cdot 200} = \dfrac{401}{400}$

12. $\displaystyle\sum_{k=1}^{5} k^2 = (1)^2 + (2)^2 + (3)^2 + (4)^2 + (5)^2 = 1 + 4 + 9 + 16 + 25 = 55$

14. $\displaystyle\sum_{k=0}^{4} (-2)^k = (-2)^0 + (-2)^1 + (-2)^2 + (-2)^3 + (-2)^4$
$= 1 - 2 + 4 - 8 + 16 = 11$

16. $\displaystyle\sum_{k=1}^{4} \dfrac{1}{2^k} = \dfrac{1}{2^1} + \dfrac{1}{2^2} + \dfrac{1}{2^3} + \dfrac{1}{2^4}$

$= \dfrac{1}{2} + \dfrac{1}{4} + \dfrac{1}{8} + \dfrac{1}{16} = \dfrac{8 + 4 + 2 + 1}{16} = \dfrac{15}{16}$

18. $a_1 = 7$, $a_2 = 9$, $a_3 = 9$, $a_4 = 2$, $a_5 = 4$.   Here $n = 5$ and the arithmetic mean is given by:

$\bar{a} = \dfrac{1}{5} \displaystyle\sum_{i=1}^{5} a_i = \dfrac{1}{5}(7 + 9 + 9 + 2 + 4) = \dfrac{31}{5} = 6.2$

20. $a_1 = 100$, $a_2 = 62$, $a_3 = 95$, $a_4 = 91$, $a_5 = 82$, $a_6 = 87$, $a_7 = 70$, $a_8 = 75$, $a_9 = 87$, and $a_{10} = 82$. Here $n = 10$ and the arithmetic mean is given by:

$$\bar{a} = \frac{1}{10} \sum_{i=1}^{10} a_i = \frac{1}{10}(100 + 62 + 95 + 91 + 82 + 87 + 70 + 75 + 87 + 82)$$

$$= \frac{830}{10} = 83.1$$

22. $a_n = (-1)^n(n-1)^2$;

$$a_1 = (-1)^1(1-1)^2 = 0$$

$$a_2 = (-1)^2(2-1)^2 = 1$$

$$a_3 = (-1)^3(3-1)^2 = -4$$

$$a_4 = (-1)^4(4-1)^2 = 9$$

$$a_5 = (-1)^5(5-1)^2 = -16$$

24. $a_n = \dfrac{1-(-1)^n}{n}$;

$$a_1 = \frac{1-(-1)^1}{1} = 2$$

$$a_2 = \frac{1-(-1)^2}{2} = 0$$

$$a_3 = \frac{1-(-1)^3}{3} = \frac{2}{3}$$

$$a_4 = \frac{1-(-1)^4}{4} = 0$$

$$a_5 = \frac{1-(-1)^5}{5} = \frac{2}{5}$$

26. $a_n = \left(-\dfrac{1}{2}\right)^{n+1}$;

$$a_1 = \left(-\frac{1}{2}\right)^{1+1} = \frac{1}{4}$$

$$a_2 = \left(-\frac{1}{2}\right)^{2+1} = -\frac{1}{8}$$

$$a_3 = \left(-\frac{1}{2}\right)^{3+1} = \frac{1}{16}$$

$$a_4 = \left(-\frac{1}{2}\right)^{4+1} = -\frac{1}{32}$$

$$a_5 = \left(-\frac{1}{2}\right)^{5+1} = \frac{1}{64}$$

28. Given 4, 5, 6, 7, … The sequence is the set of successive integers beginning with 4. Thus, $a_n = n + 3$, $n = 1, 2, … $.

30. Given -3, -6, -9, -12, … The sequence is the set of negative integers of the form $-3n$. Thus, $a_n = -3n$, $n = 1, 2, …$.

32. Given $\dfrac{1}{2}, \dfrac{2}{3}, \dfrac{3}{4}, \dfrac{4}{5}, …$ The sequence is the set of all fractions of positive integers whose denominator is 1 plus the numerator. Thus,

$$a_n = \frac{n}{n+1}, \quad n = 1, 2, … \ .$$

34. Given -2, 4, -8, 16, ... The sequence consists of positive integer powers of (-2). Thus,

$$a_n = (-2)^n, \quad n = 1, 2, \ldots .$$

36. Given 3, -6, 9, -12, ... The sequence consists of integer multiples of 3 with alternating sign. Thus,

$$a_n = (-1)^{n+1}3n, \quad n = 1, 2, \ldots .$$

38. Given $\dfrac{4}{3}$, $\dfrac{16}{9}$, $\dfrac{64}{27}$, $\dfrac{256}{81}$, ... The sequence consists of the positive integer powers of $\left(\dfrac{4}{3}\right)$. Thus,

$$a_n = \left(\frac{4}{3}\right)^n, \quad n = 1, 2, \ldots .$$

40. Given 1, $2x$, $3x^2$, $4x^3$, ... The sequence consists of non-negative integer powers of x multiplied by a number which is one more than the power. Thus, $a_n = nx^{n-1}$, $n = 1, 2, \ldots .$

42. Given x, $\dfrac{x^2}{2}$, $\dfrac{x^3}{3}$, $\dfrac{x^4}{4}$, ... The sequence consists of positive integer powers of x divided by the power. Thus,

$$a_n = \frac{x^n}{n}, \quad n = 1, 2, \ldots .$$

44.
$$\sum_{k=1}^{4} \frac{(-2)^{k+1}}{2k+1} = \frac{(-2)^{1+1}}{2 \cdot 1 + 1} + \frac{(-2)^{2+1}}{2 \cdot 2 + 1} + \frac{(-2)^{3+1}}{2 \cdot 3 + 1} + \frac{(-2)^{4+1}}{2 \cdot 4 + 1}$$
$$= \frac{4}{3} + \frac{-8}{5} + \frac{16}{7} + \frac{-32}{9}$$
$$= \frac{4}{3} - \frac{8}{5} + \frac{16}{7} - \frac{32}{9}$$

46.
$$\sum_{k=3}^{7} \frac{(-1)^k}{k^2 - k} = \frac{(-1)^3}{3^2 - 3} + \frac{(-1)^4}{4^2 - 4} + \frac{(-1)^5}{5^2 - 5} + \frac{(-1)^6}{6^2 - 6} + \frac{(-1)^7}{7^2 - 7}$$
$$= -\frac{1}{6} + \frac{1}{12} - \frac{1}{20} + \frac{1}{30} - \frac{1}{42}$$

48.
$$\sum_{k=1}^{3} \frac{1}{k} x^{k+1} = \frac{1}{1}x^{1+1} + \frac{1}{2}x^{2+1} + \frac{1}{3}x^{3+1}$$
$$= x^2 + \frac{x^3}{2} + \frac{x^4}{3}$$

50.
$$\sum_{k=0}^{4} \frac{(-1)^k x^{2k}}{2k+2} = \frac{(-1)^0 x^{2(0)}}{2(0)+2} + \frac{(-1)^1 x^{2(1)}}{2(1)+2} + \frac{(-1)^2 x^{2(2)}}{2(2)+2} + \frac{(-1)^3 x^{2(3)}}{2(3)+2} + \frac{(-1)^4 x^{2(4)}}{2(4)+2}$$
$$= \frac{1}{2} - \frac{x^2}{4} + \frac{x^4}{6} - \frac{x^6}{8} + \frac{x^8}{10}$$

52. (A) $1^2 + 2^2 + 3^2 + 4^2 = \sum\limits_{k=1}^{4} k^2$ (B) $1^2 + 2^2 + 3^2 + 4^2 = \sum\limits_{j=0}^{3} (j + 1)^2$

54. (A) $1 - \dfrac{1}{3} + \dfrac{1}{5} - \dfrac{1}{7} + \dfrac{1}{9} = \sum\limits_{k=1}^{5} \dfrac{(-1)^{k+1}}{2k - 1}$

(B) $1 - \dfrac{1}{3} + \dfrac{1}{5} - \dfrac{1}{7} + \dfrac{1}{9} = \sum\limits_{j=0}^{4} \dfrac{(-1)^{j}}{2j + 1}$

56. $1 + \dfrac{1}{2^2} + \dfrac{1}{3^2} + \dots + \dfrac{1}{n^2} = \sum\limits_{k=1}^{n} \dfrac{1}{k^2}$

58. $1 - 4 + 9 - \dots + (-1)^{n+1} n^2 = \sum\limits_{k=1}^{n} (-1)^{k+1} k^2$

60. True. Let $I = \dfrac{1}{2} + \dfrac{1}{4} + \dfrac{1}{8} + \dots + \dfrac{1}{2^n}$, then

$$I = \dfrac{1}{2} + \dfrac{1}{2}\left(\dfrac{1}{2} + \dfrac{1}{4} + \dots + \dfrac{1}{2^{n-1}}\right) = \dfrac{1}{2} + \dfrac{1}{2}\left(I - \dfrac{1}{2^n}\right)$$

So, $I = \dfrac{1}{2} + \dfrac{1}{2}I - \dfrac{1}{2^{n+1}}$ or $\dfrac{1}{2}I = \dfrac{1}{2} - \dfrac{1}{2^{n+1}}$.

Thus, $I = 1 - \dfrac{1}{2^n} < 1$.

62. True. Observe that if n is even, then

$$1 - \dfrac{1}{2} + \dfrac{1}{3} - \dfrac{1}{4} + \dots + \dfrac{(-1)^{n+1}}{n} = \left(1 - \dfrac{1}{2}\right) + \left(\dfrac{1}{3} - \dfrac{1}{4}\right) + \dots + \left(\dfrac{1}{n-1} - \dfrac{1}{n}\right)$$

$$> 1 - \dfrac{1}{2} = \dfrac{1}{2};$$

if n is odd, then

$$1 - \dfrac{1}{2} + \dfrac{1}{3} - \dfrac{1}{4} + \dots + \dfrac{(-1)^{n+1}}{n} = \left(1 - \dfrac{1}{2}\right) + \left(\dfrac{1}{3} - \dfrac{1}{4}\right) + \dots + \left(\dfrac{1}{n-2} - \dfrac{1}{n-1}\right) + \dfrac{1}{n}$$

$$> 1 - \dfrac{1}{2} = \dfrac{1}{2}.$$

64. $a_1 = 3$ and $a_n = 2a_{n-1} - 2$ for $n \geq 2$.

$a_1 = 3$
$a_2 = 2 \cdot 3 - 2 = 4$
$a_3 = 2 \cdot 4 - 2 = 6$
$a_4 = 2 \cdot 6 - 2 = 10$
$a_5 = 2 \cdot 10 - 2 = 18$

66. $a_1 = 1$ and $a_n = -\dfrac{1}{3} a_{n-1}$ for $n \geq 2$.

$a_1 = 1$

$a_2 = -\dfrac{1}{3} \cdot 1 = -\dfrac{1}{3}$

$a_3 = -\dfrac{1}{3} \cdot \left(-\dfrac{1}{3}\right) = \dfrac{1}{9}$

$a_4 = -\dfrac{1}{3} \cdot \left(\dfrac{1}{9}\right) = -\dfrac{1}{27}$

$a_5 = -\dfrac{1}{3} \cdot \left(-\dfrac{1}{27}\right) = \dfrac{1}{81}$

68. In $a_1 = \dfrac{A}{2}$, $a_n = \dfrac{1}{2}\left(a_{n-1} + \dfrac{A}{a_{n-1}}\right)$, $n \geq 2$, let $A = 6$. Then:

$$a_1 = \frac{6}{2} = 3$$

$$a_2 = \frac{1}{2}\left(a_1 + \frac{A}{a_1}\right) = \frac{1}{2}\left(3 + \frac{6}{3}\right) = \frac{1}{2}(3 + 2) = \frac{5}{2}$$

$$a_3 = \frac{1}{2}\left(a_2 + \frac{A}{a_2}\right) = \frac{1}{2}\left(\frac{5}{2} + \frac{6}{5/2}\right) = \frac{1}{2}\left(\frac{5}{2} + \frac{12}{5}\right) = \frac{49}{20}$$

$$a_4 = \frac{1}{2}\left(a_3 + \frac{A}{a_3}\right) = \frac{1}{2}\left(\frac{49}{20} + \frac{6}{49/20}\right) = \frac{4,801}{1,960} \; ;$$

$$a_4 = \frac{4,801}{1,960} \approx 2.4494898, \quad \sqrt{6} \approx 2.4494897$$

70. $b_1 = \dfrac{\sqrt{5}}{5}\left(\dfrac{1 + \sqrt{5}}{2}\right) = \dfrac{\sqrt{5}}{5}(1.618034) \approx 0.724$

$$b_2 = \frac{\sqrt{5}}{5}\left(\frac{1 + \sqrt{5}}{2}\right)^2 = b_1 \cdot \left(\frac{1 + \sqrt{5}}{2}\right) = 0.724 \cdot (1.618034) \approx 1.171$$

$b_3 = b_2(1.618034) \approx 1.894$

$b_4 = b_3(1.618034) \approx 3.065$

$b_5 = b_4(1.618034) \approx 4.960$

$b_6 = b_5(1.618034) \approx 8.025$

$b_7 = b_6(1.618034) \approx 12.985$

$b_8 = b_7(1.618034) \approx 21.010$

$b_9 = b_8(1.618034) \approx 33.994$

$b_{10} = b_9(1.618034) \approx 55.005$

The closest integer to b_n is the nth Fibonacci number

EXERCISE B-2

2. (A) 5, 20, 100, …

This is neither an arithmetic sequence ($20 - 5 \neq 100 - 20$) nor a geometric sequence $\left(\dfrac{20}{5} \neq \dfrac{100}{20}\right)$.

(B) -5, -5, -5, …

This is an arithmetic sequence with $d = 0$, and is a geometric sequence with $r = 1$; -5, -5 are the next two terms.

(C) 7, 6.5, 6, …

This is an arithmetic sequence with $d = -0.5$; the next two terms are: 5.5, 5.

(D) 512, 256, 128, …

This is a geometric sequence with common ratio $r = \dfrac{1}{2}$;

$(512)r = 256$, $(256)r = 128$;
The next two terms are: 64, 32.

4. $\sum\limits_{k=1}^{200} 3$. This series is both arithmetic with $d = 3$ and geometric with $r = 1$. $S_{200} = 3 \times 200 = 600$.

6. This is a geometric series with $r = -3$. Using sum formula we have
$$S_{20} = \frac{3(\,(-3)^{20} - 1)}{-3 - 1} = -2,615,088,300.$$

8. Neither arithmetic nor geometric, since $a_n - a_{n-1}$ is not the same for any n and $\dfrac{a_n}{a_{n-1}}$ is not the same for any n.

10. $a_1 = -2;\; d = -3$
$a_2 = a_1 + d = -2 - 3 = -5$
$a_3 = a_2 + d = -5 - 3 = -8$

12. $a_1 = 8;\; d = -10$:
$a_{15} = a_1 + (15 - 1)d = 8 + (14)(-10) = 8 - 140 = -132$
$S_{23} = \dfrac{23}{2}\,[2a_1 + (23 - 1)d] = \dfrac{23}{2}\,[16 + 22(-10)] = -2,346$

14. $a_1 = 203;\; a_{30} = 261$:
$$S_{30} = \frac{30}{2}\,(a_1 + a_{30})$$
$$= \frac{30}{2}\,(203 + 261) = 6,960$$

16. $a_1 = 32;\; r = -\dfrac{1}{2}$:
$$a_2 = a_1 r = 32\left(-\frac{1}{2}\right) = -16$$
$$a_3 = a_2 r = (-16)\left(-\frac{1}{2}\right) = 8$$
$$a_4 = a_3 r = 8\left(-\frac{1}{2}\right) = -4$$

18. $a_1 = 3;\; a_7 = 2,187;\; r = 3$:
$$S_7 = \frac{ra_7 - a_1}{r - 1} = \frac{3(2,187) - 3}{3 - 1}$$
$$= 3,279$$

20. $a_1 = 240;\; r = 1.06$:
$$a_{12} = a_1 r^{11} = 240(1.06)^{11}$$
$$= 455.59$$

22. $a_1 = 100;\; a_{10} = 300$:
$a_{10} = a_1 r^9$
$300 = 100r^9$
$r^9 = 3$
$r = 3^{1/9} = 1.13$

24. $a_1 = 8,000;\; r = 0.4$:
$$S_{10} = \frac{a_1(r^{10} - 1)}{r - 1} = \frac{8,000(.4^{10} - 1)}{.4 - 1} = 13,331.94$$
$$S_\infty = \frac{a_1}{1 - r} = \frac{8,000}{1 - .4} = 13,333.33$$

26. $S_{50} = \sum\limits_{k=1}^{50} (2k - 3)$. The sequence of terms is an arithmetic sequence.
Therefore,
$$S_{50} = \frac{50}{2}\,(a_1 + a_{50}) = \frac{50}{2}\,(-1 + 97) = 2,400$$

28. $S_8 = \sum\limits_{k=1}^{8} 2^k$. The sequence of terms is a geometric sequence with common

ratio $r = 2$ and $a_1 = 2^1 = 2$.

$$S_8 = \frac{2(2^8 - 1)}{2 - 1} = 510$$

30. Let $a_1 = 24$, $d = 2$. Then, using the formula $a_n = a_1 + (n - 1)d$ we can find n.

$$96 = 24 + (n - 1)2$$
$$2(n - 1) = 96 - 24 = 72$$
$$n - 1 = 36$$
$$n = 37$$

Therefore,

$$S_{37} = \frac{37}{2}[24 + 96] = 2,220.$$

32. (A) 16, 4, 1, ⋯ . Since $r = \dfrac{4}{16} = \dfrac{1}{4} = \cdots = \dfrac{1}{4}$ and $|r| < 1$, the sum

exists:

$$S_\infty = \frac{16}{1 - 1/4} = \frac{16}{3/4} = \frac{64}{3} \approx 21.33$$

(B) 1, -3, 9, ⋯

$$r = -\frac{3}{1} = \frac{9}{-3} = \cdots = -3. \text{ Since } |r| = 3 > 1, \text{ the sum does not exist.}$$

34. $g(t) = 18 - 3t$:

$g(1) = 15$, $g(2) = 12$, $g(3) = 9$, ⋯

This is an arithmetic progression with $a_1 = 15$, $d = -3$.

Thus, using the formula $S_n = \dfrac{n}{2}[2a_1 + (n - 1)d]$, we have:

$$S_{100} = \frac{100}{2}[2(15) + 99(-3)] = -13,350$$

36. $g(x) = 2^x$

$g(1) = 2$, $g(2) = 2^2$, ⋯, $g(10) = 2^{10}$. This is a geometric progression

with $a_1 = 2$, $r = 2$. Thus, using formula $S_n = \dfrac{a_1(r^n - 1)}{r - 1}$, we have:

$$S_{10} = \frac{2(2^{10} - 1)}{2 - 1} = 2,046$$

38. Use $a_1 = 2$ and $d = 2$ in $S_n = \dfrac{n}{2}[2a_1 + (n - 1)d]$:

$$S_n = \frac{n}{2}[2(2) + (n - 1)2] = \frac{n}{2}(4 + 2n - 2) = \frac{n}{2}(2n + 2)$$

$$= \frac{2n(n + 1)}{2} = n(n + 1)$$

40. Yes. Let $a_1 = \frac{1}{2}$ and let $0 < r < 1$, then $S = \dfrac{\frac{1}{2}}{1 - r}$. For $S \geq 1000$, we should solve the inequality $\dfrac{\frac{1}{2}}{1 - r} \geq 1000$ or $1 \geq 2{,}000 - 2{,}000r$ which has a set of solutions for $0 < r < 1$.

42. Yes. Using the sum formula $S_n = \dfrac{n}{2}(a_1 + a_n)$ with $a_1 = 1$, $a_n = 1.1$ and $S_n = 105$, we obtain $n = 100$.

44. No. Using the sum formula for infinite geometric series $S = \dfrac{a_1}{1 - r}$. For $a_1 = 10$, $S = 5$ we obtain, from this formula, $r = -1$. However, the sum of infinite geometric series is given by $\dfrac{a_1}{1 - r}$ when $|r| < 1$. Therefore such a series does not exist.

46. Consider the time line:

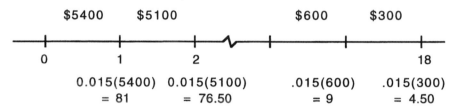

$5400 \qquad \$5100 \qquad\qquad \$600 \qquad \$300$

0   1   2   18

0.015(5400) 0.015(5100)   .015(600)   .015(300)
= 81   = 76.50   = 9   = 4.50

The total cost of the loan is:
    $4.50 + 9 + 13.50 + \ldots + 76.50 + 81$
The terms of an arithmetic progression with $n = 18$, $a_1 = 4.50$, and $a_{18} = 81$. Thus,

$$S_{18} = \frac{18}{2}(4.50 + 81) = \$769.50$$

48. This is a geometric progression with $a_1 = (1{,}200)(.65) = 780$ and $r = 0.65$. Thus, $S_\infty = \dfrac{780}{1 - 0.65} = \$2{,}229$.

50.

P

1   2

$(1 + r)P \qquad (1 + r)^2 P$

This is a geometric sequence with $a_1 = P$ and ratio $(1 + r)$.
Thus, $A = P(1 + r)^n$.

2. $7! = 7 \cdot 6 \cdot 5 \cdot 4 \cdot 3 \cdot 2 \cdot 1 = 5,040$

4. $\dfrac{20!}{19!} = \dfrac{20(19!)}{19!} = 20$

6. $\dfrac{10!}{6!} = \dfrac{10 \cdot 9 \cdot 8 \cdot 7 \cdot (6!)}{6!} = 5,040$

8. $\dfrac{7!}{3! \, 4!} = \dfrac{7 \cdot 6 \cdot 5 \cdot (4!)}{3 \cdot 2 \cdot 1(4!)} = 35$

10. $\dfrac{7!}{4! \, (7-4)!} = \dfrac{7!}{4! \, 3!} = 35$ (see Problem 8)

12. $\dfrac{52!}{50! \, 2!} = \dfrac{52 \cdot 51 \cdot (50!)}{50! \, 2 \cdot 1} = \dfrac{52 \cdot 51}{2} = 1,326$

14. $C_{7,3} = \dfrac{7!}{3! \, (7-3)!} = \dfrac{7!}{3! \, 4!} = 35$ (see Problem 8)

16. $C_{7,4} = \dfrac{7!}{4! \, (7-4)!} = 35$ (see Problem 10)

18. $C_{5,5} = \dfrac{5!}{5! \, (5-5)!} = \dfrac{5!}{5! \, 0!} = \dfrac{5!}{5!} = 1$ (0! = 1)

20. $C_{18,3} = \dfrac{18!}{3! \, (18-3)!} = \dfrac{18 \cdot 17 \cdot 16 \cdot (15!)}{3! \, (15!)} = \dfrac{18 \cdot 17 \cdot 16}{3 \cdot 2 \cdot 1} = 816$

22. $(m + n)^5 = C_{5,0}m^5 + C_{5,1}m^4 n + C_{5,2}m^3 n^2 + C_{5,3}m^2 n^3 + C_{5,4}mn^4 + C_{5,5}n^5$

$\qquad = m^5 + 5m^4 n + 10m^2 n^3 + 10m^3 n^2 + 5mn^4 + n^5$

24. $(u - 2)^5 = C_{5,0}u^5 + C_{5,1}u^4(-2) + C_{5,2}u^3(-2)^2 + C_{5,3}u^2(-2)^3$

$\qquad\qquad + C_{5,4}u(-2)^4 + C_{5,5}(-2)^5$

$\qquad = u^5 - 10u^4 + 40u^3 - 80u^2 + 80u - 32$

26. $(x - 2y)^5 = C_{5,0}x^5 + C_{5,1}x^4(-2y) + C_{5,2}x^3(-2y)^2 + C_{5,3}x^2(-2y)^3$

$\qquad\qquad + C_{5,4}x(-2y)^4 + C_{5,5}(-2y)^5$

$\qquad = x^5 - 10x^4 y + 40x^3 y^2 - 80x^2 y^3 + 80xy^4 - 32y^5$

28. The third term in the expansion of $(x - 3)^{20}$ is:

$C_{20,2}x^{18}(-3)^2 = \dfrac{20!}{2! \, 18!}x^{18}(9) = \dfrac{20 \cdot 19 \cdot (18!)9}{2 \cdot 1 \cdot (18!)}x^{18} = 1,710x^{18}$

30. The 13th term in the expansion of $(p + q)^{15}$ is:

$C_{15,12} \, p^3 q^{12} = \dfrac{15!}{12! \, 3!}p^3 q^{12} = 455p^3 q^{12}$

32. The third term in the expansion of $(2x + y)^{12}$ is:

$$C_{12,2}(2x)^{10}y^2 = \frac{12!}{2!\,10!}2^{10}x^{10}y^2 = 67,584x^{10}y^2$$

34. $C_{n,r} = \dfrac{n!}{r!\,(n-r)!} = \dfrac{n!}{(n-r)!\,r!} = \dfrac{n!}{(n-r)!\,[n-(n-r)]!} = C_{n,n-r}$

36. According to the Binomial Theorem:

$$(a + b)^n = \sum_{r=0}^{n} C_{n,r}\, a^r b^{n-r}.$$

Letting $a = b = 1$, we have

$$2^n = \sum_{r=0}^{n} C_{n,r} = \text{sum of the entries in each row of Pascal's triangle.}$$

38. $C_{n,r} = \dfrac{n!}{r!\,(n-r)!} = \dfrac{n-r+1}{r} \cdot \dfrac{n!}{(r-1)!\,(n-r+1)!}$

$$= \frac{n-r+1}{r} \cdot \frac{n!}{r'!\,(n-r')!} \quad \text{where } r' = r - 1$$

$$= \frac{n-r+1}{r}C_{n,r'} = \frac{n-r+1}{r}C_{n,r-1}$$